Fundamentals of Biochemistry
in
Clinical Medicine

Fundamentals of Biochemistry
in
Clinical Medicine

By

NIELS C. KLENDSHOJ, M.D.

Assistant Professor of Pathology
Director of the Division of Toxicology
University of Buffalo, School of Medicine
Director of the Department of Biochemistry
Buffalo General Hospital
Buffalo, New York

CHARLES C THOMAS · PUBLISHER
Springfield · Illinois · U.S.A.

CHARLES C THOMAS · PUBLISHER

Bannerstone House

301-327 East Lawrence Avenue, Springfield, Illinois, U.S.A.

Published simultaneously in the British Commonwealth of Nations by
Blackwell Scientific Publications, Ltd., Oxford, England

Published simultaneously in Canada by
The Ryerson Press, Toronto

Printed in the United States of America

Dedicated to
MY WIFE ROBERTA

PREFACE

THE physicians and surgeons of today cannot be proficient in medical practice without applying knowledge of the several basic sciences. Unfortunately, altogether too little time is available for the busy practitioner to keep abreast of more than a few medical developments which, because of their very great usefulness, come to his immediate attention. The object of the present work is to present in the form of a short review, the fundamental aspects of biochemistry and its application to clinical medicine, intentionally omitting many details of both subjects.

The book is designed to permit the reader, whose main interest is in some other field, to scan it in a reasonably short time, or to obtain a brief review of whatever subject in this field demands his attention at the moment.

The material is introduced by two chapters devoted to atomic and molecular structure. It has been the experience of the writer that much modern literature becomes more understandable to the medical practitioner if he will devote a few moments to clarify certain elementary definitions. These two chapters do not pretend to go much beyond that. The next seven chapters contain material of more fundamental biochemical nature, while the last nine chapters are dedicated mostly to practical aspects of biochemistry in clinical medicine. It is hoped that this arrangement will facilitate the approach to the various subjects and be time-saving for reviewing. The indicated division of material has not always been followed strictly as convenience has dictated the occasional inclusion of certain clinical aspects in the early part of the book and some theoretical subjects have been discussed in relation to specific disease entities.

Obviously, a book of this nature should not be considered a reference work. The bibliography, following each chapter, to a large extent omits the customary documentary references, the material selected being presented as suitable supplementary reading. Therefore, the bibliography may not necessarily represent, in the author's opinion, the most important contributions to the subject. Many monumental publications have not been listed with the understanding that the reader who seeks more detailed knowledge will resort to larger works.

Buffalo, New York   N. C. K.

ACKNOWLEDGMENTS

THE writer is indebted to numerous colleagues at the University of Buffalo School of Medicine, and to his associates at the Buffalo General Hospital for their kind suggestions and help. Appreciation is expressed toward Dr. Wilson D. Langley, Dr. Edward M. Bridge, Mr. Milton Feldstein, and Miss Alice L. Sprague for their time and effort in aiding the preparation of this book. Appreciation is also expressed toward Mrs. W. Victoria Bender who typed the manuscript.

N. C. K.

CONTENTS

Fundamentals of Biochemistry
in
Clinical Medicine

Chapter 1

ATOMIC STRUCTURE

U NDERSTANDING of the structure of the atom is founded upon an adequate
knowledge of the 'particles' which comprise the atom. The definitions
of the properties of these particles are derived from a wide variety of experimental work. The particles may not necessarily conform to the way they
are pictured or described, but they can be discussed as long as they are
defined in terms of properties established by experiment.

Early studies of the structure of the atom were based on observations of
electrical discharge in vacuum. Later, the study of radioactivity and trans-
mutation contributed greatly to the increased understanding of atomic structure. In more recent years nuclear fission of certain atoms under special
conditions has added considerably to the knowledge of the nucleus. This
process has also made available larger amounts of radioactive and isotopic
material for experimental work.

An understanding of the nature of electricity underlies all approaches to
the study of atomic structure. Electricity is commonly thought of as a form
of energy, because it is associated with the ability to perform work. J. J.
Thompson showed that electricity consists of distinct particles called electrons. The electron, therefore, is the fundamental unit of electricity and the
determination of its electrical charge is of great importance. Millikan established the physical characteristics of the electron with amazing accuracy in
his oil-drop experiments.

In studies of the nature of matter, two general laws have been supported
by all experimental approaches. These laws state that matter cannot be
created or destroyed, and that the same holds true for energy. Of course
either one can be altered in form; for instance one chemical substance can be
transformed into another, and electricity can be transformed into heat. These
two laws have guided practically all physical and chemical research, and
they are but two phases of a single principle because matter can be changed
into energy and vice versa according to definite laws. The theory of rela-
tivity leads to the conclusion that inertial mass of a moving body increases as
speed increases. Therefore, a relation between kinetic energy and mass must
exist. It is only because of the tremendous disproportion between these two
values that the laws of conservation of energy and mass are true for most
practical purposes.

In 1905, Einstein formulated the mathematical relationship between
energy and mass as follows: $E = mc^2$. In this equation E represents energy

of a particle, m its mass, and c the velocity of light. The application of this equation leads to startling consequences. For instance, the conversion of 1 kilogram of mass to energy should produce approximately 25 billion kilowatt hours of energy which corresponds to all the electrical power used in the United States for two months. If energy is measured from the combustion of 1 kilogram of coal, the corresponding figure would be 8.5 kilowatt hours. The only reason why there are no detectable changes in mass in the ordinary chemical reactions is that such changes of mass, equivalent to the ordinary energy changes, are entirely too small to be detected.

ELECTRONS

It already has been stated that electrons represent the unit of negative electrical charge. Electrons have the ability to ionize molecules with which they come in contact. If electrons are discharged in air, they will ionize molecules and make the air a conductor of electricity. This conductivity can be measured with an electroscope, and the effect on the electroscope may be used as a quantitative measure of the flow of electrons.

Cathode rays represent electrons in motion from the negative cathode to the positive anode of a vacuum tube. The transfer of electrons in a vacuum tube depends on the difference in potential between the cathode and anode and the rate at which electrons are emitted from the surface of the cathode. The hotter the cathode is the more electrons will be formed. Therefore, hot filaments are used in radio tubes, x-ray tubes, etc., to produce adequate streams of electrons.

Electrons are deflected by electrical and magnetic fields according to well-known physical laws. Their motion can be accelerated or decelerated between electrical potentials. Electrons at very high speed are used to bombard elements to transform them into other elements. The high speed of the electrons is obtained by subjecting them to very high voltage fields, or by the use of devices in which the electrical field is changing continually at a much lower voltage. Methods used to accelerate negative particles may also be used for acceleration of positive particles if the electrical or magnetic fields are designed accordingly.

The *Van de Graaff electrostatic generator* has been of outstanding importance in the development of high voltage fields. This machine is based on the principle that a moving belt of non-conducting material can transport electrical charges continually from a generating source to a large closed-surface conductor called a terminal. The terminal is usually spherical, and elementary principles of electrostatics teach that the charges are distributed over the surface, leaving the space inside free of electrical forces. The surface voltage eventually reached depends upon the charging rate and the rate at which the charge is disseminated. Special methods have been used to decrease dissemination of the electrostatic charges; such methods include the use of air low in moisture, air under pressure, and other gases such as neon. Particles to be accelerated are produced by a suitable source inside the terminal and pass through a vacuum tube running from the terminal to the ground. Van de Graaff generators have been built in which particles are accelerated in vacuum between one terminal and another charged at the opposite polarity in order to double the voltage of the accelerating field. The maximum charge obtainable on the terminal is reached when the diffuse dissemination of electrostatic charges is equal to the charges supplied by the belt. It is obvious that surroundings to which the terminal might discharge by sparking across as well as the insulating characteristics of the belt are factors limiting the ultimate voltage. Potentials of over 5 million volts have been created. The maximum energy to which a particle can be accelerated in an electrostatic generator cannot exceed the voltage to which the terminals can be charged. Other devices such as the cyclotron, overcome limitations of the voltage in the available fields by subjecting the accelerating particles repeatedly to the electrical forces. Thus the energy attained by a particle in an electrostatic generator is the result of acceleration in a single step while other devices avoid energy limitations by acceleration in multiple steps.

The *cyclotron* consists of two hollow D-shaped electrodes known as dees. These two electrodes are placed in apposition so that there is a gap between them. The dees are connected to a source of electrical potential of 10 to 100 kilovolts and the polarity across the gap changes at high frequency. The particles to be accelerated are created in the center of the cyclotron and are made to spiral in the hollow dees by a powerful magnetic field. Every time they cross the open gap between the dees the potential across the electrodes causes acceleration. When the spiralling particles have described a 180° arc in one of the dees the polarity changes so that further acceleration occurs while they cross the gap again. Because of the acceleration the particles spiral toward the periphery of the dees and eventually escape tangentially from the magnetic field.

The increase in mass which a particle undergoes during the accelerating process becomes appreciable at high energies. This increase gradually reduces the rotational frequency so that the particles cross the gap at a time when the potential between the dees is less than maximum and converging toward zero. At the zero point further increase in the energy of the particles cannot take place. Thus the relativistic increase in mass places a limit on the energy obtainable in a cyclotron. Two methods suggest themselves to obviate this limiting effect. One is a change in the magnetic field but this is impractical for structural reasons. The other is a gradual reduction in the frequency of the electrical field to synchronize it with the velocity of the particles. Such machines have been constructed and they are called *synchro-cyclotrons*.

The *betatron* uses electro-magnetic induction for the acceleration of electrons. Its construction parallels in principle that of an ordinary transformer in which the secondary coil has been replaced with a circular evacuated chamber called a 'doughnut.' The electrons are made to accelerate in the circular path by the application of a magnetic field. The accelerated electrons may be extracted from the equilibrium orbit in the doughnut by reducing the magnetic flux below the necessary magnitude to maintain a constant radius of the electron path. The electrons may also be extracted by the use of auxiliary coils.

The *synchrotron* combines the principles of the betatron and the cyclotron. The initial phase of operation consists of acceleration by the betatron principle of electrons injected at nearly the speed of light. Subsequently the electrons are accelerated to high energies by application of a constant frequency field similar to that employed in the cyclotron.

The electron is the smallest known mass. Its mass in grams would require 27 ciphers after the decimal point before the first significant figure. Electrons are constituents of all matter; chemical properties of matter depend exclusively on the arrangement of electrons in the atom as described later.

POSITRONS

C. D. Anderson, in 1932, discovered the existence of another particle in the atom equal in mass to the electron, but of opposite charge. This particle has been termed the positron. The positron has a very short life. When its energy has fallen to a relatively low value it is annihilated on encountering an electron with a consequent release of radiation of the gamma-ray type, with energy equal to the sum of the two particle masses.

PROTONS

If a cathode tube is constructed with a perforated cathode, rays extend behind it, and it can be demonstrated by use of an electrical field that these rays carry a positive charge. Electrons issuing from the cathode will collide with atoms of gas in the rarefied atmosphere of the tube, and an occasional collision will knock other electrons from the orbit of these atoms; thus the remaining part of the atom will carry a positive charge. These particles form the rays observed behind the cathode. If the atom is hydrogen, the resulting positively charged particle is called a proton.

Figure 1 shows diagrammatically the formation of a proton by collision of an electron with a hydrogen atom. The bombarding electron has enough energy to carry away the orbital electron of the hydrogen atom, leaving the positively charged nucleus (the proton). Because of its positive charge the proton will be attracted by the negative cathode and, if the electrical forces are adequate, it will continue its path through the perforations of the electrode. The positive ray can be deflected in electrical or magnetic fields. A measurable degree of deflection requires more electrical force than in the case of the electrons. This is due to the greater mass of the positive-ray particles.

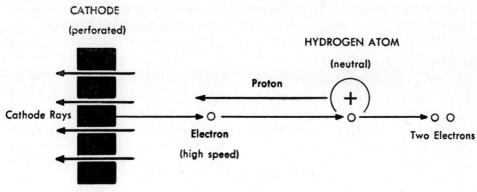

Fɪɢ. 1

The proton, the lightest of the gaseous ions, weighs approximately 1,840 times as much as the electron.

NEUTRONS

The existence of the neutron was predicted by Rutherford in 1920, later they were demonstrated by Joliot and Curie in France, and by Chadwick in England. If radiation from radon strikes a target of beryllium, a flow of radiation from the beryllium results. This radiation is capable of ejecting protons from the atoms of many elements. Energy calculations applied to such experiments show that the radiation from beryllium can be explained only by assuming that it contains particles of unit mass and without charge. In other words, these particles are of the same mass as a proton, but do not carry an electrical charge. They are called neutrons.

Neutrons, having no charge, are hard to detect because they cannot be deflected by electrical or magnetic fields. This characteristic gives neutrons the important property of being able to penetrate the electron shells of atoms and enter the atomic nuclei. Neutrons which have been slowed down by passage through screens consisting of material containing hydrogen (water, paraffin, etc.) are more useful for the penetration of atomic nuclei than high-speed neutrons. The atoms of nearly all the known elements interact with neutrons and five main types of behaviour have been observed. These are the emission of:

a) A proton
b) An alpha particle
c) Gamma radiation
d) Neutrons
e) A positron

Neutrons will eject protons from a screen containing hydrogen atoms, and it is for this reason that water, instead of lead, is used as a protective wall for modern atom-smashers. When neutrons travel through matter they are relatively unaffected by other particles because they are neutral in charge. Thus they can penetrate the strong positive field surrounding the nucleus and effect atomic disintegrations.

There is no natural supply of neutrons in spite of the fact that there are more of them than anything else in the world. They can be obtained only from nuclear disintegrations, and they can be controlled by putting atomic nuclei in their path to slow and deflect them so that they gradually lose their energy by collision.

MESONS (MESOTRONS)

The meson is the next heaviest particle known. It may be positively or negatively charged. The first mesons discovered were found to have a mass of approximately 210 to 220 times that of an electron. More recently mesons have been discovered having a mass of around 285 times the electron mass. The heavier meson rapidly decays into the lighter type. A meson has an extremely short life span; upon its disintegration it produces an electron and other particles as yet unidentified. Possibly uncharged mesons are produced during the disintegration. Light and heavy mesons appear to be fundamentally different in nature because the heavy type interacts very strongly with atomic nuclei, a property which is only weakly present in the lighter type. Yukawa originally postulated the meson as a possible 'exchange' particle operating in the as yet unknown mechanism which holds together the atomic nucleus. The heavy meson is probably the particle involved. Further studies on the meson promise to help remove some of the mystery of nuclear binding forces. Cosmic ray studies have been the major source of information on mesons, thus limiting possibilities of experimental work. Newer methods of particle acceleration are reaching the energy range in which mesons may be produced in the laboratory. Their further investigation may materially aid understanding of atomic structure.

RADIATION

The high-atomic-weight elements, such as uranium, thorium, radium, etc., exhibit natural radioactivity. The rays emitted can be divided into three types:

A. Alpha-particles are high speed, ionized helium atoms, or rather they are nuclei of helium atoms. As such they are positive particles.

B. Beta-particles consist of high speed electrons, and are negatively charged particles.

C. Gamma-rays are electromagnetic radiation without mass and without electrical charge. Gamma-rays may act like particles, and a 'quantum' of gamma radiation is called a *photon*. Gamma-rays are very penetrating. In this respect they resemble x-rays, but in general they contain more energy than x-rays.

Because alpha- and beta-rays are of opposite electrical charge, and gamma-rays do not carry any electrical charge, it becomes a simple matter to demonstrate the three types of radiation from a radioactive substance by passing the radiation through an electrical or magnetic field. The two types of charged particles will be deflected in opposite directions, while gamma-rays will proceed without any deviation.

MEASURING METHODS

For convenience a unit called the *electron-volt* (e.v.) is used to express energy in atomic physics. It is defined as the energy acquired by an electron moving under a fall of potential of 1 volt. Taking the charge of an electron as 4.802×10^{-10} electrostatic (e.s.) units and 1 volt as $1/300$ e.s. units the work done by the electron under the defined condition is $4.802 \times 10^{-10}/300 = 1.601 \times 10^{-12}$ erg. Hence this value represents the equivalent of 1 e.v. in the c.g.s. system. Because of the large figures involved in expressing energies of particles a unit of Mev equivalent to 1 million e.v. is used frequently.

Geiger-Müller counters are used to detect and measure radiation. They usually consist of a cylindrical cathode and an anode mounted coaxially. The electrodes are charged with a potential which is slightly less than that required for continuous discharge. The space between the electrodes is filled with a gas, usually under reduced pressure. An ionizing particle entering the chamber will produce charged particles which in turn are accelerated by the potential between the electrodes. These accelerated particles cause further ionization so that eventually an avalanche of ions is produced capable of being detected as a voltage pulse. It may be seen that this principle permits counting of particles independent of their ionizing power. Many modifications of the Geiger-Müller counter are available to make it suitable for specific purposes. Also electronic recording devices are capable of counting at an exceedingly rapid rate the impulses registered in the Geiger-Müller counter.

Geiger-Müller counters are used in biological investigations involving the use of radioactive isotopes by simply tracing the pathway and determining the relative distribution of the radioactive substance. The stable isotopes do not emit radiation and their measurements are made possible by their deviation in atomic weight from the naturally occurring elements. Such determinations are made in *mass spectrographs*.

GENERAL STRUCTURE OF ATOMS

The characteristics of the particles of which atoms consist may be summarized essentially as follows:

In nucleus:	proton:	mass = 1,	charge = +1
	neutron:	mass = 1,	charge = 0
In orbit:	electron:	mass = 1/1840,	charge = −1

Each element has its own atomic structure which has been pictured as a solar system with a nucleus corresponding to the sun, and electrons whirling around in orbits corresponding to the planets. When an atom is in normal balance, it is neutral electrically and consequently must contain an equal number of protons in the nucleus and of electrons in the orbits. The simplest atom is hydrogen, and the hydrogen atom can be visualized as consisting of one proton in the nucleus with one electron in the orbit to make up a neutral atom. Helium has two protons in the nucleus and two orbital electrons. In addition, the helium atom has two neutrons in the nucleus, giving it an atomic weight of 4.

In the periodic system the atoms are numbered, the atomic number being equal to the number of protons in the nucleus. In a normally balanced, electrically neutral atom, the atomic number is equal to the number of electrons. If it is remembered that the mass of the electron is very small in comparison with the mass of the proton and the neutron, it can be seen that practically all the weight of an atom is in the nucleus. Protons and neutrons are of equal mass. Therefore, the weight of the atom is the sum of the protons and the neutrons.

Atoms are mostly empty space. The approximate diameter of an electron orbit is 1/200,000,000 inches. If a nucleus is compared in size to that of a baseball, the electrons would be specks about 2,000 feet away. If these relative dimensions are kept in mind, it is much easier to understand how particles and rays can penetrate seemingly solid matter.

The electrons of an atom move around in their orbits at very high speed, but they represent relatively small amounts of energy. On the other hand, the nucleus contains tremendous amounts of binding energy which resists the separation of protons and neutrons. For example, the nuclear energy in one pound of helium corresponds to the amount of electricity needed to run a 100 watt bulb for 13,000,000 years.

The heaviest atom found in nature is uranium. It has been determined that the uranium nucleus contains 92 protons and 146 neutrons. In normal balance uranium must have 92 electrons in its orbit. By definition, the atomic number of uranium is 92, and the atomic weight is 238, equal to the sum of the protons and the neutrons.

The electrons determine the chemical behaviour of the elements. They arrange themselves in orbits in a characteristic manner which will be discussed later. Obviously an atom with a certain number of protons is chemically the same regardless of the number of neutrons in the nucleus, because the number of protons determines the number of orbital electrons, and these in turn determine the chemical properties. This means that atoms of any one of the known elements may show variation in atomic weight due to variation in the number of neutrons in the nucleus without any change in chemical properties. Such variants within the same element are called *isotopes;* in other words, isotopes are chemically identical. They contain the same number of protons in the nucleus, but the number of neutrons differ. Elements in nature are usually mixtures of isotopes, which explains the fractional ratio of atomic weights.

Hydrogen consists normally of one proton in the nucleus and one orbital electron. Natural hydrogen contains a small amount of an isotope with an additional neutron in the nucleus. The atomic weight of this hydrogen-isotope is, therefore, two instead of one. It is referred to as heavy hydrogen or *deuterium* and the nucleus is called a *deuteron.* The proportion of heavy hydrogen in natural hydrogen is approximately 1 to 5,000. Hydrogen occurs in an isotopic form containing two neutrons in the nucleus. This isotope is radioactive and has not been found in nature. It is called *tritium* (symbol T). The half-life of tritium is approximately 12 years, which makes it a suitable tracer substance for certain purposes. Tritium is formed when lithium or boron is bombarded with neutrons; its decay is associated with the emission of beta particles.

The three forms of hydrogen nuclei may be symbolized by $_1H^1$, $_1H^2$, and $_1H^3$ where the sub-number is the atomic number ($Z = 1$) and the upper number is the mass number (A). A is the nearest integral mass number equal to the sum of protons and neutrons. When $_1H^3$ emits a beta particle (an electron) the nuclear charge is changed to 2 and the new nucleus is $_2He^3$; one neutron has been changed to a proton. This process is believed to be accompanied by the emission of a tiny particle a *neutrino.* Neutrinos are hypothetical elementary particles which permit balancing of energy in the process of production of an electron in nuclear decay. Recent observations indicate that the disintegration of a meson results in the simultaneous production of one electron and two neutrinos.

Water containing deuterium instead of hydrogen is called *heavy water.* Chemically it reacts exactly like ordinary water, but the molecule of heavy water can be traced because it has a higher molecular weight. Due to this property heavy water is very useful in biological experiments.

The uranium isotopes are highly interesting, because the understanding of their behaviour resulted in procedures for the release of atomic energy, culminating in the development of the atomic bomb during World War II. There are three uranium isotopes in naturally occurring uranium. All of them, of course, contain 92 protons, but the number of neutrons is respectively 146, 143, and 142, resulting in atomic weights of 238, 235, and 234. Natural uranium contains 99.3 per cent U-238. The content of U-235 is 0.7

per cent, and U-234 is negligible. U-235 is the isotope used for release of atomic energy. The three uranium nuclei are designated $_{92}U^{238}$, $_{92}U^{235}$, and $_{92}U^{234}$.

Most atoms are stable. The unstable atoms are radioactive and tend toward stable forms. During this process the unstable atoms release particles and energy, and eventually convert themselves into new elements. This process is called nuclear disintegration. The rate at which radioactivity is lost is a characteristic of each radioactive element. Because the radiation from a radioactive nucleus gradually subsides toward the vanishing point over an infinite period of time, it becomes impossible to measure this time. It is practical to measure the time required for the radioactive element to lose half of its radioactivity. This time measure is a characteristic and unalterable constant called the half-life of the element. The half-life is not changed by any chemical process, and the radioactivity of an element is the same regardless of its chemical form.

ARTIFICIAL NUCLEAR DISINTEGRATION

The first successful experiments to demonstrate that elements can be converted into other elements were performed by Rutherford in 1919. He bombarded nitrogen with alpha-particles and found that an isotope of oxygen was formed with an atomic weight of 17 instead of 16, as in naturally occurring oxygen.

Very little is known about the forces which bind particles together in the nucleus. It is known that stability tends to occur when the neutrons and the protons are approximately equal in number in the lighter nuclei. In the heavier nuclei the proportion of neutrons apparently must be larger for stability. At the heavy end of the periodic table none of the atomic nuclei are completely stable. Stable nuclei can be made unstable by addition of neutrons or protons under special circumstances. These new unstable nuclei in turn change to stable forms and usually during the process emit one of the five types of radiation previously mentioned.

Radioactive elements gradually disintegrate into other elements of lower atomic weight. Uranium is radioactive and follows the same pattern in its breakdown as the other radioactive elements. The half-life of uranium is very long. If uranium is bombarded with neutrons, some of it will break up into new elements in a way entirely different from that resulting from natural radiation. This type of process is called *fission*. The uranium fission was discovered in 1938 by Frisch and Meitner working with Niels Bohr. The same discovery was made independently by Curie and Joliot. Hahn and Strassmann found radioactive barium to be present after bombardment of uranium with neutrons, and the presence of this form of barium could only be explained by the fission type of breakdown of the uranium nucleus.

Natural radioactivity of uranium gives off alpha-particles. Fermi found that, during the bombardment with neutrons, uranium emits electrons. If a neutron is captured by the U-238 nucleus and an electron given off from the nucleus in the process, it means that the neutron captured now becomes a proton which must be added to the natural number of protons in the U-238 nucleus. If one electron is given off, a new proton is formed and, therefore, the new atomic nucleus contains 93 protons. In other words, a new element has been created with an atomic number higher than the highest known atomic number in nature. So far six such new elements with atomic numbers of 93, 94, 95, 96, 97, and 98 have been created, and they are called *transuranic elements*. Their names are respectively neptunium, plutonium, americium, curium, berkelium, and californium.

If U-235 undergoes fission the mass of the fission products is less than the mass of the original U-235, and the difference is converted into energy. One pound of U-235 is capable of releasing 11,400,000 kilowatt hours. During the fission process new neutrons are created. If these neutrons are captured by additional U-235 nuclei, these will undergo fission, and if the number of new nuclei disintegrating is equal to or greater than the original number, the process becomes a self-propagating *chain reaction*.

BIOLOGICAL APPLICATION OF ISOTOPES

In 1923 Hevesy used lead containing thorium B (radioactive ThB^{212}) to demonstrate the rate of assimilation and the distribution of lead in plants. He also demonstrated that lead, already deposited, readily was replaced by new supplies of 'tagged' lead, drawing the conclusion that lead remained in the ionizable form and did not combine with carbon. Hevesy's work set the pattern for biological studies but the real progress had to await the availability of isotopes which could be fitted into specific metabolic problems.

The study of a metabolic process by the use of an isotope in one of the metabolites is based on the premise that the 'tagged' atom behaves exactly as the naturally occurring element. Obviously, in the case of radioactive isotopes, this can be true only if the radiation from the isotopes does not influence the process under study. Adequate dilution of the isotope with the corresponding natural element in most cases may make this assumption justifiable.

In general the stable isotopes behave like the natural element. This is not true for heavy hydrogen because deuterium oxide (heavy water) at least in certain concentrations, has toxic effects. Fermentation by yeast in 100 per cent deuterium oxide is much slower than in ordinary water. Small organisms such as bacteria, protozoa, worms, and fish may die in high concentrations of deuterium oxide. Signs of intoxication appear in mice if relatively high amounts of heavy water are ingested, the toxic effect disappearing with the elimination of the heavy water. It is likely that the differential behaviour of heavy water is caused by lower mobility of the deuterium ion as compared with that of the hydrogen ion and thus the toxic manifestations may be on a physical rather than on a chemical basis. Most of the isotopes in use have molecular weights sufficiently high so that deviations in behaviour due to differences in mass between the isotope and the natural element is not to be expected. Tritium may be found to be an outstanding exception in as much as its mass is greater than that of deuterium.

The choice between radioactive and stable isotopes is practically always in favor of the former if available. It is much easier to determine radiation quantitatively than it is to measure relative distribution of isotopes in a mass spectrograph. The practical limit of accuracy in a mass spectrograph is about 1 per cent. If, as an example, the natural abundance of an isotope is about 1 per cent the greatest theoretical dilution useful for tracer experiments would be approximately 1:10,000. Practically, the dilution should not be much more than 1:1,000. The example cited corresponds closely to the actual distribution of C^{13}. In contradistinction radioactive isotopes are commonly used in dilutions exceeding 1:1,000,000.

The half-life of a radioactive isotope is important in its use as a tracer because sufficient time must be allowed to complete observations, and, in case of tagged metabolic substances, additional time is required for their preparation. The half-life of the longest lived radioactive isotopes of nitrogen and oxygen is too short for practical purposes. Magnesium, aluminum, lithium, and boron also fall into this category. Aluminum exists in one stable form only and its radioactive isotopes have half-life values of which the longest is 6.7 minutes. For studies in organic metabolism the five most important elements, C, H, O, N, and S can be made available in the form of the less abundant stable isotopes and, in addition, C, H, and S form radioactive isotopes of convenient characteristics.

Carbon occurs in the form of 1 stable isotope C^{13} and two radioactive species C^{11} and C^{14}. Obviously 'tagging' of carbon atoms is of major importance because of their dominant role in organic chemistry. C^{11} has desirable properties from the standpoint of detectable radiation but its short half-life (20 minutes) makes it unsuitable for preparation of specific metabolites. It has been used to study metabolism of carbon dioxide and carbon monoxide. C^{13} has been extensively employed in many investigations, notably the intermediary metabolism of carbohydrates, proteins, and fats. C^{14} is produced in the neutron-pile reactors. Its half-life is approximately 5,000 years which makes it admirably suited for preparation of metabolites. C^{14} emits weak beta particles and well defined conditions are necessary for accurate measurements. While the 'turnover' of organic compounds in the living organism generally is rapid, thus tending to eliminate radiation from tracers, C^{14} may not be suitable for experiments in human subjects because it appears in the bones in the form of carbonate. Such radioactive carbonate has been found to remain relatively immobile in animals for periods of at least several weeks.

Oxygen has several radioactive isotopes of which the longest lived has a half-life of 126 seconds. Two stable isotopes O^{17} and O^{18} exist of which the latter has been used as a tracer. O^{18} has been used in investigations of photosynthetic processes, demonstrating that water, and not carbon dioxide, is the source of the released oxygen.

Hydrogen has 1 stable isotope, deuterium H^2, and 1 unstable, tritium H^3. It has been mentioned already that differences in mass between H^2, H^3, and natural hydrogen may cause deviations in behaviour which may have to be taken into consideration in tracer experiments. Deuterium has been introduced into positions of a labile nature in organic compounds as well as in direct attachment to carbon. The latter represents generally a sufficiently stable arrangement to permit deuterium to serve as an auxiliary identifier for the carbon atom. Schoenheimer and associates used deuterium to label fats in a series of metabolic experiments which are now classics (see Chapter 6). Nuclear-pile reactors are making more abundant amounts of tritium available so that future research with hydrogen isotopes may tend to place the emphasis on the use of H^3.

Nitrogen has a stable isotope N^{15} which has been used extensively as a tracer in nitrogen metabolism. Schoenheimer and associates followed up their successes in investigating fat metabolism with deuterium as a tracer by using N^{15} to demonstrate the source of creatine and creatinine (see Chapter 7). The use of two tracers such as N^{15} in conjunction with C^{14} promises to give much more information as to the relative reactivity of skeleton structure and side chains in many metabolites. An unstable isotope of nitrogen N^{13} can be produced in good amounts in the cyclotron but its half-life (10 minutes) is too short for most purposes.

Phosphorus plays a major role in inorganic and organic metabolism. Tracer experiments have shown that phosphorus atoms are interchangeable between the two groups. The metabolism of the phospholipids and the nucleoproteins has been investigated by the aid of phosphorus isotopes. Support has been found for the viewpoint that ribosenucleotides play a role in the synthesis of proteins. Ribosenucleic acid shows a much more rapid turnover in the liver as compared to desoxyribose-nucleic acid, the latter being primarily a nuclear constituent. Normal adult liver shows relatively few mitoses. In liver undergoing rapid growth as well as in other rapidly growing tissue, particularly neoplasms, the turnover of desoxyribose-nucleic acid is accelerated considerably. The relatively increased metabolic rate of nuclear compounds in malignant tissue has been utilized for diagnostic purposes. Low-Beer and associates have demonstrated that the radioactive phosphorus in sodium phosphate, administered to women with breast tumors, tends to distribute itself so that radiation over the tumor is more than 25 per cent greater than over the surrounding tissue, while the difference is less than 25 per cent in normal tissue.

Phosphorus has one stable isotope P^{31} and several radioactive forms of which P^{32} has a half-life of 14.3 days. P^{32} administered in inorganic phosphate to an animal soon appears in the nucleoproteins in the organism showing the interchangeability of inorganic and organic phosphorus atoms. Radiophosphorus P^{32} is employed in the treatment of blood dyscrasias because of the resulting selective beta irradiation of hematopoietic tissue. P^{32} has also been applied externally in the treatment of angiomas, warts, and other superficial lesions. The beta rays have a short range, about 7 mm. in tissue so that the effect of radiation from P^{32} can be well localized.

Polycythemia has been treated with radiophosphorus. Usually the patient is bled over a period of time until the cell volume per cent has been reduced significantly in order to minimize the risk of thrombosis and hemorrhage following ingestion or injection of P^{32}. The effect of radiation can be continued partly by repeated doses at proper intervals. Periodic examinations of the peripheral blood are made to insure against further administration of P^{32} if the patient develops transient leukopenia or thrombocytopenia. The irreversible effects of radiation pose the danger of overdosage with subsequent developments of hypoplastic or aplastic changes in the cell-forming tissues. Acute leukemia has been observed to develop in patients under treatment with radiophosphorus so that this disease may be considered a possible complication. The phosphorus is excreted in the urine and the consequent exposure of the nephrons to radiation may create another danger.

Radiophosphorus has been used in the treatment of leukemia, the lymphomas, and certain neoplasms. The procedure is based on the relatively high rate of uptake of phosphorus in rapidly growing cells. Dosage is adjusted to obtain maximum effect on leukopoiesis with a minimum amount of damage to erythropoiesis and thrombocytopoiesis. In chronic leukemia the results have been comparable with those of roentgen therapy while the method appears to be ineffective in acute leukemia and in Hodgkin's disease.

Sodium has one stable isotope Na^{23}. Two radioactive isotopes Na^{22} and Na^{24} can be used as tracers. The former has a half-life of three years compared to 15 hours for the latter. The isotopes have been employed in experiments on absorption, excretion, and distribution of sodium in the organism. Na^{22} as a suitable tracer for long term experiments has been used to demonstrate the depression of sodium excretion in congestive heart failure. Na^{24} has been used to determine degree of impairment in circulation in the extremities in diseases affecting the blood vessels.

Potassium metabolism has been investigated by using the radioactive isotope K^{42}. Its half-life is 12 hours limiting studies to short time experiments. More abundant supplies of K^{40} (radioactive) and K^{41} (stable) may increase the range of investigations. Experiments with both sodium and potassium have demonstrated the permeability of the red cell membrane for these ions; of particular interest is the diffusion of sodium in and out of the erythrocyte. Permeability and exchangeability of sodium and potassium show significant differences in various species.

Iodine in the radioactive form has become a valuable remedy in the treatment of hyperthyroidism, obviously because of the great selective affinity of thyroid tissue for iodine. While cures in malignancy of the thyroid gland have not been reported, the use of radioiodine appears to be of considerable benefit as a palliative remedy. I^{130} has been used most extensively but more recently a mixture of I^{130} and I^{131} has been employed. The half-life of the two isotopes is 12 hours and eight days respectively.

Many other tracers are aiding metabolic investigations. *Iron* isotopes can be used to demonstrate the life span of the erythrocyte and the conservation of iron in the mammalian organism. The role of trace elements such as *copper, magnesium, cobalt, zinc,* and *boron,* may be much better understood through the use of the corresponding isotopes.

Possibly the greatest single contribution of metabolic studies involving isotopes is the revelation that atoms as well as radicals and whole molecules are in a constant state of exchange. The old concept of static deposition of the building stones of the organism until their re-entry into the general metabolism is specifically demanded, has been abandoned.

SUPPLEMENTARY READING

KELSEY, F. E.: Radioactive isotopes in medical research, diagnosis and therapy. J.A.M.A., *146*:1131, 1951.

LAWRENCE, J. H.: The use of isotopes in medical research. J.A.M.A., *134*:219, 1947.

SIRI, W. E.: *Isotopic Tracers and Nuclear Radiations.* McGraw-Hill Book Company, Inc., 1949.

SMYTH, H. D.: *Atomic Energy for Military Purposes.* Princeton University Press, 1945.

SOLOMON, A. K.: *Why Smash Atoms?* Harvard University Press, 1946.

STRANATHAN, J. D.: *The "Particles" of Modern Physics.* The Blakiston Company, 1948.

A Symposium on the Use of Isotopes in Biology and Medicine. The University of Wisconsin Press, 1948.

Chapter 2

MOLECULAR STRUCTURE: ORGANIC CHEMISTRY

BIOCHEMISTRY comprises the application of inorganic, organic, and physical chemistry to processes in living organisms. Most of the chemical structures associated with life are organic or carbon-containing compounds. One of the outstanding features of the carbon atom is its ability to combine with other carbon atoms to form chains or rings; this property accounts for the exceedingly large size of some of the molecules. Because of the great number and variety of these substances it is impossible to generalize in regard to their common properties without citing many exceptions; however, certain general differences become evident when carbon compounds are compared with inorganic substances. Organic materials are gaseous, liquid, or solid with relatively low melting points. Nearly all carbon compounds are combustible and differ in this respect from most inorganic materials. Properties such as solubility, ionization, reaction velocities, etc., of organic compounds tend to deviate from those of inorganic substances.

Obviously the carbon atom must have characteristics which explain its specific ability to form chains or rings. Current views in regard to the forces which bind atoms together cast light on this unique property and the student of biochemistry should have some understanding of the theory underlying the processes whereby atoms unite to form molecules.

VALENCE

Simple studies on the quantitative relationship by which atoms form stable molecules give rise to the concept of valence, and from the rules of valence it can be predicted in what proportions elements will unite to form specific substances. These rules have been correlated with the electron arrangement in the atoms. Electrons are segregated into concentric shells, or energy levels, and the atomic configuration attains its greatest stability when the outer shell contains eight electrons. The electron shell closest to the nucleus is exceptional in that maximum stability is achieved by the presence of two electrons. The chemical stability of the inert gases is accounted for by the presence of eight electrons in each of the outer shells except in the case of helium which has only two. The valence of an atom is presumed to be determined by the number of electrons in the outer shell and atoms with fewer than eight electrons in this shell tend to add or lose electrons, and in this manner to assume the configuration of an inert gas by achieving an octet in the outer shell. Union occurs when atoms accept electrons from, or share them with

18

TABLE I

Periods	Element	Number of Electrons		
		First Shell	Second Shell	Third Shell
1	Hydrogen	1		
	Helium	2		
2	Lithium	2	1	
	Beryllium	2	2	
	Boron	2	3	
	Carbon	2	4	
	Nitrogen	2	5	
	Oxygen	2	6	
	Fluorine	2	7	
	Neon	2	8	
3	Sodium	2	8	1
	Magnesium	2	8	2
	Aluminum	2	8	3
	Silicon	2	8	4
	Phosphorus	2	8	5
	Sulfur	2	8	6
	Chlorine	2	8	7
	Argon	2	8	8

other atoms, and in the case of carbon atoms, the process may repeat itself indefinitely. This simple picture of the fundamental properties of atoms gives a working theory to explain their chemical behaviour. However, energy changes, which occur in the transfer of electrons in the outer shell, do not always harmonize with this simplified concept.

The structures of the first 18 atoms in the periodic system are listed in Table 1, showing the arrangement of electrons in the various shells. These 18 elements include most of those occurring in organic compounds.

Activity of an atom is determined by its tendency to form an outer shell containing eight electrons. The simplest way for atoms with less than four outer electrons to form an octet is by losing these electrons to some other atom. Usually those with a relatively large number of outer electrons complete the octet by adding electrons. Atoms of these two types are the electropositive and electronegative elements respectively. For instance, lithium and sodium each have one electron in the outer or valence shell. They become stable by losing this electron and forming monovalent cations. Fluorine or chlorine, with seven outer electrons may add the electron lost by lithium or sodium to the outer shell and become stable monovalent anions. In a similar manner beryllium and magnesium may lose their two outer electrons to form divalent cations. Oxygen and sulfur exhibit divalent properties because of the necessity for adding two electrons to complete their valence shell. The trivalent properties of boron, nitrogen, aluminum, phosphorus, etc., may be explained similarly. The transfer of electrons is assumed to become increasingly difficult as the number of electrons involved increases. The carbon atom has four valence electrons; theoretically it may either lose these or add four more to form an octet. Carbon is situated midway between helium and neon, and it is difficult for carbon to attain the configuration of either of these inert gases. This may be expressed differently by saying that carbon has little tendency to gain or lose electrons, and is therefore comparatively unreactive. It may be argued that all elements with four valence electrons should behave similarly, which they do, but it is to be remembered that carbon has the smallest total number of electrons of elements within the fourth group, and that its outer electrons are subjected much more forcefully to electrostatic forces than those elements which have their outer shell at a greater distance from the nucleus. These considerations make it evident that carbon occupies a unique position among the atoms.

It has been determined that electrons tend to form pairs and that these paired electrons usually spin about their axes in opposite directions; each electron thereby neutralizing the magnetic moment created by the other. If they spin in the same direction the atom is paramagnetic which means that it is affected by outside magnetic forces.

NATURE OF THE CHEMICAL BOND

There are two principal ways in which bonds can be established between atoms.

(A) *Electron transfer:* Such a bond is established by an atom's losing one or more electrons to another atom or atoms. The combination of sodium with chlorine to form sodium chloride may be used as an example. Table 1 shows that sodium atoms become more stable if they lose their outer electron, and that the same applies to chlorine if it gains an electron. Sodium tends to donate one electron to a chlorine atom resulting in eight electrons in the outer shell of each. Sodium becomes a positively charged, monovalent cation, and chlorine becomes a monovalent, negatively charged anion. The bond described is *electrovalent* or *ionic*. Substances containing such bonds are generally non-volatile and water-soluble. They dissociate electrolytically in water. The electrostatic fields of force around the individual ions cause them to arrange themselves in orderly patterns which determine the crystalline structure of the substance. Crystals of salts are giant aggregates of ions rather than of molecules.

(B) *Electron sharing:* Those atoms which neither lose nor gain electrons readily, share electrons with one another. Consequently the electron systems of the atoms interpenetrate and the atomic nuclei are closer together than in those with ionic bonds. Bonds of this nature are called *non-polar* or *covalent*. At times the term *electron-pair bond* is applied. Whereas in ionic structures the binding forces (fields of force) are exerted in all directions in space, in covalent structures the 'field of force' is exerted between the atoms rather than in space around them. This gives the binding force a definite direction. For this reason the bond is referred to as '*directed valence*' and specific '*bond angles*' must exist between such bonds.

The covalent bond may be illustrated by the structural formula for methane. This substance is a gas containing one carbon atom with four outer electrons and four hydrogen atoms with one electron each. When combination occurs one hydrogen electron and one carbon electron form a pair which are shared by the two atoms. If electrons are represented by dots, methane may be pictured as:

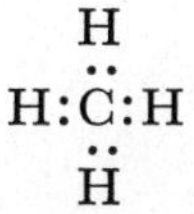

$$H$$
$$H:\overset{..}{\underset{..}{C}}:H$$
$$H$$

METHANE

Double and triple bonds of other molecules can be represented similarly as follows:

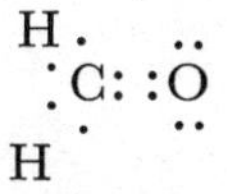

$$\overset{H\;.}{\underset{H}{\;\overset{.}{\underset{.}{C}}::\overset{..}{\underset{..}{O}}}} \qquad \text{and} \qquad H:C::C:H$$

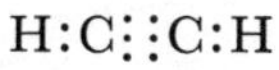

FORMALDEHYDE   ACETYLENE

It may be seen in these formulas that all the participating atoms have attained the configuration of inert gases by sharing the necessary number of electrons to form octets. Absence of the powerful external field of electrical forces which is characteristic of the ionic compounds accounts for many of the physical characteristics such as the comparatively low melting and boiling points of the covalent structures.

OPTICAL ISOMERISM

Many substances have a specific optical effect on polarized light which is frequently utilized in identifying the substance. The degree of rotation of the plane of polarized light by an optically active substance depends upon its concentration, the wavelength of the light used, the temperature, and the distance the light travels through the solution. The measurement of optical rotation is usually performed in a *polarimeter* under specified conditions. The *specific rotation* is the rotation of polarized light in degrees by a solution containing 1 gram of substance per cc. of solution viewed through a thickness of 10 cm. The temperature and the wavelength of the light used must be stated. The light from a sodium lamp is frequently employed and is designated by the letter D (indicating the wavelength of the spectral D line). The symbol $[\alpha]_D^{20°}$ means the specific rotation of light of the wavelength of the D line at 20°C. If the plane of the light is rotated clockwise the substance is *dextrorotatory*, and if the rotation is in the opposite direction it is *levorotatory*.

The structure of lactic acid may be used to illustrate optical isomerism. The formula is:

$$CH_3 - \underset{\underset{OH}{|}}{\overset{\overset{H}{|}}{C}} - COOH$$

LACTIC ACID

The center carbon atom in this formula has four different atoms or groups of atoms attached to it and is, therefore, *asymmetric*. The asymmetry gives rise to the specific property of rotating the plane of polarized light.

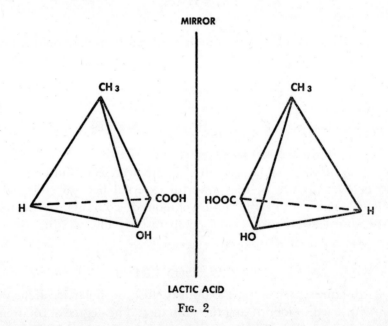

LACTIC ACID

FIG. 2

Figure 2 shows the conventional way of picturing the two possible forms (isomers) of the lactic acid molecule in a spatial arrangement so that one is the mirror image of the other one. These two forms represent the substances corresponding to right and left rotation of the plane polarized light. They are referred to as D-lactic acid and L-lactic acid respectively. If the two forms

are mixed in equal proportions the effect of one on polarized light counter-
acts that of the other. Such a mixture is called *racemic*.

Many organic substances contain more than one asymmetric carbon atom
and thus may give rise to numerous isomers. Tartaric acid has two asymmetric carbon atoms in the molecule. Two of the forms are mirror images
of each other and correspond to D- and L-forms. A mixture of equal amounts
of these is racemic tartaric acid. Figure 3 shows a third arrangement of the

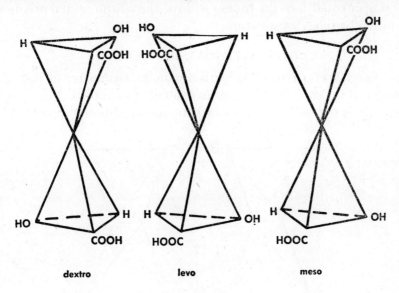

TARTARIC ACIDS

Fig. 3

atoms. In this structure there is symmetry between the two halves of the molecule. No effect on polarized light can be observed because each half of the
molecule compensates the rotatory effect of the other. The substance having
this structure is mesotartaric acid. The three structures of Figure 3 are written
in planar formulas as follows:

```
      COOH              COOH              COOH
        |                 |                 |
   H—C—OH            OH—C—H             H—C—OH
        |                 |                 |
  OH—C—H             H—C—OH             H—C—OH
        |                 |                 |
      COOH              COOH              COOH
     DEXTRO-            LEVO-             MESO-
```

TARTARIC ACIDS

These conventional ways of representing stereoisomers are convenient for
purposes of illustration. They depict the relative spatial arrangement of the

atoms in these substances, although their absolute position in space cannot be defined.

It is usually observed that only 1 of several possible stereoisomers occurs in nature, and that the 'unnatural' isomers cannot replace the 'natural' ones in normal biological processes. Such for instance is the case with the D- and L-forms of the amino acids. Certain microrganisms will metabolize one form and not the other. If racemic tartaric acid is exposed to penicillin glaucum under proper conditions the fungus will use the D-form preferentially so that the solution becomes levorotatory.

GEOMETRICAL ISOMERISM

The existence of a type of isomerism without asymmetry of the molecule was predicted by Van't Hoff before an example was known. The basis for his prediction was the belief that two carbon atoms combined through a double

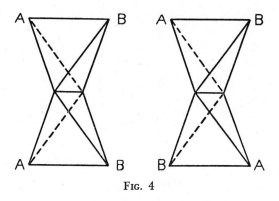

Fig. 4

bond cannot rotate freely around their mutual axis. Therefore, the presence of two unlike substituents upon each carbon can give rise to two different structures. Such isomerism is not associated with any specific optical activity, nor does it, of course, depend upon the presence of asymmetric carbon atoms. The tetrahedron of Figure 4 illustrates the fixed position of the carbon atoms, and that two substitutes A and B can be arranged to give two substances. These two 'geometrical' isomers can also be depicted by planar structure as follows:

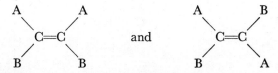

In the one structure the two substituents are fixed on the same side of the ethylenic system tnd in the other on opposite sides. The two configurations are referred to as the *cis-form* and the *trans-form,* and the phenomenon is sometimes called *cis-trans isomerism*. It is not always possible to determine the exact relationship of the substituents to the plane of the molecule even if geometrical isomerism can be demonstrated. In such cases it is common to refer to the two structures as the α- and β-forms. Geometrical isomerism plays an important practical role in clinical biochemistry and examples of such spatial arrangements will be discussed in relationship to the steroids.

NOMENCLATURE

At the present time there are several hundred thousand organic compounds which are well defined in relation to their molecular structure and general chemical characteristics. These formulas are complex and differ widely in type, and their systematic classification naturally requires an involved nomenclature. There are three large divisions of organic chemistry covering aliphatic, aromatic, and heterocyclic compounds. The *aliphatic* division consists of open-chain structures which may be straight or branched. If the chain is straight it means that no carbon atom is attached to more than two others while in the branched type of structure at least one carbon atom is connected to three or four other carbon atoms. Some aliphatic compounds exhibit ring formation but the chemical characteristics of these rings are quite different from those of the aromatic and heterocyclic compounds. Chemical reactions involving aliphatic ring structures often open the ring in contradistinction to the more stable aromatic and heterocyclic types of rings.

The *aromatic* compounds may be considered derivatives of benzene. The benzene ring consists of 6 carbon atoms. It is usually depicted with every alternate bond as a double bond. This accounts for the tetravalency of carbon in benzene and benzene derivatives, although the way in which the binding forces are actually distributed is not definitely established. The benzene ring is usually indicated by a hexagon in which the alternating single and double bonds are shown or assumed.

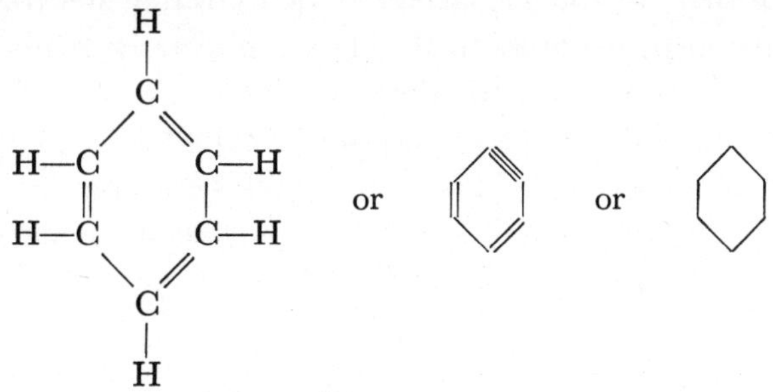

BENZENE

Stable carbon ring structures having fewer or more than six atoms are called *alicyclic*.

The *heterocyclic* division of organic compounds comprises ring structures in which atoms other than carbon occur in the ring. Many important bio-logical substances are included in this division. Nitrogen frequently occurs in the ring.

Organic acids. An acid contains hydrogen which can be replaced by posi-tive elements or groups to form salts. The acidic properties are attributed to the great activity of the hydrogen ions when they become dissociated. The replaceable hydrogen in organic acids is usually that in the carboxyl group ($-COOH$), although other hydrogen containing groups may impart acid characteristics. The OH-group in phenol (C_6H_5OH), for instance, is acid in character. The estrogenic hormones contain such OH-groups and they can be separated from other steroid hormones through their acid properties. Monobasic acids contain one carboxyl group as in acetic acid (CH_3COOH) or benzoic acid (C_6H_5COOH). Dibasic acids contain two carboxyl groups as in oxalic acid ($COOH-COOH$) or succinic acid ($COOH-CH_2-CH_2-COOH$).

Alcohols are hydroxides of organic radicals as exemplified by methyl alcohol (CH_3OH), ethyl alcohol (C_2H_5OH), benzoyl alcohol ($C_6H_5CH_2OH$), etc. . . . *Primary, secondary, tertiary* alcohols have the configurations $-CH_2OH$, $=CHOH$, and $\equiv COH$ respectively. A newer system of nomen-clature uses the ending *ol* to indicate an alcohol; thus methyl alcohol is called methanol and ethyl alcohol is ethanol. The terms *diol, triol,* etc. denote the number of OH groups in the molecule.

Ethers, which are oxides of organic radicals, are usually considered as de-rivatives of alcohols because they are most commonly prepared by removal of H_2O from the hydroxyl groups of two molecules of alcohols. The two alkyl groups are linked together by the oxygen atom as in methyl ether (CH_3OCH_3) and ethyl ether ($C_2H_5OC_2H_5$). Ethers may be considered as derived from water in which the two hydrogen atoms are replaced with alkyl groups. Sometimes the term *alkyloxides* is applied.

Esters are formed by the replacement of ionizable hydrogen in an acid with a hydrocarbon or other radical. They are usually formed by the inter-action of alcohols and acids with the loss of water, the acid may be either organic or inorganic. This type of reaction is called *esterification.* Examples are ethyl acetate ($C_2H_5OOCCH_3$) and ethyl benzoate ($C_2H_5OOCC_6H_5$).

Aldehydes are intermediate in oxidation between primary alcohols and carboxylic acids. The characteristic radical is

$$
\begin{array}{c}
H \\
| \\
(-C=O)
\end{array}
$$

and it may be derived from the primary alcohol group ($-CH_2OH$) by removal of two hydrogen atoms.

Ketones have two hydrogen atoms less than a secondary alcohol group

(=CHOH). The specific ketone radical (=C=O) is called a *carbonyl* group.

Amines are derived from ammonia by substitution of one or more of the hydrogen atoms with certain organic radicals belonging to the aliphatic or aromatic divisions. As ammonia contains three hydrogen atoms the number of substituents may be one, two, or three and the corresponding compounds are designated as *primary* (RNH_2), *secondary* (R_2NH) and *tertiary* (R_3N) amines.

Alkyl halides are halogen derivatives of the alcohols and are usually derived through replacement of the hydroxyl group of an alcohol by a halogen as in ethyl chloride (C_2H_5Cl) and methyl bromide (CH_3Br). Alkyl halides are also derived by replacement of one or more of the hydrogens of a saturated hydrocarbon with halogen as in chloroform ($CHCl_3$) or carbon tetrachloride (CCl_4).

Acid halides are derived from acids by replacement of the hydroxyl group with halogen. They are characterized by the fact that the halogen atom can be removed easily by hydrolysis. Examples would be acetyl chloride, derived from acetic acid

$$CH_3\overset{\|}{\underset{O}{C}}Cl,$$

and benzoyl chloride, derived from benzoic acid

$$C_6H_5\overset{\|}{\underset{O}{C}}Cl.$$

Acid amides result from the replacement of the hydroxyl group of an acid by NH_2 as in

$$\text{ACETAMIDE } CH_3\overset{\|}{\underset{O}{C}}{-}NH_2$$

and

$$\text{BENZAMIDE } C_6H_5\overset{\|}{\underset{O}{C}}{-}NH_2.$$

Alkyl cyanides or nitriles are derived by replacement of one hydrogen atom of an alkane by the cyanide radical as in methyl cyanide (CH_3CN).

Nitro compounds are derived by replacement of hydrogen with the nitro group as in nitromethane (CH_3NO_2) or nitrobenzene ($C_6H_5NO_2$).

Nitroso compounds result from the replacement of hydrogen by the nitroso radical (−N=O). Aliphatic nitroso compounds are known only when the alkyl group is tertiary as in t-nitroso butane (($CH_3)_3C{-}N{=}O$). The aromatic nitroso compounds are quite common. Nitrosobenzene ($C_6H_5N{=}O$) will serve as an example.

Oximes are obtained from aldehydes and ketones by replacement of oxygen with $=N-OH$. The oximes can exist as geometrical isomers due to the spatial restrictions of the double bond. Aldoximes are derived from aldehydes (acetoxime, $CH_3=N-OH$), and ketoximes from ketones

$$\text{Acetone Oxime} \quad \begin{array}{c} CH_3 \\ \diagdown \\ \quad C=N-OH. \\ \diagup \\ CH_3 \end{array}$$

Hydrazines are derivatives of hydrazine (H_2NNH_2) by replacement of hydrogen with alkyl or aryl groups as in methyl hydrazine (CH_3NHNH_2) and hydrazobenzene ($C_6H_5NHNHC_6H_5$).

Osazones are derived by replacement of oxygen in aldehydes or ketones with $=N-NHC_6H_5$. They are useful in the identification of sugars by reaction of aldehyde or ketone sugars with phenylhydrazine ($C_6H_5NHNH_2$).

Hydroxylamines are derivatives of hydroxylamine (H_2N-OH) by replacement of one hydrogen with an alkyl or aryl group. Methyl hydroxylamine (CH_3NHOH) or phenylhydroxylamine (C_6H_5NHOH) will serve as examples.

Diazo compounds result from the diazotization of amines with nitrous acid. The alkyl diazonium compounds are unstable, and lose N_2 at once. The aromatic diazonium compounds are quite stable and can be represented by benzene diazonium chloride ($C_6H_5N:N-Cl$). The aromatic diazonium compounds are of importance in the dye industry.

Azo compounds are of the general structure $R-N=N-R$, where R is any aryl grouping. These compounds are colored. Azobenzene ($C_6H_5-N=NC_6H_5$) will serve as an example.

Amino acids are compounds which contain both the carboxyl and amino grouping. The alpha amino acids are the building blocks of proteins.

$$\text{Alanine} \quad \begin{array}{c} CH_3CHCOOH \\ | \\ NH_2 \end{array}$$

and

$$\text{Tyrosine} \quad \begin{array}{c} C_6H_4(OH)CHCOOH \\ | \\ NH_2 \end{array}$$

are representative of the amino acids.

Sulfonic acids are sulfur derivatives of organic compounds. They are in effect derivatives of sulfuric acid, where a hydroxyl group of $HO-SO_2-OH$ has been replaced by an aryl or alkyl group as in ethyl sulfonic acid ($CH_3CH_2SO_2OH$) or benzene sulfonic acid ($C_6H_5SO_2OH$).

Sulfinic acids are derivatives of sulfurous acid (H_2SO_3) in which one of the hydroxyl groups has been replaced by an aryl or alkyl group as in benzene sulfinic acid ($C_6H_5SO_2H$). The sulfinic acids are auto-oxidizable to sulfonic acids.

Mercaptans may be considered as sulfur derivatives of alcohols, in which the oxygen of the alcohol group has been replaced by sulfur as in ethyl mercaptan (CH_3CH_2SH).

Aromatic ring structures: The nomenclature of ring structures will be discussed as they are encountered in the text. The systematic classification of organic substances uses definite rules for the numbering of the carbon atoms in the various formulas so that a number written before a substituent radical indicates the carbon atom to which it is attached. The capital letter N- is used as a prefix in the names of certain nitrogen compounds to show that such groups have displaced hydrogen from a nitrogen atom. This designation should not be confused with a small n- which denotes a so-called normal or straight chain compound of a series. N-Methylpyrrole may be cited as an example of a compound in which the methyl group has replaced a hydrogen atom bound to the nitrogen atom. Its formula is $C_6H_4=N.CH_3$.

THE STUDY OF ORGANIC STRUCTURAL FORMULAS

In spite of their complexity structural formulas constitute the simplest and most precise way of expressing chemical changes and they are indispensable in presentation of biochemical reactions. Most of these reactions involve only a comparatively small part of the molecular structure and if the reader's attention is focused on the part involved he can frequently study organic equations with great benefit even if he does not possess expert knowledge of organic chemistry. Wherever possible this text will direct attention to reacting groups by presenting them in heavy type. The same will apply to formulas in which distinct groups within the molecule are responsible for specific biological activity.

SUPPLEMENTARY READING

PAULING, L.: *The Nature of the Chemical Bond.* Cornell University Press, 1940.
SHRINER, R. L., ADAMS, and MARVEL, C. S.: Stereoisomerism, in H. Gilman, *Organic Chemistry*, Vol. I., p. 214. John Wiley and Sons, Inc. 1943.

Chapter 3

ACID BASE RELATIONS

CHEMICAL EQUILIBRIUM

MOST chemical reactions do not proceed to their theoretical end point; they stop when the reacting components reach stable equilibrium. Biochemical reactions frequently involve a relatively small change in the proportions of the participating components from one stable equilibrium to another. Organic reactions proceed at rather slow rates, and biochemical equilibria involving organic compounds are generally attained through changes between a number of substances so that an appreciable delay may occur between an event initiating a reaction and the ultimate result.

These considerations have certain practical aspects. For instance, the clinician may wish to accomplish changes in the organism by intravenous administration of suitable substances, and often he measures the result by determination of the concentration of the involved components in the blood. The changes in the blood may be accomplished long before the cellular changes have come to equilibrium, and it should not be presumed that such equilibrium has been reached because blood determinations so indicate.

LAW OF MASS ACTION

This law states that the rate of a chemical reaction is proportional to the active masses of the reacting substances. A simple reversible chemical reaction may be expressed as follows:

$$A+B \rightleftarrows C+D.$$

This equation indicates that two components A and B can be converted into two other substances C and D and also that the reaction can occur in the opposite direction. Obviously an equilibrium of the two systems will exist when the rates of the two reactions are equal. If the masses of the participants are indicated by bracketing their symbols the two reaction speeds can be expressed by the equations:

$$s_1 = k_1[A][B]$$

and

$$s_2 = k_2[C][D]$$

in which k_1 and k_2 are proportionality constants. When the two reaction rates are equal, i.e., $s_1 = s_2$, the equilibrium is determined by the expression:

$$\frac{[C][D]}{[A][B]} = \frac{k_1}{k_2} = K.$$

K is called the *equilibrium constant* for the reaction.

The law of mass action may be applied to the electrolytic dissociation of a weak electrolyte. For example the dissociation of acetic acid into hydrogen and acetate ions may be written:

$$CH_3COOH \rightleftharpoons H^+ + CH_3COO^-$$

and equilibrium of this system is indicated by

$$\frac{[H^+][CH_3COO^-]}{[CH_3COOH]} = k.$$

In an ionizable system such as this, k is called the *ionization constant*.

If a system is considered in which there is more than one replaceable hydrogen atom, a similar equation can be written for each step in the electrolytic dissociation. Carbonic acid may be cited as an example of a substance with two replaceable hydrogen atoms, and the dissociation equations for each step are

$$H_2CO_3 \rightleftharpoons H^+ + HCO_3^-$$

$$HCO_3^- \rightleftharpoons H^+ + CO_3^{--}.$$

These two reactions are represented by their individual ionization constants:

$$\frac{[H^+][HCO_3^-]}{[H_2CO_3]} = k_1$$

$$\frac{[H^+][CO_3^{--}]}{[HCO_3^-]} = k_2.$$

Ionization equilibria are at times expressed by the symbol pK which is defined as the negative logarithm of the dissociation constant:

$$pK = \log \frac{1}{k}.$$

SOLUBILITY PRODUCT

When a substance AB dissociates into its components A and B the law of mass action can be applied as follows:

$$\frac{[A][B]}{[AB]} = k^1.$$

If a saturated solution AB is produced the concentration AB becomes constant, and the addition of more AB to the solution would remain undissolved. At the saturation point AB is, therefore, constant and the equation can be written:

$$[A][B] = k.$$

[A] [B] expressed by k is called the solubility product and this value represents the relative solubility of AB under the particular physical circumstances. Any further addition of either A or B will cause precipitation of undissociated AB. The deposition of calcium salts in the bone matrix may be considered as an important example of the application of solubility products to biochemical reactions (see Chapter 16).

NEUTRALIZATION

The acidic or basic properties of a substance depend on the number or concentration of hydrogen ions formed by its dissociation. It is convenient to use the term *pH* to express hydrogen ion concentrations. This term may be understood by consideration of the reaction of an acid with a base such as the neutralization of hydrochloric acid with sodium hydroxide.

$$HCl + NaOH \rightleftharpoons NaCl + H_2O.$$

This reaction involves the ions of the highly dissociated acid and base:

$$H^+ + Cl^- + Na^+ + OH^- \rightleftharpoons Na^+ + Cl^- + H_2O.$$

It will be seen that the neutralization is accomplished by hydrogen and hydroxyl ions combining to form undissociated water and that sodium and chloride ions are present in equivalent amounts on both sides of the equation. The neutralization reaction, therefore, can be expressed by the equation:

$$H^+ + OH^- = H_2O.$$

It may equally well be stated that this expression can be used to evaluate the electrolytic dissociation of water, the ionization constant being determined by:

$$\frac{[H^+][OH^-]}{[H_2O]} = K.$$

The electrolytic dissociation of water proceeds only to a very minor degree so that the value for H_2O may be considered constant and therefore:

$$[H^+][OH^-] = k_w.$$

The value of k_w is equal to 1×10^{-14} molar at 24°C. The dissociation of water gives rise to equal numbers of hydrogen and hydroxyl ions and the concentration of each of these at neutrality is therefore 1×10^{-7} molar. Any solution containing hydrogen ions in this concentration is neutral. Neutrality may be expressed by

$$[H^+] = [OH^-] = 10^{-7}.$$

Any other concentration of hydrogen ions may be indicated by a corresponding numerical value of the exponent. Example: A solution having $H = 1 \times 10^{-4}$ has a pH = 4. The term pH is defined arbitrarily as the positive value of the exponent. The relationship of pH to the concentration of hydrogen ions is as follows:

$$pH = \log \frac{1}{[H^+]}.$$

BUFFERS

If a certain amount of acid or base is added to a given solution the change in hydrogen ion concentration of this solution depends upon both the amounts of acid or base added and on the chemical properties of the solution itself. Certain chemical combinations have the ability to resist large changes in pH upon the addition of acid or base. Such solutions are called buffers and they are usually composed of slightly dissociated acids or bases and their respective salts. A buffer system may be indicated by:

$$\frac{HA}{BA}$$

where HA is the weakly dissociated acid and BA is its salt. Buffers remove hydrogen or hydroxyl ions from solution by a shift in their internal equilibrium. For example.

$$H^+ + \frac{CH_3COOH}{Na^+ + CH_3COO^-} \leftrightarrows CH_3COOH + Na^+.$$

STRONG ACID	ACETIC ACID SODIUM ACETATE BUFFER	WEAK ACID	NEUTRAL SALT OF STRONG ACID

Sodium ions as well as undissociated acetic acid molecules are present on both sides of the equation and the hydrogen ions are removed by a change in the ratio:

$$\frac{CH_3COOH}{CH_3COO^-}.$$

A buffer system will tend to prevent change in hydrogen ion concentrations as long as there is sufficient material present to affect the necessary alteration in the ratio of the components. It should not be thought that a buffer system is capable of keeping hydrogen ion concentrations constant until its point of exhaustion is reached. Actually changes in the ratio of the components permit a fairly wide range of pH to be obtained, but this range is narrow compared to the fluctuations caused by small amounts of acids or bases in non-buffered solutions.

The relationship of hydrogen ion concentration to changes in buffer systems is important for the understanding of many biochemical phenomena of great practical significance. The law of mass action applied to the dissociation of a weak acid may be expressed thus:

$$\frac{[H^+][A^-]}{[HA]} = k \quad \text{or} \quad [H^+] = k\frac{[HA]}{[A^-]}.$$

Most salts are highly ionized regardless of the ionization constant of the corresponding acid, so that the concentration of a salt of a weak acid, BA is practically equal to A⁻. Therefore:

$$[H^+] = k \frac{[HA]}{[BA]} \quad \text{or} \quad \frac{1}{[H^+]} = \frac{1}{k} \times \frac{[BA]}{[HA]}.$$

If the definitions of pK and pH are recalled the last equation may be re-written as

$$pH = pK + \log \frac{[BA]}{[HA]}.$$

This is *Henderson-Hasselbalch's equation* which in effect states that the hydrogen ion concentration of a solution is determined by the ratio of the buffer components and can be calculated from the equation if the values of this ratio and of pK are known.

BLOOD BUFFERS

Metabolic products comprise many substances of acid and alkaline nature which in solution deviate considerably from the pH range of normal body fluids. They must, therefore, be buffered during their transport in the organism to their point of excretion. Blood contains very efficient buffer systems so that its normal range of pH is maintained between 7.3 and 7.45. The limits of pH compatible with life are usually stated to be 6.8 to 7.8. It is only in extremely abnormal conditions that these limits are approached.

The cells and the plasma buffers are separated by the cell membranes so that those in the plasma serve as the primary buffers and those in the cells constitute a secondary group which helps to maintain the efficiency of the plasma buffers. The most active chemical groups in the blood buffer systems are bicarbonates, phosphates, and proteins. They are contained in cells and plasma as follows:

Cell Buffers:

$$\frac{HHb}{KHb}; \quad \frac{HHbO_2}{KHbO_2}; \quad \frac{KH_2PO_4}{K_2HPO_4}$$

Plasma Buffers:

$$\frac{H_2CO_3}{NaHCO_3}; \quad \frac{NaH_2PO_4}{Na_2HPO_4}; \quad \frac{HProt}{NaProt}$$

When a metabolic product is buffered the reaction is not confined to any one of the above systems. Changes in one of the buffer systems imply changes in the rest as they are all in equilibrium. However, it is convenient to study the buffering mechanism of each individual system, keeping in mind that a shift in the components of one system results in changes in all of them.

The action of the *bicarbonate system* may be illustrated by the equation:

$$H^+ + \frac{H_2CO_3}{Na^+ + HCO_3^-} \rightleftarrows H_2CO_3 + Na^+ \rightleftarrows CO_2 + H_2O + Na^+$$

This is a rapid reaction and is accelerated by a zinc-containing enzyme, *carbonic anhydrase*. The CO_2 liberated by the process is eliminated through the lungs. The base in the form of sodium ions is not lost by this process.

A buffer system has a maximum capacity for its buffer effect when the components are present in a ratio equal to one. In a bicarbonate system this ratio would exist at pH = 6.1, as determined by the Henderson-Hasselbalch equation. At the normal pH of blood the ratio of the carbonic acid to bicarbonate is approximately 1 to 20.

The following equation applies to the mechanism of the *phosphate system:*

$$H^+ + \frac{NaH_2PO_4}{2Na^+ + HPO_4^{--}} = NaH_2PO_4 + Na^+$$

The acid phosphatase, NaH_2PO_4, is eliminated in the urine. This is a comparatively slow process and is attended by loss of base.

A special process takes place in the kidney tissues whereby *ammonia* is substituted for part of the base reaching this organ. Feeding experiments with isotopic ammonia and urea result in quantitative recovery of the isotope in the form of urea in the urine, while heavy nitrogen introduced into amino acids appears in the urinary ammonium salts. This indicates that the source of the ammonia is in the direct deamination of amino acids without urea as an intermediate product. Van Slyke and his associates believe that glutamine may be the sole source of the ammonia. The formation of ammonia by the kidneys is regulated by the demand for base in the body in order to regenerate the blood buffers adequately. There is an increase in urinary ammonia output during acidosis and in conditions causing a deficiency of base in the body. During alkalosis when excess of base is available the ammonia excretion is diminished.

The ammonia mechanism is not the only method employed by the kidneys to save base. Part of the dibasic phosphate, B_2HPO_4, is converted to the monobasic salt, BH_2PO_4, by interaction with carbonic acid. Bicarbonate is formed during this reaction and is absorbed by the tubular epithelium. Thus a certain amount of phosphoric acid present in the blood as dibasic phosphate can be excreted as a monobasic phosphate with loss to the body of only half the amount of base originally present as phosphate.

$$B_2HPO_4 + H_2CO_3 = BH_2PO_4 + BHCO_3$$

The bicarbonate excretion in the urine may vary greatly. Alkaline urine may contain as much as 10 grams of $NaHCO_3$ daily while very acid urine contains only a small fraction of a gram.

Although acid components must be buffered in the plasma to maintain its normal pH, the kidneys are able to excrete a certain amount of acid in the free form and in this manner to conserve base. For instance the acetone bodies in diabetic acidosis are excreted to an appreciable extent as free acids.

The *hemoglobin system* in the red cells constitutes an important buffer

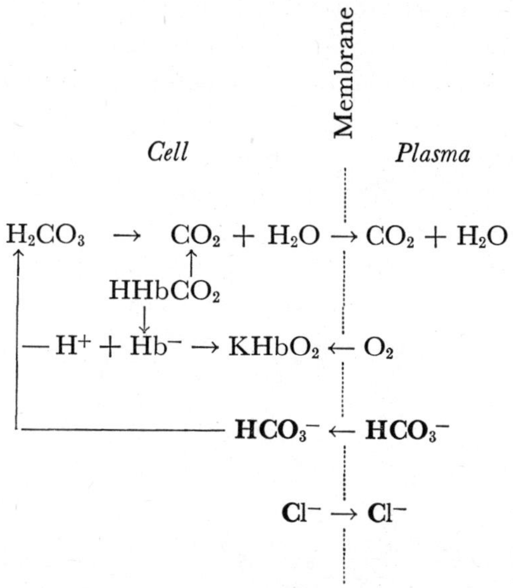

$$\begin{array}{c}
\text{Cell} \qquad\qquad\qquad\qquad\qquad \text{Plasma} \\[2pt]
H_2CO_3 \;\rightarrow\; CO_2 + H_2O \rightarrow CO_2 + H_2O \\
\uparrow \qquad\qquad \uparrow \\
HHbCO_2 \\
\downarrow \\
-H^+ + Hb^- \rightarrow KHbO_2 \leftarrow O_2 \\
HCO_3^- \leftarrow HCO_3^- \\[6pt]
Cl^- \rightarrow Cl^-
\end{array}$$

Membrane

CHLORIDE SHIFT DURING OXYGENATION OF HEMOGLOBIN

FIG. 5

mechanism. The action is more complex than that of the buffers considered up to this point. The buffer effect of hemoglobin is due to its amphoteric properties as a protein, but this is of minor importance quantitatively. Oxyhemoglobin is a stronger acid than hemoglobin and therefore combines with more base at the pH of blood. When oxyhemoglobin is reduced to hemoglobin, less base bound by hemoglobin is needed to retain the proper pH and considerable base is thus made available for combination with CO_2. At the pH of blood oxyhemoglobin unites with approximately eight times more base than hemoglobin. Furthermore carbon dioxide and hemoglobin form a direct combination through an amino group, the resulting substance being a carbamino acid or carbhemoglobin. About 20 to 25 per cent of the carbon dioxide liberated in the lungs is transported in the form of carbhemoglobin.

The physico-chemical characteristics of the red cell membranes play a major role in the buffering action of blood. These membranes are selectively permeable and in general are more permeable to anions than to cations. Sodium and potassium ions are distributed with most of the potassium inside the cells and probably all the sodium in the plasma. Isotopic hydrogen on the contrary can be shown to pass freely back and forth through the cell membranes.

A large portion of the plasma sodium is present in the form of sodium chloride. If hydrochloric acid is added to sodium bicarbonate in a test tube the following reaction takes place:

$$HCl + NaHCO_3 \rightarrow NaCl + H_2O + CO_2.$$

Sodium in the sodium chloride cannot be made available as base for combination with carbon dioxide unless the reaction proceeds in the opposite direction. This cannot occur in a test tube but a special mechanism operating through the red cell membranes makes it possible in blood. Essentially the change of sodium chloride to sodium bicarbonate takes place in the tissue capillaries by migration of chloride ions into the cells where they participate in the internal shift of the cell buffers to maintain a normal pH. In the lungs the reverse reactions take place. This migration of chloride ions into and out of the red cells is called the *chloride shift*. Figure 5 indicates graphically the ion exchange inside and outside of the cells during oxygenation in the lungs. In the tissues where oxygen is being utilized all these processes go in the opposite direction. It should be recalled that the anions shown in the diagram exist with potassium ions inside and with sodium ions outside the cells.

CARBON DIOXIDE TRANSPORT

The bicarbonate buffer system consists of carbon dioxide dissolved both in the free form and as bicarbonate. At a normal pH the ratio of the two forms is 1:20 so that approximately 5 per cent of the total carbon dioxide in blood is present as dissolved CO_2. The amount of CO_2 combined as carbhemoglobin depends upon the state of oxygenation of the hemoglobin and is thought not to exceed 10 per cent. The rest of the carbon dioxide is present as bicarbonate.

Oxygenation or deoxygenation of hemoglobin initiates the changes in the various systems participating in the transport of carbon dioxide which result in the CO_2 release in the lungs. The amount of carbon dioxide transported by these systems does not bear a direct relationship to their CO_2 content in the blood. Approximately $\frac{1}{2}$ of the total carbon dioxide released is transported to the lungs through the mechanism of the chloride shift and $\frac{1}{4}$ of the total may be accounted for by the carbhemoglobin combination. The remainder of the CO_2 is transported through the buffer actions of hemoglobin and of the plasma proteins. The role played by the plasma proteins is rather insignificant and fluctuations in their concentration have little effect upon the transport of carbon dioxide.

It is important from a clinical standpoint to be able to detect abnormal changes in the relative amounts of the blood buffers. It is impractical to do this by determination of the pH of blood as the buffers are efficient enough to prevent readily detectable changes until extreme conditions have been reached. It is much simpler to determine the *alkali reserve* which is represented by the bicarbonate content of the blood. The CO_2 in the bicarbonate in a certain amount of plasma can be measured in the well known Van Slyke apparatus and may be expressed as the *carbon dioxide combining power*. Actually the dissolved carbon dioxide is included in the Van Slyke determination, but it introduces an error of only about 5 per cent. Normal blood contains 50 to 70 volumes-per-cent carbon dioxide as determined by the Van Slyke method.

SUMMARY

Metabolic intermediates and waste products in solution may deviate considerably in their hydrogen ion concentration from the normal pH of blood. The general metabolism introduces material of both acid and alkaline nature although the acid is usually in excess. The various buffer systems of the blood ordinarily prevent significant changes of pH while these metabolic constituents are being transported. The blood buffers are regenerated by two major methods:

A. Elimination of CO_2 in the expired air. This is a rapid process and does not entail the loss of base.

B. Elimination in the urine of phosphates and bicarbonates in proportions according to the amount of excess acid in the blood. This is a relatively slow process and results in the loss of base. Certain mechanisms, such as the formation of ammonia, operate in the kidneys to reduce this loss of base.

Less important means of elimination of waste products of acid and alkaline nature are available, such as direct urinary excretion of acids, the oxidation of organic acid to CO_2 and water and disposal of some acid constituents in the perspiration and intestinal secretions.

ACIDOSIS AND ALKALOSIS

These terms are usually employed according to the definitions given them by Van Slyke and Cullen, namely to signify decrease and increase respectively in the alkali reserve. It is essential that these definitions be kept in mind, as changes in the pH of the blood may not necessarily occur in the directions indicated by the two terms. Actual acidity of blood (pH less than 7) only occurs in extreme conditions; blood is normally slightly alkaline (pH 7.30-7.45) and changes in the alkalinity are associated with shifts in the ratio of the components of the bicarbonate buffer system rather than with changes in the absolute value of the bicarbonate concentration.

The relationship of the two components of the bicarbonate system can be presented diagrammatically as shown in Figure 6 (after Van Slyke). The abscissa measures the CO_2 tension in mm. Hg. pressure and the ordinate the total CO_2 in vol. per cent. Any point in this graph represents definite amounts of H_2CO_3 and $BHCO_3$ and a line drawn through such a point and the origin represents variations in total amounts of components in the same ratio. As the ratio determines the pH according to Henderson-Hasselbalch's equation, any straight line through the origin will pass through points representing the same pH. The line near the abscissa indicates CO_2 present as H_2CO_3. The value of this curve deducted from the total at any point is the amount of CO_2 in the form of bicarbonate. Two lines marked pH 7.3 and pH 7.5 border the area in which the ratios of the buffer systems are within normal limits. Two other lines, pH 7.0 and pH 7.8 comprise the limits of pH compatible with life. The two curved lines are the CO_2 dissociation curves corresponding to oxygenated and reduced blood. The lower curve is that for oxygenated blood. Van Slyke used the term 'compensated' for any change in the buffer system within the normal pH range and the term 'uncompensated' for conditions outside this range. The diagram shows that it is divided into nine areas by the H_2CO_3 dissociation curves and the two lines representing normal

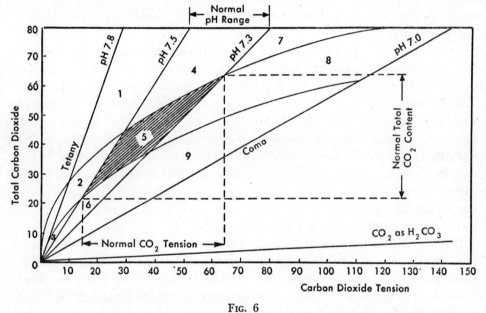

FIG. 6

limits of pH. The conditions corresponding to these nine areas are described by Van Slyke as follows:

1. Uncompensated alkali excess.
2. Uncompensated CO_2 deficit.
3. Uncompensated CO_2 deficit.
4. Compensated alkali or CO_2 excess.
5. Normal acid-base balance.
6. Compensated alkali or CO_2 deficit.
7. Uncompensated CO_2 excess.
8. Uncompensated CO_2 excess.
9. Uncompensated alkali deficit.

Alkali excess may occur as the result of loss of hydrochloric acid by vomiting or by the ingestion of large amounts of alkali. In extreme degrees of un-compensation the ionized calcium concentration may be depressed to such an extent that tetany occurs (see Chapter 16). As this condition is generally associated with persistent vomiting the term 'gastric tetany' has been applied.

Alkali deficit is the result of conditions which place excessive demands upon the alkali reserve. Such conditions are diabetic acidosis, retention of acid waste products in renal failure, and the administration of acid or acid-producing substances.

CO_2 *excess* occurs when there is obstruction to the elimination of carbon dioxide or depression of normal respiration. This condition may, therefore, occur in emphysema and pneumonia or as the effect of morphine on the respiratory center. The uncompensated state is sometimes referred to as 'gaseous acidosis.'

CO_2 *deficit* is commonly associated with hyperventilation. Breathing at high altitudes also tends to produce a CO_2 deficit. The uncompensated condition is referred to as 'gaseous alkalosis.'

It should be realized that the uncompensated and compensated states are sharply divided only because of the arbitrary limits set for the normal pH of blood. Actually the uncompensated conditions represent the same phenomena causing the compensated conditions but are more extreme.

A study of the above acid-base relations will reveal that a decrease in the pH of blood may be caused by either metabolic or respiratory disorders. In the metabolic disorders the alkali reserve is less than normal while in the respiratory types it may be normal or elevated.

Ketosis may cause severe acidosis. The most common cause of ketosis is the disturbance in fat metabolism in diabetes mellitus resulting in the accumulation of β-hydroxybutyric and aceto-acetic acids. There is a continual loss of base in the urine because of the attempt to remove these acid end products of faulty metabolism. Certain other conditions such as starvation, high fat diets, fever, anaesthesia, and impairment of liver function may cause milder forms of ketosis. Ketosis is not always associated with acidosis for ketones may be formed during excessive vomiting resulting in alkalosis. Acidosis is induced easily by administration of acid substances. Ammonium chloride is employed frequently for therapeutic purposes. Mandelic acid or ammonium mandelate has the same effect, and by their use the pH of the urine can be lowered to levels advantageous for the treatment of specific infections.

In progressive renal failure the kidneys lose their ability to excrete the acid metabolites buffered in the blood and the gradual accumulation of these eventually cause exhaustion of the buffer systems terminating in extreme acidosis and coma. A contributory factor in the acidosis of kidney failure may be found in the destruction of tubular tissue and the resulting lack of production of ammonia to conserve base.

The distressing symptoms of acidosis may be relieved by the administration of alkali. The intravenous injection of alkaline or alkali-producing substances temporarily furnishes a new supply of alkali reserve and such therapy is of material benefit to patients temporarily in acidosis from remediable causes. When the underlying pathological state cannot be corrected, as for instance in chronic glomerulonephritis, the availability of a new supply of alkali reserve only postpones the eventual outcome for a matter of hours.

Sodium bicarbonate may be given by proctoclysis or veneclysis. It is more common to use sodium lactate for intravenous therapy. This substance is a good source of base as the lactic acid is gradually oxidized, leaving the sodium ions free to combine with carbon dioxide:

$$H^+ + \frac{CH_3CHOHCOOH}{Na^+ + CH_3CHOHCOO^-} = CH_3CHOHCOOH + Na^+$$

Alkalosis is a common result from severe vomiting. The continuous loss of hydrogen ions in the form of hydrochloric acid leaves an uncompensated alkali excess. It is important to remember that large amounts of sodium chloride are lost in the vomitus and that a serious depletion of chloride ions may ensue. Prolonged gastric lavage or continuous duodenal decompression may produce the same physiological state as persistent vomiting. A decompression outfit should be allowed to function only to the extent necessary for the patient's comfort and the prevention of gastric distention. Assimilation of sodium bicarbonate adds to the alkali reserve and thus may produce alkalosis. It is common practice among many people to use sodium bicarbonate in self-medication of gastro-intestinal disorders, and this may add to the degree of alkalosis initiated by vomiting.

If emesis is severe and persistent the patient eventually passes into a state of dehydration which may change the entire acid-base balance. Electrolytic balance in dehydration will be discussed in Chapter 4.

SUPPLEMENTARY READING

GAMBLE, J. L.: *Chemical Anatomy, Physiology and Pathology of Extracellular Fluid.* Harvard University Press, 1950.

VAN SLYKE, D. D.: The normal and abnormal variations in the acid-base balance of the blood. *J. Biol. Chem., 48:*153, 1921.

VAN SLYKE, D. D., and CULLEN, G. E.: The bicarbonate concentration of blood plasma; its significance and its determination as a measure of acidosis. *J. Biol. Chem., 30:*289, 1917.

Chapter 4

BODY FLUIDS

Most of the cells in the body do not have direct contact with the atmosphere, but are surrounded by fluids through which all metabolic exchanges must be mediated. Pathological states may cause demonstrable changes in the composition of *extracellular fluid,* and abnormal states of this surrounding fluid may effect profoundly the normal biological processes of the cells. Claude Bernard recognized the extracellular fluid as a physiological entity, and referred to it as the 'milieu interieur.' It is made up of the *blood plasma* and the *interstitial fluid* which includes the circulating lymph. *Intracellular fluid* constitutes most of the fluid in the body. The amounts of these fluids relative to total body weight are approximately: plasma 5 per cent, interstitial fluid 15 per cent, and intracellular fluid 50 per cent.

The extracellular fluid supplies the medium in which the transport of metabolic nutrient and waste materials takes place. The constancy of environment necessary for normal cell life is maintained by the various regulatory mechanisms which assure small changes of pH, concentrations of essential mineral and organic constituents, osmotic pressure, water balance, fluid volume, temperature, etc. Under ordinary conditions the two principal organs which regulate these variables are the kidneys and lungs, but under extreme or abnormal conditions other secretory and excretory organs such as the sweat glands contribute materially to the adjustments of body fluid composition.

FLUID COMPOSITIONS

An idea of the importance of the body fluids as functional physiological entities may be obtained by considering the differences in their composition. Any one body fluid is as distinctive from the others in its characteristic make-up as one organ from others in anatomical structure. Interstitial fluid may be considered the evolutionary replacement for the original environment of the unicellular or simple multicellular organism. In composition it resembles sea water of prehistoric times.

Measurements of the concentrations of constituents of body fluids are expressed in various units. Milligrams or grams per 100 cc. are commonly employed by clinical laboratories. This system is satisfactory if applied to non-dissociating substances, but electrolyte concentrations are better stated in equivalents, because the concentration effects of anions and cations may be readily compared when expressed in equivalent amounts, but not from

42

weight-volume relations. A gram equivalent of an atom or molecule is equal to the atomic or molecular weight in grams for monovalent substances. If the functioning group is divalent, trivalent, etc., the atomic or molecular weight must be divided by 2, 3, etc., to obtain the equivalent weight.

Amounts dealt with in body fluid concentrations are usually so small that it is more convenient to use a unit 1,000 smaller. This is called a *milliequivalent* and concentrations may be stated as milliequivalents per liter. As normality of a substance in solution means the number of gram-equivalents present in one liter, it may be seen that 1 milliequivalent per liter comprises a 1/1000 normal solution. An example may help to clarify the use of these terms. Sodium is present in plasma in the amount of approximately 315 mg. per 100 cc. As it is a monovalent element with atomic weight of 23, its concentration is 315/23 = 13.7 mEq./per 100 cc. or 137 mEq. per 1,000 cc. The molecular weight of sodium chloride is 58.5 and the average NaCl concentra-

tion in plasma is $\dfrac{600 \times 10}{58.5} = 103$ mEq. per liter.

In the example given the difference between the total sodium and the sodium as NaCl is 34 mEq. This amount of sodium is mainly sodium bicarbonate with a small part accounted for otherwise. Obviously, the expression of the sodium values in mEq. permits a ready calculation of sodium other than as chloride, which cannot be estimated without conversion of the values in mg. per 100 cc. to mEq. In all biochemical calculations involving electrolyte balance, the mEq. system facilitates the quantitative balancing of anions and cations.

BLOOD COMPOSITION

Normal circulation requires maintenance of the blood volume within rather narrow limits. Whole blood is approximately 1/11 or 9 per cent of the body weight. Changes of blood volume are rapidly counteracted either by diffusion of extravascular fluids, or by elimination of fluid through the usual excretory channels.

The common inorganic cations of plasma are Na^+, K^+, Ca^{++}, and Mg^{++} of which normal concentrations are approximately:

	mg./100 cc.	*mEq./liter*
Sodium	315 ± 10	137 ± 5
Potassium	18 ± 2	4.6 ± 0.5
Calcium	10 ± 1	5.0 ± 0.5
Magnesium	2.1 ± 0.3	1.7 ± 0.3

The anions which balance these cations are mainly Cl^- and HCO_3^- with smaller amounts of HPO_4^{--}, SO_4^{--}, organic acid radicals, and protein. The normal limits of plasma sodium chloride are 600 ± 20 mg. per 100 cc., or 103 ± 3.4 mEq./liter. The bicarbonate concentration is usually stated in terms of carbon dioxide combining power. It may be recalled that CO_2 determinations in the Van Slyke apparatus include also the free carbon dioxide dissolved in the plasma. Extracellular fluid contains small amounts of non-electrolytes representing metabolites in transit to and from the tissue cells. For a discussion of blood proteins see Chapter 7.

Alterations in *blood volume* are associated with a number of pathological states with which the clinician has to deal. The principal change usually is in the water content of the plasma or of the cell, but changes in the dissolved components may occur without change in the water content. The subject of dehydration, because of its clinical importance, will be discussed in a separate section.

Polycythemia and leukemia may be accompanied by increased cell volume which is apt to be more pronounced in the former condition than in the latter. Clinical states associated with hyperproteinemia may result in small increases in blood volume. Anemias may be responsible for slight reductions. In anemia of chronic types this effect is frequently compensated for by an increase in plasma proteins.

Diminution of the concentration of plasma proteins as in burns is associated with a decrease of blood volume. The effect of hemorrhage on the blood volume depends upon the rapidity of the loss of blood. Because of various compensatory mechanisms a slow loss of blood is much less serious than a sudden hemorrhage entailing a comparable loss of red cells. If the loss of blood is not severe enough to cause death, fluid and protein are mobilized from the tissues to restore the blood volume.

The hematopoietic system gradually replaces the lost cells but this process is much slower than the mobilization of fluid. Therefore red cell counts following sudden hemorrhage give an approximate measure of the restoration of volume. Actually the picture is not as simple as described because other compensatory factors are present, such as reduction in the capacity of the vascular bed and the discharge of red cells into the blood stream by contraction of the spleen. The latter process probably is unimportant in the human species.

INTERSTITIAL FLUID COMPOSITION

This fluid is quite similar to plasma in its composition except that it contains only a small amount of protein. Since blood and intracellular fluid volumes remain very constant, fluctuations in fluid content are confined almost entirely to changes in the volume of the interstitial fluid.

INTRACELLULAR FLUID COMPOSITION

There is a great difference in the composition of extracellular and intracellular fluids. The cations in the latter consist mainly of K^+ and Mg^{++}; it is doubtful if any sodium at all is present. These cations are balanced by the anions HPO_4^{--}, SO_4^{--}, and protein. The potassium content of cells is very high compared with that of plasma; its concentration in the red cells of the normal subject is approximately 420 mg. while the plasma value is 16 to 20 mg. per 100 cc.

WATER BALANCE

This term implies that water intake equals water output. Most of the required intake is satisfied by ingestion of water but a part is satisfied by water formed in metabolic processes. An average diet yields approximately 300 grams of water daily from the latter source. Water loss from the body depends on many factors. The daily excretion of urine averages approximately 1,500 cc. but this amount is subject to wide fluctuations. The perspiration and invisible evaporation from the skin may account for a loss of about 500 cc. in 24 hours with wide variations, depending on energy expenditure of the individual and upon the temperature and humidity of the surroundings. Expired air contains moisture, occasioning a water loss of 300 to 400 cc. in 24 hours. This figure depends on the same variable factors as loss from the skin. Finally the feces account for the loss of about 200 cc. from the intestinal tract. In studying the water loss of patients, it is easy enough to measure fluid output in the form of urine, vomitus, surgical drainage, feces, etc., but the loss by direct evaporation, the *insensible loss,* ordinarily can only be estimated.

The daily excretion of water may give a very erroneous impression of its function in the body. The kidneys and the secretory structures in the digestive tract filter out tremendous volumes of fluids daily, and the small intake required for normal water balance is only possible because these organs have very efficient methods of reabsorbing this water. The glomerular filtrate varies in volume within wide limits. The daily amount may easily be 50 to 100 liters and on occasion far exceeds these amounts. The digestive fluids represent volumes of several liters. The gastric and the intestinal secretions in the average adult each comprise approximately 3 liters. The volume of saliva may be approximately 1.5 liters and the bile and pancreatic juice bring the total fluid secreted into the intestinal tract up to 8 liters or more in 24 hours.

URINE

The average adult excretes 1,000 to 1,800 cc. of urine daily. If his fluid intake is insufficient this volume may decrease. The kidneys require at least 500 cc. of fluid excretion daily to maintain normal elimination of waste products. When the amount of urine is small, it becomes highly concentrated in the healthy individual and the specific gravity is usually about

1.030. From 2/5 to 3/5 of the daily water intake eventually is eliminated as urine unless environmental factors deviate considerably from normal. Pathological states may alter the ratio of water intake to urinary output. Diabetes insipidus and diabetes mellitus for instance cause polyuria. If the insensible loss is high or loss of water by other means predominate the urine volume may be relatively small. Cardiac and renal insufficiency reduce the amount of urine excreted.

The composition of urine is very complex, as the kidneys excrete a great many metabolic waste products. The urine also contains normal body constituents in excess of body needs. The elimination of buffer components in the urine to maintain normal acid-base balance has been discussed in Chapter 3. The inorganic urinary constituents are mainly chlorides, phosphates, and sulfates of sodium, potassium, ammonium, calcium, and magnesium, with varying amounts of bicarbonates. Organic waste products are urea, creatinine, uric acid and other nitrogenous substances such as amino acids. Certain components of urine such as glucose, proteins, ketone bodies, bile pigments, etc., are found only in traces in the urine of normal individuals, but may increase to major proportions in disease.

The specific gravity is a reliable index of the total solids in the urine. Normal kidneys are able to excrete concentrated or diluted urine according to the dilution of the blood. Normally the extreme range of specific gravity may extend from 1.001 to 1.036; under average conditions the range is generally 1.015 to 1.025. Progressive destruction of kidney function results in loss of ability to concentrate or dilute the urine, and the outside limits of specific gravity converge toward 1.010, which is the approximate specific gravity of the glomerular filtrate.

OSMOTIC PRESSURE

The distribution of fluid between the tissues and the vascular system is controlled by several factors. Capillary walls are semipermeable, and allow substances of small molecular size to pass through, while large molecules like the plasma proteins cannot diffuse to an appreciable extent. As the force which propels the fluid through the vascular system is supplied through the contraction of the heart, the pressure within the vessels is higher than that of the surrounding tissue fluids and this *hydrostatic pressure* difference forces fluid from the vascular system into the tissues. The other force which helps to maintain proper fluid distribution is *osmotic pressure*.

The osmotic pressure in a system depends upon the number of particles present per unit of volume and not upon the kind of molecules. Thus, undissociated large molecules in concentrated solution contribute comparatively slightly to the osmotic pressure, while small non-diffusible molecules in large number exert a considerable effect, particularly if they are dissociated.

The difference in osmotic pressure on two sides of a membrane is determined by non-diffusible substances, as the diffusible components will pass through freely and distribute themselves in osmotic equilibrium. That the diffusible molecules or ions do not necessarily attain identical concentrations on both sides of the membrane was shown by *Donnan,* who developed mathematical expressions which define the relations between the diffusible ions and lyophilic colloidal complexes in biological systems. The capillary membrane is permeable to most of the inorganic ions and to the organic substances of relatively small molecular size. Therefore, the difference in osmotic pressure between blood and interstitial fluid is determined largely by the protein concentration of the blood. When the level of plasma proteins is less than about 5 per cent the osmotic pressure is reduced to the point where escape of intravascular fluid causes edema. Note that the osmotic relationship between intravascular and interstitial fluid is considered as a difference in osmotic pressure. This should be distinguished from absolute osmotic pressure which is almost exclusively determined by the concentrations of the ionic components. In plasma the colloid osmotic pressure is probably less than 1 per cent of the total absolute osmotic pressure, but because of their non-diffusible nature the colloids regulate the diffusion of water out of or into the small branches of the vascular bed.

The total concentration of cations in the extracellular fluid determines its osmotic pressure as there is a reciprocal relationship between the bicarbonate ions and other anions. For practical purposes the cation value is taken to be that of the sodium ions, and the renal control of sodium level is necessary for osmotic stability of the extracellular fluid. Sudden variations in Na^+ concentrations may occur as the result of intake of sodium salts in the food, and transitory adjustments in osmotic relationships take place by diffusion of water into and out of the cells.

DEHYDRATION

It has already been pointed out that changes in volume of the fluid compartments of the body are largely confined to the interstitial fluid which may undergo variations of considerable magnitude from day to day. The other fluid volumes are more constant and it has just been shown that changes in sodium concentration of the extracellular fluid reflect the change in volume of the intracellular component. The change in extracellular fluid volume may be expressed simply as being the variation in weight of the individual over a short period of time.

Under normal conditions the daily fluid loss is made up by an equal intake of water. If this replacement is not made, the result is dehydration. Excretion of water is accompanied by excretion of electrolytes. Thus, the loss of fluid is not simply a loss of water, but a loss of dissolved electrolytes and of organic

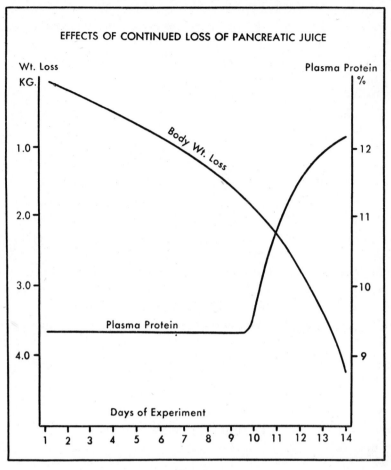

EFFECTS OF CONTINUED LOSS OF PANCREATIC JUICE

FIG. 7

substances, and the term 'dehydration' describes only part of the actual state of affairs when body fluids are depleted. The integrity of osmotic relationships in the body depends upon the maintenance of electrolyte concentrations within narrow limits. Thus, in the dehydrated individual a proper state of hydration cannot be reinstated by administration of water alone. The clinician will do well to consider the word 'dehydration' as meaning 'water and electrolyte depletion' in spite of its direct implication of water only.

Figure 7 (from J. L. Gamble: *Chemical Anatomy, Physiology and Pathology of Extracellular Fluid*), shows graphically the effect of gradual electrolyte loss on the plasma volume. The experiment illustrated was performed on a dog with a pancreatic fistula. Dehydration resulted from the continuous loss of sodium in the pancreatic juice. The water loss was replaced by adequate administration of water, but the sodium ion was not replenished as the dog was fed meat from which practically all sodium had been removed. The weight loss was taken as an index of the dehydration, and the concentration of the plasma proteins served as an estimate of plasma volume. The diagram shows that the decrease in the interstitial reserve of fluid served to maintain a normal plasma volume for the first 10 days of the experiment. After the exhaustion of the interstitial fluid resources the plasma volume diminished rapidly.

Apparently the interstitial reservoir compensates for the fluid loss in the early stages of dehydration, and the eventual failure of this supply of water results in the manifestations of severe dehydration. During the more or less symptomless period of dehydration, the shrinking of the amount of water in the interstitial fluid is accompanied by a corresponding excretion of sodium as a means of maintaining the osmotic balance. As the degree of dehydration becomes more severe, the interstitial fluid begins to draw on the resources of the intracellular fluid which also requires electrolyte adjustment. As the dominant cation within the cells is potassium, the excreta contain proportionately larger amounts of K^+ as the dehydration progresses. Determination of the potassium excretion gives an approximate estimate of the loss of intracellular fluid.

Dehydration occurs when the fluid intake is inadequate to balance normal losses or when the loss of fluid exceeds the amount the individual is able to assimilate. Dehydration also may result from a negative electrolyte balance.

Dysfunctions of the gastro-intestinal tract, associated with persistent vomiting or diarrhea, constitute the most frequent cause of dehydration. Gamble states that the distribution of digestive secretions in 24 hours average as follows:

Saliva	1,500 cc.
Gastric secretions	2,500 cc.
Bile	500 cc.
Pancreatic juice	700 cc.
Secretion of intestinal mucosa	3,000 cc.
Total	8,200 cc.

It is evident that a continuous loss of these secretions may produce a significant depletion of body fluids in a short time. Also it should be remembered that severe disturbances in gastro-intestinal function usually prevent the patient from ingesting fluids.

Gamble's method of presenting fluid compositions graphically illustrates the manner in which the electrolytes may be apportioned as a result of losses of fluid from the gastro-intestinal tract. Figure 8 is reprinted from his book.

The diagram shows the concentrations of cations and anions in the various fluids and their relation to those of plasma. If a serious loss of one of these fluids is sustained by an individual the result eventually must be an alteration in the structure of the plasma since it is the ultimate source of the gastro-

ELECTROLYTE COMPOSITION OF GASTRO-INTESTINAL SECRETIONS

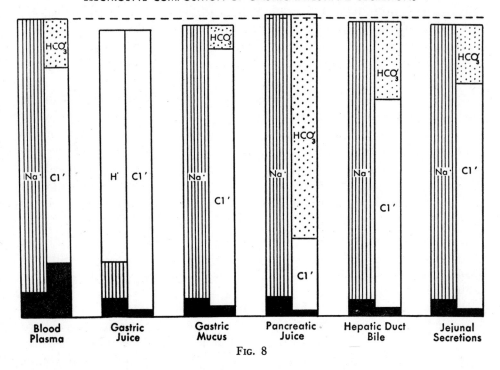

FIG. 8

intestinal secretions. Gastric and pancreatic juice show the greatest departure from plasma in composition. The gastric juice may not derive any sodium by secretions from the digestive glands. However, it always contains a certain admixture of gastric mucus. This may be markedly increased in inflammatory states of the mucosa, and thus may add materially to the loss of sodium by emesis.

Loss of sodium and chloride ions can only be replaced by sources outside the body while practically all the other components can be supplied by the metabolism during normal or pathological conditions. Thus the factors which determine the change in plasma composition are not only the amounts, but also the ratio of sodium and chloride in the fluid lost.

If the loss of fluid is confined mainly to the gastric secretion it is obvious from its acid nature that the loss of chloride far exceeds that of sodium. Therefore, the excess of sodium retained in the plasma forms sodium bicarbonate and alkalosis results. The alkalosis then is partly countered by diuresis with an increased excretion of base in the urine.

The water loss in persistent vomiting may thus be accounted for by (1) direct loss in the vomitus; and (2) by diuresis. The low sodium content of the blood is the result of (1) loss of gastric mucus in the vomitus; and (2) loss of base in the urine.

The dehydration effect of sustained loss of pancreatic juice has been discussed previously. It may be recalled that dogs with pancreatic fistulas become dehydrated in proportion to their loss of sodium. Continued loss of pancreatic juice eventually results in acidosis because of this loss of base.

When the degree of dehydration approaches a state of anuria the failure of the kidneys to remove excess of acid metabolic products contributes to disturbances in the acid-base balance. This factor must be taken into consideration when the carbon dioxide combining power of blood is evaluated during advanced pathological states involving the gastro-intestinal tract. For instance, in diffuse peritonitis with dehydration to the point of oliguria or anuria, the CO_2 combining power is usually less than normal in spite of persistent vomiting. Only a determination of the total base in the plasma of such patients, of course, would reveal the actual extent of loss of base. Because of the quantitative importance of sodium, the loss of total base is practically equal to the loss of sodium.

Diarrhea often results in dehydration which may develop very rapidly in infants. Acidosis associated with diarrhea is more likely to be a secondary effect due to renal failure caused by dehydration rather than to removal of sodium in excess over chloride ion.

TREATMENT OF DEHYDRATION

This is designed to accomplish two ends: (1) restoration of fluid volume and (2) replacement of electrolyte loss. It has already been pointed out that sodium and chloride ions are the only ones which must be supplied and physiological saline solution is, therefore, well suited for the parenteral administration of these two essential ions. Regulation of excretion by the kidneys will eventually accomplish a normal distribution of sodium and chloride ions in the various fluid compartments provided there is enough water available for adequate renal function. This can be assured by the additional use of isotonic glucose solution. The glucose serves a dual purpose because it not only replaces water which has been lost, but it helps to prevent ketosis occasioned by starvation.

Effectual guidance for the clinician in his treatment of dehydration may be furnished by determinations of urea or non-protein nitrogen, CO_2 combining power, and serum or plasma NaCl. If the sodium chloride content has been markedly depleted the administration of fluid should be initiated with saline solution in sufficient amounts. When normal NaCl concentration in the plasma has been reached, NaCl and glucose solutions should be used in such proportions that the sodium chloride concentration remains within normal limits. If too much NaCl is given the patient will retain an excess of water and edema of the tissues will ensue.

Simple treatment of dehydration can only be successful if the kidneys retain their ability to function normally if adequate amounts of fluid are supplied. If the kidneys are damaged bilaterally their regulating function may be lost to such an extent that attempts to treat dehydration by administration of water and electrolytes may be useless or harmful.

A number of different conditions may result in acute renal insufficiency which anatomically exhibits damage primarily to the distal tubular segments of the nephron. The more or less typical histological picture may be seen in fatal cases of hemolysis following incompatible blood transfusions, prolonged hypotension, burns, the crush syndrome, heat stroke, and a number of conditions brought about by various infectious and toxic agents. In hospital practice acute renal failure associated with long periods of hypotension is likely to be observed following extensive hemorrhage in surgical and obstetrical cases.

Macgraith and associates concluded that circulatory failure led to renal anoxia and this in turn to the characteristic pathological changes. The term 'renal anoxia syndrome' has been applied as well as 'lower nephron nephrosis' and 'hemoglobinuric nephrosis.' The syndrome presents a serious prognosis as various observers have found that, in patients with persistent oliguria, the chance of survival appears to be less than 20 per cent.

Most fatal cases of lower nephron nephrosis die within eight days. The morphological changes in the lower part of the nephron are probably reversible in most cases and regeneration of renal tubules may be well advanced after eight days. If patients can survive the initial stage of damage, very rapid recovery of renal function may be observed. Treatment of lower nephron nephrosis is entirely a matter of carrying the patient along until tubular regeneration provides adequate renal function.

The clinical course in lower nephron nephrosis is characterized by three phases. *The first phase* is the period of injury whether this be due to circulatory failure with hypotension, hemolysis, or toxins. This phase is relatively short, lasting at most a few hours, but the length of time has a profound bearing on subsequent events. In *the second phase* renal insufficiency develops. The patient may exhibit persistent oliguria or may become anuric; the latter is infrequent. In the oliguric phase azotemia develops rapidly and, toward the end of this phase, blood urea concentrations may be encountered comparable to those seen in advanced chronic diffuse glomerulonephritis. Plasma sodium and chloride concentrations are decreased. The plasma potassium concentration may remain constant or show a moderate increase. The patient tends to be in acidosis as evidenced by the relatively low concentration of bicarbonate ions in the plasma. Because of failure of the regulatory function of the kidneys, specific gravity of the urine is low and becomes generally fixed in a range below 1.010. It is common for the urine in the oliguric stage to contain large amounts of protein. If the injury to the kidneys is produced by transfusion of incompatible blood, the urine will contain hemoglobin. The excretion of hemoglobin diminishes quite rapidly and usually becomes negligible after the first two days. Thus the prognosis in hemolytic transfusion reactions should not be based on the rate of disappearance of hemoglobin from the urine; fatalities in such cases occur, as in other cases of lower nephron nephrosis toward the eighth day.

The third phase is the period of recovery which is initiated by diuresis. In the second phase the amount of urine excreted in 24 hours varies, and there is commonly a perceptible increase in this volume during the first five to eight days. Diuresis in the later stages of recovery may be prominent and characterized by loss of large amounts of salt. While this diuresis may be spectacular, thus giving the impression of rapid recovery, the actual period of healing of the damage to the tubules may be a matter of several months before return to near normal function occurs. During this extensive period of convalescence polyuria is common.

In patients with a good prognosis the ability of the kidneys to concentrate urine shows rapid gain, and the excretion rate of urea exhibits considerable improvement during the diuretic phase.

The treatment of lower nephron nephrosis varies greatly with the stage of the disease. During the first phase therapy is directed toward combatting the hypotension with such measures as transfusions of blood, the use of other fluids intravenously, and oxygen. In most cases the initial hypotension is caused by loss of blood and prompt transfusion may be demanded not only from the standpoint of restoring the blood volume, but also to prevent secondary damage from anoxia, particularly to the central nervous system. Needless to say that all measures should be employed to insure perfect compatibility of the donor blood.

Treatment of the second phase is directed toward maintaining water and electrolyte balance in the patient as near normal as possible until the kidneys can resume their regulatory function. Replacement of water should equal as closely as possible the insensible loss. The underlying cause of the acidosis which develops during the second phase cannot be corrected while severe oliguria or anuria are present, but the carbon dioxide combining power of the plasma may be prevented from reaching low levels by the administration of sodium bicarbonate orally or 1/6 molar sodium lactate intravenously. Just as in other cases of renal failure the retention of phosphates with the attendant lowering of the concentration of calcium in the plasma may make it advisable to administer calcium ions to prevent tetany. The sodium chloride intake must be restricted and any sign of edema should be a signal to reduce further the administration of salt as well as water. It is usually useless to attempt to stimulate the kidneys to produce urine during the second phase.

The approach of the diuretic phase is often heralded by definite daily increments in urine volume toward the end of the oliguric phase. Diuresis may be copious, volumes of 5,000 to 10,000 cc. frequently being observed, and the extent of the diuresis seems to have some relationship to the severity of the oliguric phase. Successful treatment of the third phase depends upon adequate replacement of loss of water, sodium, and potassium.

SUPPLEMENTARY READING

CAMPBELL, K. N., and IOB, V.: The treatment of renal insufficiency in the surgical patient. *Ann. Surg. 128:*379, 1948.

GAMBLE, J. L.: *Chemical Anatomy, Physiology and Pathology of Extracellular Fluid.* Harvard University Press, 1950.

LANDIS, F. M.: The passage of fluid through the capillary wall. *Harvey Lectures, 32:*70, Charles C Thomas, Publisher, 1936-37.

MUIRHEAD, E. E., and HILL, J. M.: The treatment of acute renal insufficiency. *Surg. Gynec. and Obst., 87:*445, 1948.

PETERS, J. P.: *Body Water.* Charles C Thomas, Publisher, 1935.

RICHARDS, A. N.: Processes of urine formation. *Proc. Roy. Soc., London, 126:*398, 1938.

ROWNTREE, L. G., and BROWN, G. E.: *The Volume of the Blood and Plasma in Health and Disease.* W. B. Saunders Co., 1929.

SMITH, H. W.: *The Physiology of the Kidney.* Oxford University Press, 1937.

WANGENSTEEN, O. H.: *The Therapeutic Problem in Bowel Obstruction.* Charles C Thomas, Publisher, 1937.

WIES, C. H., and PETERS, J. P.: The osmotic pressure of proteins in whole serum. *J. Clin. Investigation, 16:*93, 1937.

Chapter 5

ENZYMES

C HEMICAL equations do not indicate at what speed the stated reaction may proceed. Systems capable of reacting may do so at such a slow *reaction velocity* that the observer is unable to detect any change under the particular circumstances. By appropriate changes in physical state such as temperature or pressure of the system the reaction velocities may be increased so that significant changes may be determined easily. A reaction velocity is approximately doubled for each 10 degrees rise in temperature. Most ionic reactions proceed so rapidly that they appear to be completed instantaneously, while organic reactions are usually slow, and in many instances heat must be applied to obtain sufficient speed for practical purposes.

The rate of a reaction frequently may be accelerated by the presence of a substance which apparently does not enter into chemical union with any of the reacting components because it is found unchanged at the end of the reaction; nor does it have any stoichiometric relationship to them. Such substances are *catalysts* and the process *catalysis*. A catalyst does not change the ultimate equilibrium. Theoretically a catalyst can serve its function indefinitely but practically most catalysts gradually lose their activity, in many instances having participated in reactions involving up to 200,000 times their own weight in reacting material. It is quite likely that all catalysts operate by forming intermediate compounds which subsequently decompose leaving the catalyst to be used over again. Certain substances in minute amounts may alter the activity of a catalyst. They are called *catalytic poisons* if they retard the action and *promoters* if they accelerate it.

ENZYMES

Living cells require a number of substances of both inorganic and organic nature to perform their normal functions and most of these substances must be synthesized from suitable components of food. These synthetic processes require a steady supply of energy which is ordinarily obtained by a stepwise oxidation of part of the food which supplies the necessary energy for the reaction to proceed. When in vitro organic reactions are compared with the same processes in vivo it is indeed surprising that the latter progress at sufficient speed to supply the ordinary demands of the living organism, and it is remarkable that they can be speeded up to supply the demands of an organism under stress. Adequate velocities of organic reactions at body temperature could not be attained were it not for the catalytic action of complex organic substances called enzymes.

Enzymes are produced by living cells but they exert their effect even when they are separated from the cell. In contradistinction to many inorganic catalysts the enzymes exhibit definite *specificity,* and it is thought that the reason for this is that their action is localized to definite structural configurations within the reacting molecule. This specificity may be broad in its scope as exemplified by protein or carbohydrate splitting enzymes, while in other instances it may be limited to one reaction: for example urease acts only on urea.

The detailed mechanism of enzyme reactions is uncertain although it is likely that the enzyme momentarily combines with the molecule for which it is specific and that in doing so it decreases the energy barrier for the reaction. Kinetic data strongly suggest the formation of intermediate compounds and in a few instances spectroscopic evidence for their existence has been obtained. The general rule that a catalyst does not alter the ultimate chemical equilibrium also applies to enzymic reactions.

CATALYTIC PROPERTIES OF ENZYMES

A substance upon which an enzyme has a specific action is a substrate for that particular enzyme. Interpretations relative to the action of an enzyme are based upon its effect on a substrate. Such observations must be made under well standardized conditions as many factors influence the rate of an enzymic reaction. The reaction velocity is linearly proportional to the *enzyme concentration* except toward the end of the reaction, and the velocity also increases with the *concentration of the substrate* but not linearly. Beyond a certain substrate concentration the reaction velocity tends to become constant.

As is true of other catalysts, increased temperature increases the activity of enzymes. However, most enzymes are heat-labile proteins which undergo destructive changes (denaturation) at higher temperatures. The optimum temperature of an enzyme, therefore, is that point at which the balance between these two effects is most favorable, and usually falls close to the range of normal body temperature. There are two other temperatures below and above the optimum at which the activity falls close to zero. These two temperatures are called minimum and maximum respectively. The reader should distinguish between the meaning of optimum and of maximum.

Hydrogen ion concentration also influences enzyme action and the terms minimum, maximum, and optimum are used with the same meaning as when applied to temperature effects.

Light occasionally accelerates or decelerates enzymic reactions. The destructive effect of ultraviolet light is especially great.

Many enzymes are present in cells and secretions in an inactive form called *proenzymes* or *zymogens.* Proenzymes may become activated by various agents such as inorganic ions (*activators*) or specific non-protein organic substances (*kinases* or *coenzymes*). Some proenzymes are self activating, the action of another substance not being required. The kinases are colloidal while the coenzymes are non-colloidal, dialyzable, heat-stable substances. A coenzymic group is called a *prosthetic radical*. Enzymes are very sensitive to the action of certain substances. Such ions as silver, gold, mercury, fluoride, cyanide, iodoacetate, etc., are powerful poisons. All enzymes are large molecules and it is quite likely that all of them are proteins. A number of enzymes have been isolated in pure and crystalline form.

TERMINOLOGY

It is accepted practice to name enzymes by attaching the suffix 'ase' to the name of the specific substrate. Examples are lipase, amylase, phosphatase, carboxylase, etc. When this nomenclature was adopted a number of enzymes such as pepsin, trypsin, ptyalin, and papain were known and their original names are still in use.

CLASSIFICATION

It is not possible to classify all enzymes in a simple and satisfactory manner. Two large groups are the *hydrolytic* and the *oxidizing-reducing* enzymes. The former group includes the digestive enzymes which produce hydrolytic splitting of carbohydrates, fats, proteins, nucleoproteins, phosphoric acid esters, etc. The latter group comprises the dehydrogenases, oxidases, peroxidases, catalases, and others.

Desmolases act specifically either to form or to break carbon chains. Hydrases bring about the addition of water to substrates without causing hydrolysis. Special classes of enzymes such as the phosphorylases are concerned with the intermediary metabolism of carbohydrates.

OXIDATION-REDUCTION REACTIONS

Oxidation involves either combination of oxygen with or removal of hydrogen from an atom or molecule. A more general statement is that the term oxidation implies the removal of electrons from molecules, atoms, or ions, and reduction the addition of electrons. In an electrolytic process electrons are supplied at the cathode (negative pole) and removed at the anode (positive pole) so that reduction takes place at the cathode and oxidation at the anode. A few examples will makes this clear. The ferrous ion is oxidized at the anode by the removal of one electron.

$$Fe^{++} \rightarrow Fe^{+++} + \ominus$$

At the cathode the opposite takes place. Here a ferric ion will combine with an available electron and become a ferrous ion.

$$Fe^{+++} + \ominus \rightarrow Fe^{++}$$

A molecule of chlorine may combine with 2 electrons at the cathode yielding 2 chloride ions. Therefore chloride ions are formed by the reduction of chlorine molecules or atoms.

$$Cl_2 + 2\ominus \rightarrow 2Cl^-$$

An ion may accept an electron from another ion so that one becomes reduced while the other is oxidized. A ferric ion will accept an electron from a stannous ion, the iron becoming reduced to the ferrous form and the tin oxidized to stannic ions.

$$2Fe^{+++} + Sn^{++} \rightarrow 2Fe^{++} + Sn^{++++}$$

The relative ability of a chemical system to participate in oxidation-reduction reactions may be expressed by its *oxidation-reduction* potential. This is an electromotive force measured in volts. Since no satisfactory method for measuring the absolute potential of a single electrode has been devised, it is general practice to measure the difference in potential between two electrodes, one of which is used as a reference. The generally accepted reference electrode is the standard hydrogen electrode, the potential of which is arbitrarily called zero. The potential of the substance in question is then determined relative to the hydrogen electrode.

The actual potential existing between an electrode (usually platinum) and an oxidation-reduction system is the result of an equilibrium between them in regard to their affinity for electrons. If, for example, an electrode is placed in a solution containing both ferrous and ferric ions, the reducing ion (Fe^{++}) will make the electrode more negative by giving up electrons to it and the oxidizing ion (Fe^{+++}) will make it more positive by accepting electrons from it. The potential of the platinum electrode is determined by the relative concentrations of ferrous and ferric ions and this potential is a measure of the oxidation-reduction potential of the Fe^{++}/Fe^{+++} solution under consideration. The oxidation-reduction potential depends not only upon the relative concentrations of the ions but also upon the actual energy exchange in the reaction.

In biological reactions the oxidizable substance is frequently referred to as an *oxygen acceptor* while a reducible substance is a *hydrogen acceptor*.

Biochemical oxidations and reductions usually take place in steps which are generally reversible. Many of these reactions mediate the exchange of hydrogen and electrons between intermediary components which serve, therefore, as *mediators* or *carriers*. These systems enable the organism to derive energy for physiological work, and for maintenance of body heat from food substrates and oxygen.

The oxidation of food takes place through the activation and removal of hydrogen by specific enzymes. Thunberg discovered these *dehydrogenases* and Weiland showed that a food substrate usually loses two hydrogen atoms at each stage of its oxidation. The dehydrogenases transfer the hydrogen to successive bridging systems which act as hydrogen acceptors. It is thought that the electrons are passed along the cytochrome system to cytochrome oxidase. This substance (and *oxidases* in general), is capable of activating molecular oxygen to accept these electrons forming hydroxyl ions which eventually unite with the released hydrogen ions to form water. In this way the potential energy of the food substrate is liberated as the heat of formation of water. The process may be presented diagrammatically as follows:

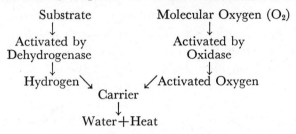

Each side of this reaction can be studied separately by using appropriate poisons for the enzymes on the other side. Dehydrogenases are inhibited by certain narcotics and by iodoacetate while the oxidases are inhibited by cyanides, sulfides, and carbon monoxide. The poisonous properties of cyanides are due to this specific action on oxidases. Death from exposure to carbon monoxide is caused by its reaction with hemoglobin rather than its inhibitory action on cell oxidases.

DEHYDROGENASES

These enzymes may be divided into anaerobic and aerobic types. Thunberg used methylene blue as an artificial hydrogen acceptor to study the anaerobic type of reaction in mixtures of substrates and dehydrogenases. Because the reduced form of methylene blue (leuco form) is colorless the loss of color indicated the transfer of hydrogen from the substrate to the dye. When molecular oxygen was admitted to the reacting mixture it combined with hydrogen of the leuco dye, forming hydrogen peroxide or water, and the blue color was rapidly regenerated. The methylene blue in this experiment exemplifies the function of carriers. If a carrier is not present in a cell the dehydrogenase cannot transfer the hydrogen obtained from the substrate and its action soon stops because the original form cannot be regenerated ready to repeat the reaction. In natural biological dehydrogenation reactions cozymases, cocarboxylases, etc., serve as hydrogen acceptors.

The aerobic type of reaction appears to transfer hydrogen directly to molecular oxygen. However, the aerobic dehydrogenases are probably all bound firmly to prosthetic hydrogen acceptor radicals which serve the same purpose as the free carriers in anaerobic reactions, and therefore, the two types of reactions are fundamentally similar.

OXIDASES

As already mentioned these enzymes activate molecular oxygen and make it available for combination with hydrogen of the reduced hydrogen acceptor systems. A number of specific oxidases are known such as *phenol oxidases* which transfer activated oxygen to phenols to form quinones. *Dopaoxidase* belongs in this category as it forms quinones from tyrosines; these quinones condense to form melanin.

Cytochrome oxidase, the 'respiratory enzyme of Warburg,' is a specific enzyme for the oxidation of cytochrome. Formerly it was called indophenol oxidase because of its apparent ability to form an indophenol from p-phenylenediamine and α-naphthol in the presence of molecular oxygen. However, this oxidation reaction must be mediated by the cytochromes. Cytochrome oxidase has an oxidizable iron-porphyrin complex as a prosthetic radical. The iron functions by shifting from the reduced to the oxidized form and vice versa. As previously shown this is accomplished by the loss or addition of an electron respectively and this enzyme illustrates well the concept of electron transfer as the actual mechanism in biological *oxidation-reduction* systems.

Catalase is an anomalous enzyme found in all tissues of the body, and capable of two possible functions, the decomposition of hydrogen peroxide to water and oxygen, and a peroxidative effect which permits the oxidation of substances by hydrogen peroxide directly. It has also been suggested that catalase functions in the red cells to prevent the breakdown of hemoglobin to choleglobin and methemoglobin in the presence of peroxide. In view of the toxic effect of peroxide on living cells, it is obvious that accumulation of this substance cannot occur to any great extent. However, some investigators doubt that peroxide is formed in appreciable amounts in vivo, and the concentration of catalase found normally in cells is not high enough to carry out the peroxidative function. Consequently in the absence of definite evidence, the function of catalase in the body must remain uncertain.

Peroxidase also is capable of liberating oxygen from hydrogen peroxide and equally little is known about this. It is found in relatively large quantities in pus cells and in the blood of patients with myeloid leukemia. The peroxidases have iron-porphyrin prosthetic groups, which are responsible for the specific oxidation of phenols in the presence of hydrogen peroxide. This reaction can be utilized to detect traces of blood, which contains iron-porphyrin radicals, as these for instance will catalyze the oxidation of guaiaconic acid to guaiac blue. Peroxidases are also capable of destroying certain toxins such as those from diphtheria and tetanus bacteria. In vitro they can oxidize di-iodotyrosine to thyroxin, but this has not been shown to occur in vivo.

HYDROGEN AND OXYGEN ACCEPTORS

The preceding pages have given a brief outline of enzymes which activate hydrogen and oxygen respectively. Now it remains to discuss some of the intermediary chemical systems whereby activated hydrogen from food substrates and oxygen eventually are brought together to form water. The process of oxidation of food is completed only when this has occurred. The reader is reminded again that both hydrogen and oxygen acceptors are referred to as carriers, bridging systems, or electron transporters.

Harden and Young discovered in yeast a coenzyme, *cozymase,* essential for alcoholic fermentation. Later Warburg and Christian found another cozymase and the two enzymes were called *coenzyme I* and *coenzyme II* respectively. Analytical studies proved these substances to be phosphopyridine nucleotides and they were found to be identical except for the number of phosphoric acid molecules in the structures. Coenzyme I contains two molecules of phosphoric acid and it is therefore called *diphosphopyridine nucleotide* while coenzyme II contains three phosphoric acid molecules and is called *triphosphopyridine nucleotide.* The term *codehydrogenases* is sometimes used for these coenzymes.

The phosphopyridine nucleotides are important hydrogen acceptors and they are widely distributed in nature. The largest concentrations are found in liver, kidney, muscles, and adrenal cortex. The gray matter of the brain and the retina also contain relatively high concentrations of these coenzymes, while their content in blood is practically confined to the red cells.

The coenzyme molecules are complicated structures containing nicotinic acid amide (niacin), d-ribose, and adenine in addition to the phosphoric acid. The formula for diphosphopyridine nucleotide is given below.

Only a small part of this molecule serves as the actual hydrogen acceptor. Reduction takes place in the pyridine ring of the nicotinic acid amide converting the double bond involving the nitrogen atom to a single bond. This process permits the acceptance of two hydrogen atoms as indicated below.

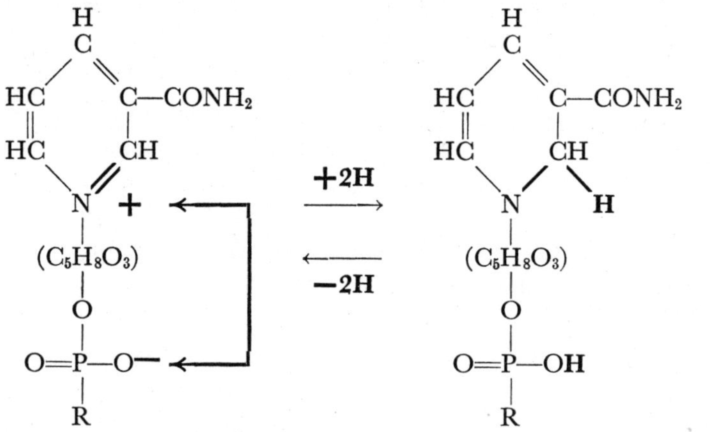

(Note the neutralization of charges when hydrogen is accepted)

The cozymases accept hydrogen from dehydrogenases. The latter are specific within very narrow limits while the specificity of the cozymases is somewhat broader. The hydrogen is passed on from the cozymases to other carriers, namely the flavoproteins and certain metabolic intermediates. Some of these reactions will be discussed in greater detail in Chapter 8.

Niacin is the antipellagra vitamin of the B group. In pellagra the contents of cozymases of the liver and the muscles are decreased while in other organs normal concentrations are found. Niacin is the dietary substance deficient also in 'blacktongue' of dogs.

In the catalysis of carbohydrates the intermediate α-keto acids (such as pyruvic acid) undergo decarboxylation under the influence of *carboxylase* with production of carbon dioxide. Decarboxylation may proceed either as an oxidative or as a non-oxidative reaction. In the former the process goes through an intermediate hydroxyderivative—

$$CH_3CO.COOH + H_2O \rightarrow CH_3.\overset{\displaystyle OH}{\underset{\displaystyle OH}{C}}.COOH \rightarrow CH_3COOH + CO_2 + 2H$$

(Pyruvic Acid)   (Acetic Acid)

In the non-oxidative reaction the CO_2 is split off converting a 3 carbon to a 2 carbon chain.

$$CH_3COCOOH \rightarrow CH_3CHO + CO_2$$

(Pyruvic Acid)   (Acetaldehyde)

The aldehyde formed undergoes the so-called Canizzaro reaction which consists of simultaneous oxidation and reduction of two aldehyde molecules:

$$2RCHO+H_2O \rightarrow RCH_2OH+RCOOH$$

ALDEHYDE   ALCOHOL   ACID

The Canizzaro reaction is catalyzed by the enzyme *mutase*.

Cocarboxylase is a carrier with a prosthetic radical which is specific for pyruvic acid dehydrogenase and for carboxylase. This radical contains vitamin B_1 or thiamin and the hydrogen carrying property is due to an unsaturated bond in this molecule as indicated in the formula:

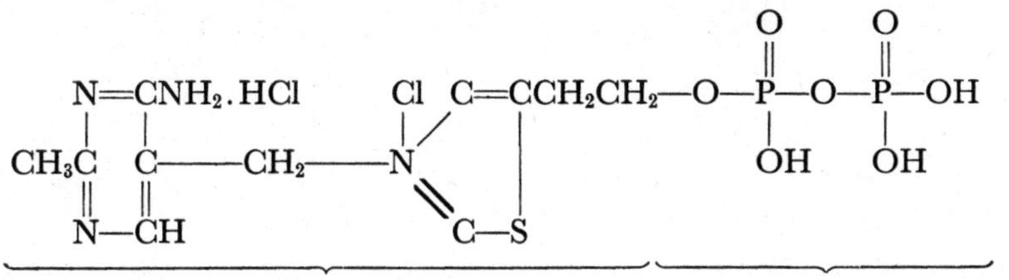

(THIAMIN)   (PYROPHOSPHORIC ACID)

Beri-beri develops in thiamin deficiency and this condition is associated with an accumulation of lactic and pyruvic acids.

Flavoproteins contain the water soluble vitamin B_2 or *riboflavin*. This vitamin forms a flavin nucleotide, *cytoflavin,* containing the flavin (or dimethylisoalloxazine) group, a carbohydrate (d-ribitol), and phosphoric acid. Its structure is as follows:

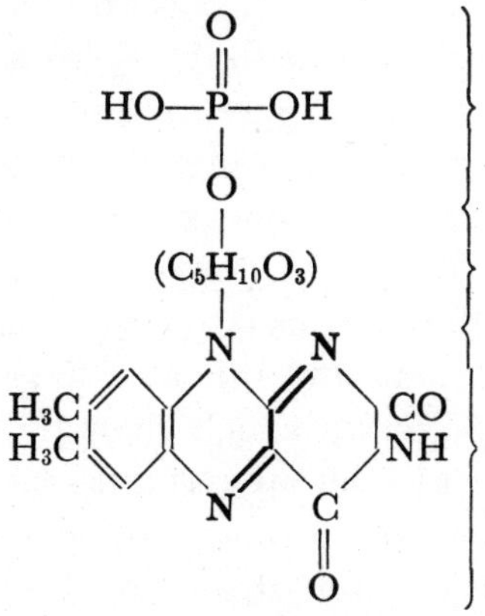

(PHOSPHORIC ACID)

(d-RIBITOL)

(DIMETHYLISOALLOXAZINE) (FLAVIN)

Cytoflavin combines with specific dehydrogenases to form the flavoproteins or *yellow enzymes.* Cytoflavin can combine with adenylic acid through the phosphoric acid radical to form alloxazine-adenine dinucleotide which is the prosthetic radical of *diaphorase* or *coenzyme factor.* Diaphorase is the most important flavoprotein but others exist with the same prosthetic radical. Thus it appears that the specificity of the enzymes resides in the protein of the combination rather than in the prosthetic radical. Xanthine oxidase and d-amino acid oxidase are examples of enzymes containing the flavin-adenine dinucleotide. If the structure of flavinadenine dinucleotide is compared with that of cozymase I, it may be seen that one contains riboflavin and the other niacin, but that they are similar otherwise.

The flavin radical of the molecule serves as the hydrogen carrier, the above formula for cytoflavin indicating the specific part concerned with this function. The reversible oxidation-reduction process may be depicted thus:

OXIDIZED FORM   REDUCED FORM

Flavoproteins accept hydrogen from cozymases. It is questionable if the simpler flavoproteins can accept hydrogen and transfer it to molecular oxygen at a rate sufficiently rapid to be of biological significance. The transfer of hydrogen proceeds rapidly in the presence of diaphorase and of oxygen activated by the cytochrome system.

Cytochromes are porphyrin complexes combined with protein. They are three in number and are designated as cytochromes a, b, and c. Cytochrome c has been studied more than the others. Identification of each is based on its spectral characteristics. Their oxidation depends on the action of cytochrome oxidases as previously described and their reduction is brought about by the transfer of hydrogen from metabolites activated by dehydrogenases. The largest amounts of cytochromes are found in skeletal and cardiac muscles; smaller amounts are present in liver, kidney, lungs, brain, etc. The cytochromes are responsible for making available most of the molecular oxygen for biological oxidations.

It is considered that most, if not all, electrons removed by dehydrogenases must pass through the cytochrome system and this mechanism may be the final pathway of most of the enzyme systems which virtually supply all the energy for body functions. Cyanide is without appreciable effect on the cytocromes, but it does inhibit 80-90 per cent of the oxygen uptake by cytochrome oxidase, probably by combining with the iron of the prosthetic radical.

A number of biological substances are capable of undergoing oxidation and reduction with great facility although their activity is not necessarily dependent on the action of specific enzymes. They may therefore participate in oxidation-reduction reactions in the organism.

Glutathione is widely distributed in cells and body fluids. Its exact function is not well understood at present, as it does not act as an hydrogen acceptor in conjunction with any known dehydrogenase. It is present in the tissues mostly in its reduced form, and is thought to keep ascorbic acid and enzymes containing the sulfhydryl group (-SH) in their reduced forms. Glutathione has an additional function as an activator of certain proteolytic enzymes *(cathepsin)*.

Structurally glutathione is a tripeptide containing glutamic acid, cysteine, and glycine. The oxidized form consists of two molecules combined through the disulfide (-S-S-) linkage. In the reduced form glutathione is

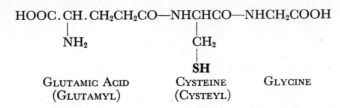

Ascorbic acid (Vitamin C), is also a substance which undergoes oxidation and reduction readily. It is an essential food factor, and a deficiency in the diet results in scurvy. Like glutathione its function as an hydrogen acceptor has not yet been associated with any known dehydrogenase. Oxidation of ascorbic acid produces dehydroascorbic acid, the reaction being reversible. The latter substance can be oxidized further by an irreversible reaction, resulting in the loss of biological activity. Possibly glutathione functions to prevent irreversible oxidation of ascorbic acid. Details of the functional mechanism of vitamin C are not known.

Szent-Györgyi has shown that certain intermediate metabolic products can serve as hydrogen carriers in so-called *linked dehydrogenase systems*. His experimental data deal with 4-carbon dicarboxylic acids, succinic and fumaric acids, which are very reactive. Szent-Györgyi's original cycle of oxidations may represent only one of several systems which are involved in cellular oxidations, but there is little doubt that simple intermediate metabolic systems such as the C_4 dicarboxylic acids may serve as important hydrogen carriers.

SUPPLEMENTARY READING

Barron, E. S. G.: The application of biological oxidation-reduction systems to the study of cellular respiration. *Biol. Symp., 10:*27, 1943.

Elliott, K. A. C.: Intermediary metabolites and respiratory catalysis. *Physiol. Rev., 21:*267, 1941.

Green, D. E.: *Biochemistry from the Standpoint of Enzymes.* Interscience Publishers, Inc., p. 149, 1946.

Harrow, B.: "One Family"—Enzymes, Vitamins and Hormones, Burgess Publishing Co., 1950.

Lardy, H. A.: *Respiratory Enzymes*, Burgess Publishing Co., 1949.

Northrop, J. G.: *Crystalline Enzymes.* Columbia University Press, 1948.

OCHOA, S.: Chemical Processes of oxidative recovery of muscle. *Ann. New York Acad. Sc., 47*:835, 1947.

SCHLENK, F.: Enzymic reactions involving nicotinamide and its related compounds. *Adv. in Enzymol., 5*:207, 1945.

SUMNER, J. B., and MYRBACK, K.: *The Enzymes: Chemistry and Mechanism of Action.,* Vol. I., Academic Press, New York, 1950-51.

Symposium on Respiratory Enzymes: University of Wisconsin Press, 1949.

Chapter 6

LIPIDS

A NUMBER of important physiological substances may be grouped conveniently under this general classification. Most lipids are insoluble in water and soluble in the so-called 'fat solvents' such as ether, chloroform, benzene, etc. Some of them, such as the bile acids, phospholipids, and soaps readily form emulsions in water. The solubility properties of the lipids give them certain physiological characteristics which are more responsible for their being grouped under one heading than specific chemical similarity in structure or reactions.

Lipids may be divided into four groups of which each constitutes a collection of substances of definite chemical similarity. The four groups are:

1. Simple lipids
2. Compound lipids
3. Derived lipids
4. Related substances

Chemical properties of the lipids are determined by their unit or units. If they contain more than one structural unit, each individual one can usually be determined after hydrolysis of the complex molecule, and they permit further classification and chemical characterization.

The simple lipids upon hydrolysis yield fatty acids and alcohols. If the alcohol is glycerol the original lipid is a *fat;* if any other alcohol the compound is called a *wax.* Sterols combine with fatty acids to form *sterol esters* which are included in the group of simple lipids.

Compound lipids are divided into two groups. These can be described in the same manner as above through their products of hydrolysis. The *phospholipids* yield fatty acids, phosphoric acid, a nitrogen-containing base, and usually glycerol, while the *glycolipids* yield fatty acids, a carbohydrate, and a nitrogenous base.

The derived lipids are those structural parts in the first two groups which as individual units retain the general properties of the lipids. Fatty acids, fatty alcohols, and fatty aldehydes belong in this group.

The related substances comprise the sterols and steroid compounds derived from phenanthrene, lipochromes, etc. These substances are extremely important and are usually of major physiological effect in comparatively small amounts.

FATS

Fats are esters of glycerol and fatty acids. The formation of organic acid esters takes place through the reaction of the hydrogen in the carboxyl group of the organic acid and the OH-group of the alcohol. As glycerol has three alcoholic OH-groups it forms esters containing three fatty acid radicals according to the following structure:

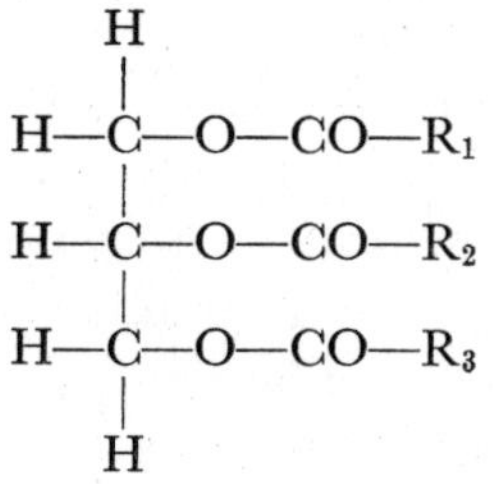

$$
\begin{array}{c}
\text{H} \\
| \\
\text{H—C—O—CO—R}_1 \\
| \\
\text{H—C—O—CO—R}_2 \\
| \\
\text{H—C—O—CO—R}_3 \\
| \\
\text{H}
\end{array}
$$

The fat can easily be broken down again to its components by hydrolysis with alkali; the glycerol is liberated and the fatty acids form salts with the cation (sodium, potassium, etc.) of the alkali. These salts are soaps and the hydrolytic process is called *saponification*. Fats will hydrolyze in an acid medium but with much more difficulty than in an alkaline medium. Specific enzymes are able to cause the hydrolytic splitting of fats with great facility under certain conditions. Such enzymes are called *lipases*.

The fatty acids in naturally occurring fats usually have straight chains of an even number of carbon atoms. Palmitic and stearic acids are examples of straight chain fatty acids, commonly found in ordinary fats, and containing 16 and 18 carbon atoms respectively. Fatty acids with more than 18 carbon atoms are widely distributed in nature, but frequently are present only in very small amounts. Phthioic and tuberculostearic acids from tubercle bacilli, and the acids in chaulmoogra oil, used in the treatment of leprosy, are examples of fatty acids with branched carbon chains.

Fatty acids occur in the form of *saturated* or *unsaturated* compounds. If they are saturated all the bonds between the carbon atoms are single bonds, but if they are unsaturated two or more carbon atoms are linked with double or even triple bonds. These multiple bonds can be converted to single bonds by saturating the corresponding place in the molecule with hydrogen. This process is used commercially to produce edible fats of higher melting point from oils, and the process is called *hydrogenation*. Iodine reacts in the same way as hydrogen in this addition process, and therefore, the quantitative measure of the amount of iodine to cause saturation is a measure of the degree of unsaturation. The *iodine number* measures the iodine in grams that combines with 100 grams of fat or fatty acid.

Any of the naturally occurring fatty acids may be found in the fat molecule. The designations R_1, R_2, R_3, in the structural formula indicate that different fatty acid radicals may enter into the composition of the fat molecule. Fats usually contain more than one kind of fatty acid in the individual fat molecule, and the fat in the tissue consists of mixtures of such mixed *triglycerides*. Different animals have a tendency to select their own characteristic fatty acid as predominating in the mixture. The structure of the triglycerides also is influenced by the composition of the food.

PHOSPHOLIPIDS

Phospholipids can be divided into three types, *lecithins, cephalins,* and *sphingomyelins*. All of them contain fatty acids, phosphoric acid, and a nitrogenous base. The first two types are triglycerides like the fats, except one of the fatty acid radicals has been replaced by the complex of phosphoric acid and nitrogenous base as indicated in their structural formulas:

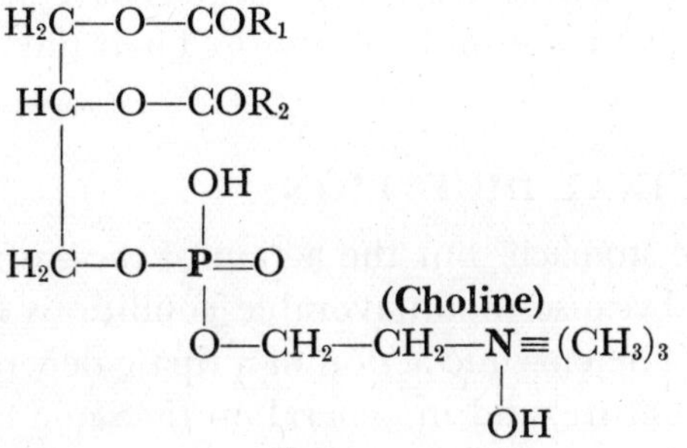

$$H_2C—O—COR_1$$
$$HC—O—COR_2$$
$$OH$$
$$H_2C—O—P{=}O$$
$$(Choline)$$
$$O—CH_2—CH_2—N{\equiv}(CH_3)_3$$
$$OH$$

LECITHIN

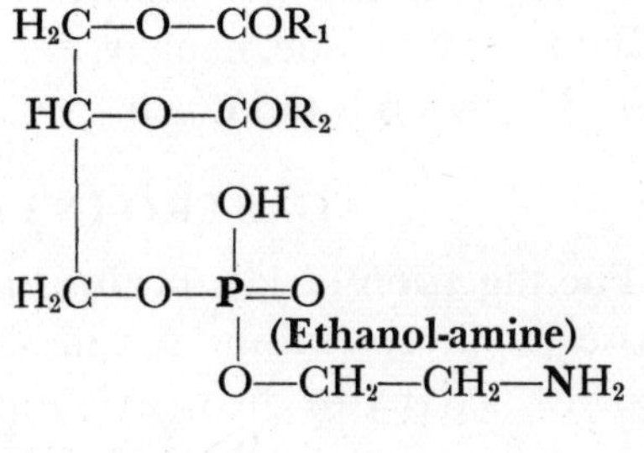

$$H_2C—O—COR_1$$
$$HC—O—COR_2$$
$$OH$$
$$H_2C—O—P{=}O$$
$$(Ethanol{-}amine)$$
$$O—CH_2—CH_2—NH_2$$

CEPHALIN

Sphingomyelins can be hydrolyzed into four compounds: fatty acids, phosphoric acid, and the nitrogenous bases choline and sphingosine.

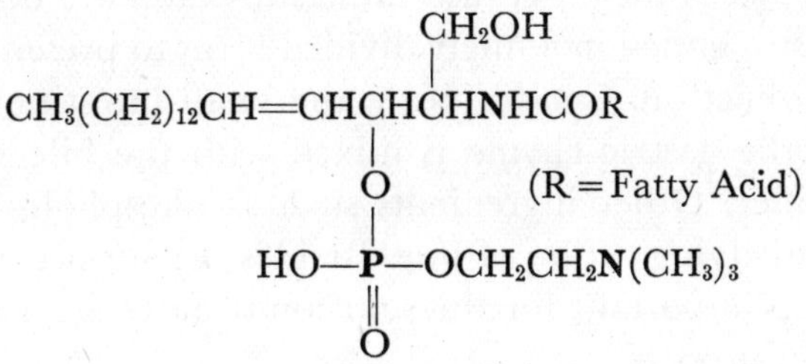

$$CH_2OH$$
$$CH_3(CH_2)_{12}CH{=}CHCHCHNHCOR$$
$$O \qquad (R = Fatty\ Acid)$$
$$HO—P—OCH_2CH_2N(CH_3)_3$$
$$O$$

SPHINGOMYELIN

It will be seen from the structures that lecithins and cephalins are mono-amino-monophosphoric acid lipids, while sphingomyelins are diamino-mono-phosphoric acid lipids. The ratio of nitrogen to phosphorus in the two groups is 1:1 and 2:1 respectively.

Phospholipids are probably present in all cells. Their concentration remains relatively constant under all conditions including starvation. French workers, therefore, refer to this fat portion as the 'element constant.'

Liver and spleen contain approximately equal amounts of lecithin and cephalin, while in the kidneys, lungs, and heart the lecithin content predominates. The brain content of cephalin is higher than that of lecithin. Most of the sphingomyelin is present in brain and nerve tissue.

The function of the phospholipids has been studied by introduction of isotopes into various components of the fatty food of the diet and determination of their rate of appearance in the phospholipids of the organs. Such studies show that they are continuously undergoing rapid turnover suggesting that they participate as intermediaries in fat metabolism.

GLYCOLIPIDS

These substances yield sphingosine, fatty acids, and galactose on hydrolysis. They do not contain phosphoric acid. The glycolipids are found in the medullary sheath of nerves and in brain tissue which is the basis for the name *cerebrosides* frequently applied to them. Three distinct glycolipids have been found in brain tissue, namely, *kerasin, nervone,* and *phrenosin.* Their physiological function is unknown.

GASTRO-INTESTINAL DIGESTION

The digestion of fats begins in the stomach, but the action of the gastric lipase is of very minor significance because of unfavorable conditions for lipolytic activity in the gastric juice. The enzymic action of a lipase depends on certain factors, such as pH, temperature, and in general on the same factors as any other enzyme reaction. However, the rate of conversion of any substrate (fat in this case) also depends on the degree of physical contact between the substrate and the enzyme. When enzymes act on carbohydrates or proteins the contact is ideal because these substrates are dissolved in water. Fats need to be suspended in a finely divided form to present enough surface for the enzyme to act on. Conditions in the small intestine are ideal in this respect because the gastric chyme is mixed with the bile which acts as an excellent emulsifier. Other ingredients such as phospholipids and proteins enhance the emulsifying action of bile. Besides the surface action of the bile salts they are also important for the solution of fatty acids produced by the enzymic digestion process.

The main fat splitting enzymes are formed by the pancreas and secreted in the pancreatic juice, the name *steapsin* being applied to them. The presence of bile and pancreatic juice together is required for normal fat digestion. Fat digestion continues through the small intestine and comparatively small amounts of undigested fat reach the colon. Some additional digestion of fat particles in the colon may proceed through the action of bacteria.

Under normal physiological conditions very little fat is excreted in the stool. The amount is frequently less than 5 per cent, although great variations may be found without being associated with any pathological condition. Some of the lipid excreted in the stool consists of secretory products from the intestinal mucosa.

FAT ABSORPTION

The products of fat digestion are absorbed by and resynthesized in the mucosal cells. The fatty acids are thought to penetrate the epithelial cells in the form of complexes with the bile salts. Inside the cells these complexes are split and the bile salts returned to the liver through the portal system. The fatty acids then reunite with glycerol to form neutral fat. The mechanism is not fully understood, although there is considerable evidence that it is influenced by a phosphorylating enzyme which converts the fatty acids to phospholipids at one stage of the process. Some investigators doubt this.

FAT TRANSPORTATION

There is very little known about the transfer of fat from the epithelial cells to the central lacteals. It is unlikely that fat is absorbed directly into the portal system. Most of the absorbed fat is transported in the chyle through the thoracic duct. The chyle may contain 2 to 8 per cent lipid material following a meal. Whether in transit to or from storage fat may be transported in the form of droplets (chylomicrons) or as phospholipids or cholesterol esters. Some fat may be transported as lipoproteins.

Blood lipids represent mostly the lipids in transit as neutral fat, phospholipids, free cholesterol, and fatty acids in esterified cholesterol. Normal plasma values for total lipids average about 700 mg. per 100 cc. with outside limits roughly estimated at 500 to 900 mg. per 100 cc. These values are considerably lower in infants.

CONVERSION OF OTHER STRUCTURES TO FAT

The body does not depend entirely on the dietary fat for its supply of tissue fats. Proteins are partly converted to carbohydrates in their metabolism and these, together with the ingested carbohydrates, are available for fat synthesis. The fact that fat can be formed from carbohydrates by synthesis in the organism was demonstrated by Liebig in 1852.

FAT STORAGE

Fat is stored in the interstitial tissues of all organs except the brain. The diet influences the amount and character of the fat deposited but not its distribution. The largest amounts of fat are stored in subcutaneous tissues, the tissues around such organs as heart and kidney, mesentery and omentum, and intermuscular connective tissue. Fat is the ideal form in which to store energy in the body because it is deposited with very little water, while storage of protein and carbohydrate requires approximately 3 times their own weight in water.

If an animal is in nutritional equilibrium, it presumably maintains constancy of weight and chemical composition, and it would be an obvious assumption that fat deposits may remain as such until needed, and that the active metabolism of fat would be confined to the nutritional intake. That such is not the case has been demonstrated in a series of brilliant experiments by Schoenheimer and his associates.

Ordinary metabolic balance studies are only possible where definite end products can be measured, but they do not give any insight into reactions between body constituents unless chemical groups of a readily detectable nature are introduced. Special radicals in intermediary metabolic compounds may alter their physiological behaviour so, at best, conclusions in regard to normal behaviour must be drawn from observations on abnormal compounds. Isotopes constitute the ideal 'label' for metabolic studies as the isotope atom can be traced by physical means and the chemical behaviour of the compound is not altered in any way from that of the normal. Schoenheimer used deuterium, substituted for hydrogen, and his original feeding experiments were done with linseed oil hydrogenated with deuterium. In a few days it was found that the tagged fat could be found in large quantities in the depot fat, and consequently a corresponding amount of the depot fat apparently had been metabolized.

These experiments were repeated by feeding pure tagged palmitic acid and subsequently, when the individual fatty acids in the depot fat were analyzed, it was found that over 24 per cent of the depot palmitic acid was newly introduced, and that part of the tagged compound had been degraded to shorter-chain fatty acids. It was also found that palmitic acid seemed to condense with two additional carbon atoms from unknown sources to form stearic acid as 10 per cent of the stearic acid isolated under the experimental circumstances contained deuterium. Isotopic oleic acid was found to be present, and this could not readily be explained except by desaturation of the newly formed isotopic stearic acid. Linoleic acid with two double bonds in the molecule did not contain deuterium, proving that linoleic acid was not formed synthetically from the tagged palmitic acid. This supports the viewpoint that the highly unsaturated fatty acids are essential ingredients of food as they cannot be produced from other fat components in the body.

Studies on fat synthesis with isotope compounds indicate that fat and fatty acids are built up from smaller units as the tracer isotope is fairly evenly distributed over the carbon chain. The same applies to cholesterol showing that the complicated ring structure of this substance is synthesized from many small molecules. Corresponding studies on phospholipids can be followed in detail because three different isotopes can be used at the same time, namely deuterium, radioactive phosphorus, and heavy nitrogen. It has been observed that these three isotopes are more or less rapidly introduced into the phospholipids showing that these must constantly be broken into their components and then reformed with identical compounds from other sources.

If the animal in perfect nutritional equilibrium is considered, it must be taken for granted that the amount and constitution of fat in a certain tissue do not undergo changes. Therefore, any component of the fat from this tissue depot entering into the general fat metabolism must be replaced at once with an identical compound. The sum of these reactions as measured by the aid of an isotope has been called 'molecular regeneration' by Schoenheimer. This molecular regeneration is an expression of the amount of activity in the fat and measurements show that the regeneration takes place much more rapidly in the liver than in the storage tissues. In fact, this process is so rapid in the liver that the actual rate has not been determined exactly. As most of the fat is present in the tissue depots it is obvious that there must be continuous and extensive transport of fat between the depot tissues and organs such as the liver.

The important viewpoint to have in mind in studying fat metabolism is that it is a very dynamic process where molecular components are in a constant flux, and that the apparently static state of affairs in the nutritionally balanced individual is only an expression of a biochemical equilibrium and not a state of inactivity.

THE LIVER AND FAT METABOLISM

There is considerable evidence that the liver plays an important part in the metabolism of fats. The lipids found in the liver are more unsaturated than those in other tissues. This could be explained on the basis of a selective ability of the liver to retain unsaturated fatty acids, but Schoenheimer's experiments with isotopes have proved conclusively that the increased quantity of unsaturated fat is at least partly due to a direct desaturation of lipids in the liver. Phospholipids are considered to serve as intermediaries in fat metabolism. The turnover of phospholipids has been observed to be very rapid in the intestinal mucosa during fat absorption and similar observations have been made on phospholipid turnover in the liver in the postabsorptive stage.

During abnormal feeding of fat-rich foods or cholesterol, the liver tends to accumulate an excessive amount of fat. A number of pathological conditions result in excessive deposition of fat in the liver. This may occur during starvation, and enlarged livers due to excessive fat accumulation frequently are observed in patients with uncontrolled diabetes. Large livers in diabetics may reduce rapidly towards their normal size when the patient is treated adequately with insulin. Fatty livers are occasionally associated with pregnancy and pernicious anemia. Certain poisons, such as phosphorus, chloroform and carbon tetrachloride, effect a rapid destruction of liver tissue and accumulation of fat. The fatty infiltration, seen occasionally in acute infections, may be a similar toxic effect.

The change in the fat content of the liver in uncontrolled diabetes is not just an effect associated with deficiency in insulin because depancreatized dogs on adequate insulin intake develop fatty livers. Raw beef pancreas added to the diet will prevent the fatty changes. Feeding experiments have shown that certain substances have a *lipotropic* effect so that their addition to the diet tends to prevent hepatic accumulation of fat. *Choline* is now recognized as a powerful lipotropic factor. Certain proteins such as casein, exhibit lipotropic effect. In casein, the active constituent of the molecule is *methionine*, which apparently is able to transfer methyl groups to ethanolamine to form choline. *Betaine* (trimethyl glycine) has a similar action. The cholesterol ester content of fatty livers appears to be reduced by *inositol* which is a member of the vitamin B complex. Choline presumably exerts its lipotropic activity by permitting synthesis of lecithin for fat transport. Pancreatic extracts may contain other lipotropic factors besides choline and protein. The theoretical pancreatic substance '*lipocaic*,' has not been identified as a lipotropic factor with certainty.

In experimental animals hemorrhagic lesions are at times associated with dietary deficiency of lipotropic factors. Under the same experimental conditions such animals eventually will show cirrhotic changes in the liver; these changes can be prevented by adding choline to the diet. Furthermore, the toxic effect of chloroform on the liver tissue at least may be partly prevented by administration of choline or methionine. Cholesterol added to the diet acts as an antilipotropic factor.

OXIDATION OF FAT

The importance of the liver in the metabolism of fat is particularly emphasized in the studies on the formation of *ketone bodies,* as these represent steps in the catabolic breakdown of fats to carbon dioxide and water. The 'ketone bodies' include acetoacetic acid, β-hydroxybutyric acid, and acetone. β-Hydroxybutyric acid is actually not a ketone. The chemical interrelations are as follows:

$$CH_3CHOHCH_2COOH \underset{(Reduction)}{\overset{(Oxidation)}{\rightleftarrows}} CH_3COCH_2COOH$$

(β-Hydroxybutyric Acid)   (Acetoacetic Acid)

$$CH_3COCH_2COOH \xrightarrow{(Decarboxylation)} CH_3COCH_3 + CO_2$$

(Acetoacetic Acid)   (Acetone)

The first reaction is reversible and the equilibrium is established rapidly under the control of oxidation-reduction systems. The second reaction is assumed to occur spontaneously. Acetone is not an acid and its presence as such does not influence acid-base equilibrium but it indicates that an equivalent amount of the other two ketone bodies has been converted. Experimental evidence points to acetoacetic acid as the first ketone body to be formed.

Many, and possibly all, tissues utilize the energy from fat oxidation and, therefore, observations on the rate of formation of ketone bodies actually estimate the formation of ketone bodies in excess of utilization in that particular tissue. Perfusion experiments indicate that rapid formation of ketone bodies in the liver occurs from fatty acids with an even number of carbon atoms. Odd numbered fatty acids from normal fat intake may give rise to small amounts of ketone bodies. Other substances, such as pyruvic acid and certain amino acids, can produce minor amounts of ketone bodies in perfused livers, and similarly, small amounts can be formed by perfusion of other tissues with these various substances.

It is especially important to note that the liver can produce ketone bodies at an exceedingly rapid rate, and that for all practical purposes the liver is the only important site of formation of these substances. The ketosis following pancreatectomy in dogs rapidly diminishes after the removal of the liver, and substances with toxic effect on the liver tend to reduce experimental ketosis. Chaikoff and Soskin found that the rate of utilization of sodium acetoacetate was the same in eviscerated normal and diabetic dogs indicating that the original ketosis of the diabetic dogs was due to ketogenesis in the liver. Mirsky has shown that the ketogenic effect of pituitary extracts is not demonstrable after hepatectomy.

The actual mode of degradation of fatty acids to ketone bodies and their eventual complete oxidation to carbon dioxide and water, is of major importance. In the normal organism the entire chain of reactions proceeds with great facility. This has been the major reason for the difficulties in studying it experimentally. For many years the β-oxidation theory of Knoop was accepted quite uncritically in spite of the fact that most of the conclusions were drawn from the behaviour of short-chain fatty acids and determination of their urinary excretion products. To be able to follow the experimental material along its metabolic pathway, Knoop used phenyl-substituted fatty acids whose end products were readily identifiable.

The Knoop theory assumes that two carbon atoms split off simultaneously from the fatty acid chain by oxidation at the β-position forming acetic acid which subsequently oxidizes to carbon dioxide and water. This gradual splitting off of two carbon components proceeds stepwise down to a four carbon fatty acid oxidized at the β-position explaining that only one molecule of ketone body can be formed from each fatty acid molecule regardless of the original length of its carbon chain. Much experimental evidence shows that the Knoop theory is not tenable. As a matter of fact the acetic and butyric acids postulated to be present in the liver during ketone formation have never been isolated from this organ. It can be demonstrated by use of octanoic acid in perfusion experiments that more ketone bodies are formed than from an equimolar amount of butyric acid. Liver slice experiments show that more than one molecule of ketone body is formed per molecule of fatty acid. Stadie, Zapp, and Lukens found in experiments with liver slices in vitro that the oxygen consumption indicated that the fatty acid with 16 carbon chains breaks down to form four molecules of acetoacetic acid. That this is the actual pathway of the catabolism of fatty acids is substantiated by the finding that ketone bodies increased four times more rapidly than fatty acids decreased.

Evidence available at present indicates that the major portion of fatty acid oxidation in the liver results in the entire fatty acid being converted to ketone bodies. It cannot be denied that Knoop and others proved that β-oxidation does occur, and Schoenheimer used isotopes to follow the stepwise degradation of palmitic acid (C_{16}) to lauric acid (C_{14}) and myristic acid (C_{12}): however, the successive β-oxidation only accounted for a very small part of the total fatty acid oxidation in the liver.

Hurtley in 1916, after careful search failed to find even traces of acetic acid and butyric acid in the liver during ketogenesis, and he proposed that the carbon chain of a fatty acid is first oxidized at each alternate carbon atom and then split off into sections containing four carbon atoms each. Hurtley called this process *multiple alternate oxidation,* and the theory would account for the absence of acetic and butyric acid in the liver even as transitory metabolic intermediaries. Hurtley's theory also satisfies the observations on the ratio of ketone formation to that of fat depletion, but it failed to advance any reason for the selective splitting of the oxidized carbon chain at every fourth carbon atom, representing every second keto group.

More recent experiments with short chain fatty acids have given more insight into the likely mechanism of the fat breakdown. MacKay and co-workers fed propionic acid (C_3) to animals and found that it resulted in the accumulation of glycogen in the liver without formation of ketone bodies. Earlier experiments had already shown that sugar may be formed from short-chain fatty acids such as valeric acid (C_5) by degradation to propionic acid and further to lactic or succinic acid. In MacKay's experiments the feeding of valeric acid (C_5) and heptanoic acid (C_7) resulted in the accumulation of glycogen, just as did propionic acid, but in addition, ketones were formed and the C_7 carbon chain produced more ketones than the C_5 chain. MacKay drew the conclusion that multiple alternate oxidation takes place, but that the breakdown of the fatty acid chain occurs at each keto group, and that two of the acetic acid molecules formed by this process condense to form acetoacetic acid. That such a condensation actually can take place had already been demonstrated by Friedmann in 1913. MacKay and his colleagues called their theory the '*β-oxidation acetic acid condensation hypothesis*,' and at present it represents the most satisfactory explanation of the experimental facts as known.

Medes and associates have studied the production of ketone bodies by the aid of isotopic carbon C^{13}. They found that it is not necessary for a fatty acid to be fractionated into two carbon structures to form ketone bodies. Using butyric acid these investigators discovered that direct oxidation to ketone bodies may take place as a minor mechanism involving the last four carbon atoms of a fatty acid chain. In Medes experiments acetic acid containing C^{13} in the carboxyl position produced ketone bodies if incubated with liver slices in phosphate buffer, the isotopic carbon being found in the carbonyl as well as the carboxyl positions. Other experiments were performed designed to study the metabolic pathways of acetic and acetoacetic acid in their utilization by tissues. Such experiments showed that, in liver, ketone bodies were formed from acetic acid, but were not utilized. In the kidney acetoacetic acid disappeared more rapidly than acetic acid, a small amount being converted to hydroxybutyric acid. Other tissues exhibited relatively more rapid utilization of acetoacetic acid as compared with acetic acid thus indicating that failure to isolate ketone bodies does not prove their non-formation. In spite of the experimental results showing that acetoacetic acid does not accumulate in the kidneys, Medes proved its synthesis from acetic acid by the use of material containing C^{13}.

Lehninger has performed experiments with an enzyme system in the presence of which acetoacetic acid is formed from fatty acids with chains containing more than two carbon atoms but not from acetic acid. Such experiments argue against acetic acid being the active intermediary but they do not exclude some other fundamental metabolic unit containing two carbon atoms.

After oxidation of fats to the ketone body stage these ketones still retain approximately 70 per cent of the total energy of the fat. This energy is readily available to the peripheral tissues. It was thought for many years that this energy was not available to the diabetic organism, and a peculiar concept of obligatory coupling of normal carbohydrate metabolism to utilization of ketones was developed without adequate experimental evidence for its support. The oft-repeated statement that 'fats burn in the flame of the carbohydrate' should be dismissed as utter nonsense; there is no demonstrable relation between the degree of ketosis and the rate of oxidation of carbohydrates. Chaikoff and Soskin have shown that ketone bodies can be oxidized in the peripheral tissues of the diabetic animal at the same rate as in nondiabetic tissue. The fact that the diabetic animal eventually develops acidosis indicates that the limit of utilization of ketone bodies by peripheral tissues is exceeded by their formation under these abnormal metabolic conditions. Ketosis and diabetes mellitus will be discussed in Chapter 13.

STEROIDS

While the lipids considered up to this point serve mostly to supply the fuel in the general energy metabolism of the organism, the steroids are endowed with specific physiological effects exerted by their presence in comparatively minute amounts. Most of the steroids have a four-ring structure in common; a few of them exhibit rather extensive modifications of this complex. Phenanthrene constitutes the fundamental structural unit with an additional five-membered ring attached to one of the benzene rings. In the steroid complex most or all of the double bonds of the benzene rings are saturated with hydrogen, so that the corresponding carbon atoms are united by single bonds. The saturation with hydrogen is indicated by the prefix perhydro- and the sterols are therefore derivatives of a perhydro-cyclopentenophenanthrene structure. The following is the formula in which the three saturated benzene rings represent the original phenanthrene molecule:

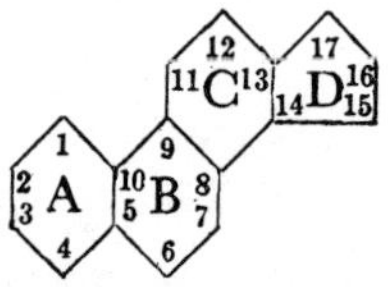

In the conventional method of identifying the individual rings, they are designated A, B, C, and D, and the carbon atoms are numbered as shown in the structure.

STEROLS

Sterols are crystalline alcoholic steroids found in animals and plants. The principal animal sterol is cholesterol, which has the alcoholic OH-group at position 3 and methyl groups at C_{10} and C_{13}. There is also an 8-carbon side chain attached at position 17. The structure is as follows:

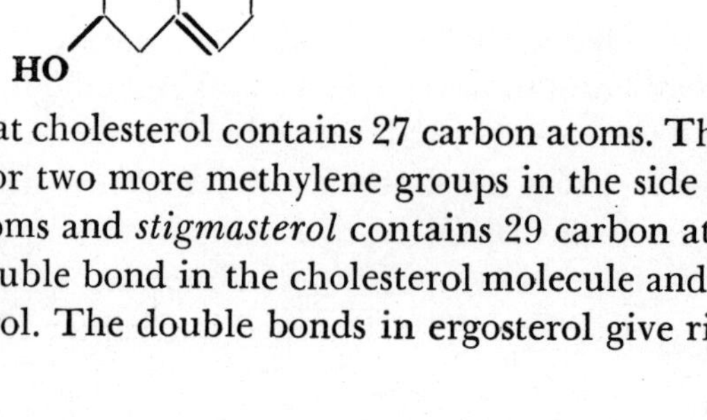

It may be seen that cholesterol contains 27 carbon atoms. The principal plant sterols have one or two more methylene groups in the side chain. *Ergosterol* has 28 carbon atoms and *stigmasterol* contains 29 carbon atoms in the molecule. Note the double bond in the cholesterol molecule and the three double bonds in ergosterol. The double bonds in ergosterol give rise to a characteristic ultra-violet absorption spectrum, while the double bond in cholesterol at C_5, gives a specific color in the *Liebermann-Burchard* reaction used clinically for the quantitative determination of cholesterol.

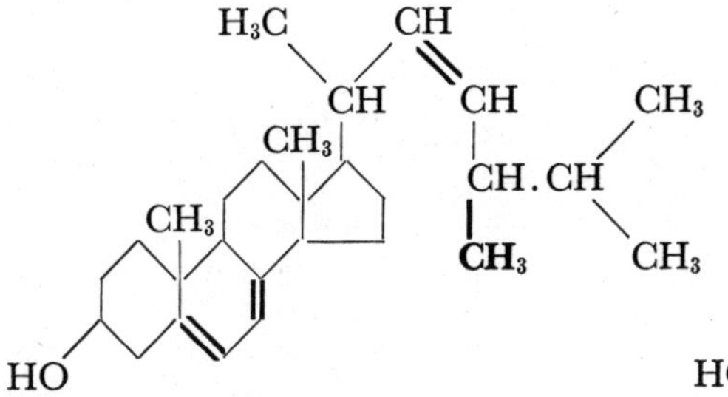

ERGOSTEROL 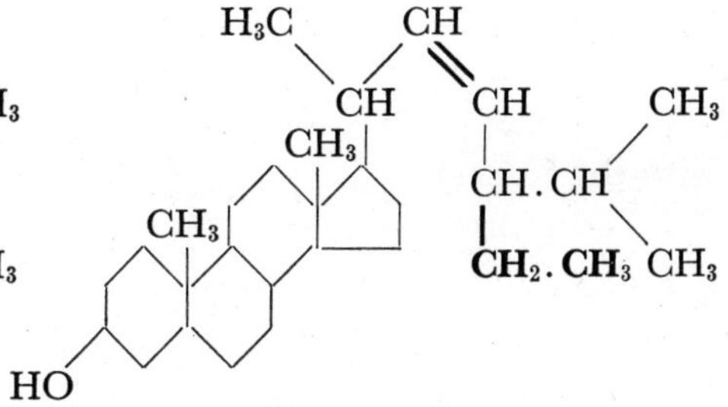   STIGMASTEROL

Plants synthesize sterols from simpler substances such as sugars. For a long time it was thought that animal sterols were derived from ingested plant sterols *(phytosterols)*. However, balance studies demonstrate that excretion of cholesterol may exceed the steroid intake, and the cholesterol content of the animal must, therefore, be maintained by its synthesis in the animal organism. The intestinal mucosa has a markedly selective action in the absorption of sterols. For example, ergosterol is not ordinarily absorbed, but the products formed by irradiation are readily absorbable.

In nature, cholesterol is accompanied by about 25 per cent of a dihydro-derivative β-*cholestanol*. An isomer, *coprosterol,* is excreted in the feces. The reduced cholesterol molecule contains nine asymmetric centers giving a theoretical possibility of 512 isomers, but β-cholestanol and coprosterol are the only two known to occur in nature. This isomerism is referable to the C_5 carbon atom: in β-cholestanol the CH_3-group at C_{10} and the hydrogen at C_5 are on opposite sides of the plane of the rings, while in coprosterol they are on the same side of the plane. The structural difference is indicated by connecting the hydrogen with a dotted line when it is located on the side opposite to the methyl group. This configuration is referred to as the trans- or allo-series, while molecules with the two groups on the same side comprise the cis- or normal-series.

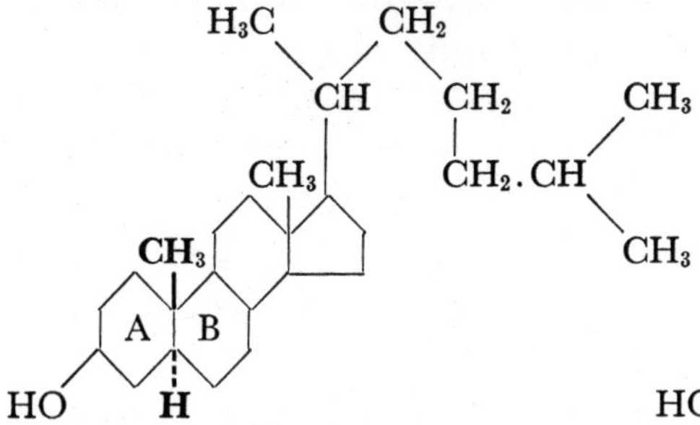

β-CHOLESTANOL   COPROSTEROL
A/B TRANS, ALLO SERIES   A/B CIS, NORMAL SERIES

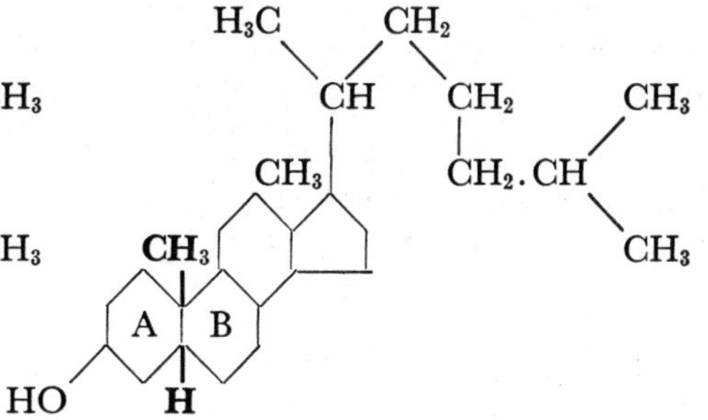

Another point of importance from the standpoint of structure is the C_3 carbon atom because the alcoholic OH-group attached here may assume two stereo-chemical variations. Cholesterol, β-cholestanol, and coprosterol have the same steric arrangements indicated by a solid line and conventionally referred to by the β-designation. The epimeric configuration is called the α-form and is graphically denoted by a dotted line connecting the OH-group with the C_3 carbon.

It is important that the student of steroid chemistry becomes familiar with the above terminology, as these isomeric variants are identified with physiological properties of clinical significance. For instance, the β-hydroxy-steroids are precipitated by digitonin and, therefore, free cholesterol, having this structure, is precipitated by this substance. If this OH-group is modified as in the esters of cholesterol the precipitation does not take place. Digitonin precipitation thus constitutes a simple chemical means of separating free cholesterol from its esters. It will be shown later that α and β forms of the 17-ketosteroids can be separated by the same procedure.

CHOLESTEROL

Cholesterol is very extensively distributed throughout the various tissues, and it is thought to be an essential component of all cells, although its actual function is practically unknown. Because of similarity in structure, cholesterol is possibly the precursor of other steroids, such as the bile acids, the sex hormones, and the adrenocortical hormones. Cholesterol occurs both in free form and as esters with fatty acids. The conversion of one form to the other is reversible, and it is presumed that an enzyme, *cholesterolesterase*, catalyzes the reaction in both directions. In the blood cells cholesterol is nearly all in its free form while plasma cholesterol is approximately from 50 per cent to 80 per cent in the ester form.

Normally the cholesterol content of blood of a given individual is quite constant and undergoes only slight increases after ingestion of large amounts of fats. This does not hold true in feeding experiments on rabbits and dogs as these animals show a significant postprandial increase in total cholesterol in the blood. The dietary cholesterol esters are hydrolyzed to free cholesterol and fatty acids under the influence of the intestinal digestive enzymes and may be resynthesized by the mucosa before entering the lymph stream. The ingested cholesterol is partly absorbed by the aid of the bile and pancreatic juice. Cholesterol is found in its free form in the bile and is partly reabsorbed and partly excreted in the feces. Some of the cholesterol is hydrogenated by bacteria to coprosterol and found as such in the feces.

A number of pathological conditions are reflected in the concentration of cholesterol in the blood. Normally this value may vary from about 100 mg. to 240 mg. per 100 cc. These limits have frequently been stated to be a good deal narrower, but the clinician will find that he will encounter a fairly large number of abnormal cholesterol values, both high and low that he cannot account for on clinical grounds, if he makes his limits too narrow.

There is a well-known inverse relationship between the total blood cholesterol concentration and the degree of thyroid activity. Very low values may be seen in hyperthyroidism, and values well above 240 mg. per 100 cc. are frequently encountered in hypothyroidism. These observations may be accounted for by a dependence of the rate of the sterol metabolism upon the activity of the thyroid gland.

Uncontrolled diabetes usually exhibits an increase in cholesterol associated with a general increase in the total lipid content of the blood. The cholesterol values in this disease may exceed 500 mg. per 100 cc., although there is not necessarily a correlation between the cholesterol and the blood glucose concentrations. Under treatment with insulin the cholesterol values diminish slowly, and the insulin effect in this regard is probably of an indirect nature. The level of the cholesterol concentration in the blood stream may be an index of the severity of the diabetes, and therefore, may have some prognostic significance. Hypocholesterolemia in diabetes mellitus has been postulated to result from decreased ability of the liver to excrete cholesterol, but it is more likely that it is associated with a primary effect in lipid metabolism.

In lipoid nephrosis the total blood cholesterol reaches exceedingly high values. Concentrations of from 600 to 800 mg. per 100 cc. are not uncommon. Pregnancy tends to increase the cholesterol content of blood and some increase may be associated with menstruation.

Pernicious and perhaps secondary anemias are frequently accompanied by low cholesterol values. In contradistinction to these, aplastic anemia and hemorrhage often result in increases in the cholesterol level. Hemolytic jaundice and acute yellow atrophy of the liver are usually associated with low cholesterol values, while in jaundice due to biliary obstruction the blood cholesterol content may increase in approximately the same proportion as the bilirubin.

BILE ACIDS

These constituents of bile contain the steroid ring complex, and part of the C_{17} side chain is similar to the hydrocarbon chain in cholesterol but ends with a COOH-group. The OH-group at C_3 is that of the α series of sterols, so that the bile acids are not precipitated by digitonin. *Cholic acid,* present in moderate amount in human bile, is conjugated with the amino acids glycine or taurine, as *glycocholic acid* and *taurocholic acid.*

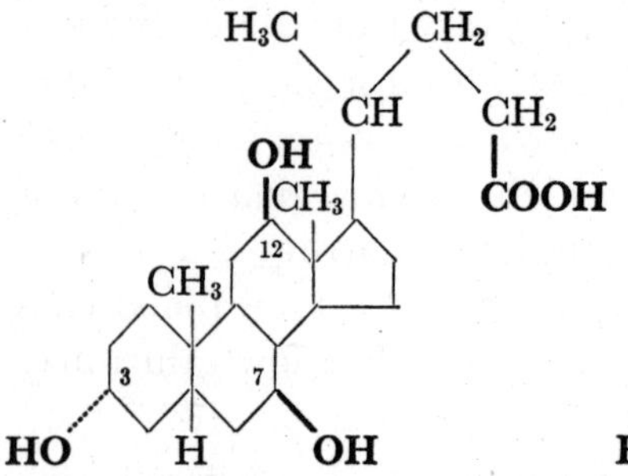

$$H_3C \quad CH_2$$
$$CH \quad CH_2$$
$$OH$$
$$CH_3$$
$$12$$
$$CH_3$$
$$COOH$$
$$3 \quad 7$$
$$HO \quad H \quad OH$$

CHOLIC ACID

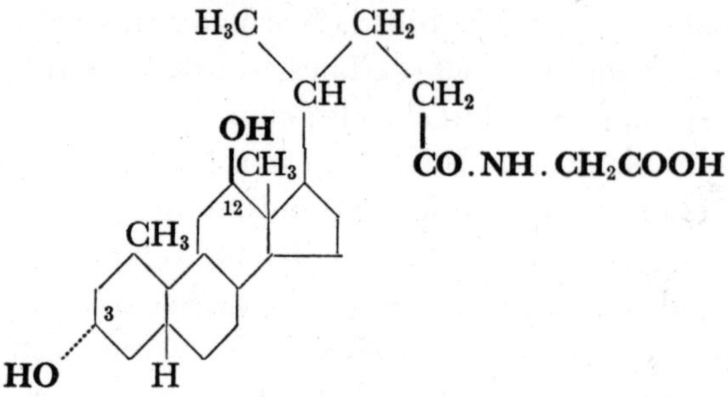

$$H_3C \quad CH_2$$
$$CH \quad CH_2$$
$$OH$$
$$CH_3$$
$$12$$
$$CH_3$$
$$CO.NH.CH_2COOH$$
$$3$$
$$HO \quad H$$

GLYCOCHOLIC ACID

Bile is weakly alkaline in reaction and the conjugated bile acids are present as salts. Because of the 'hydrophilic' character of the carboxyl group and the 'hydrophobic' nature of the rest of the molecule the bile salts are excellent emulsifiers as previously discussed under digestion of fats. The emulsifying effect is essential for absorption of certain lipoidal food factors, such as *vitamin K*, which is not absorbed in adequate amounts from the intestinal tract in obstructive jaundice.

Another bile acid of physiological importance is *desoxycholic acid:*

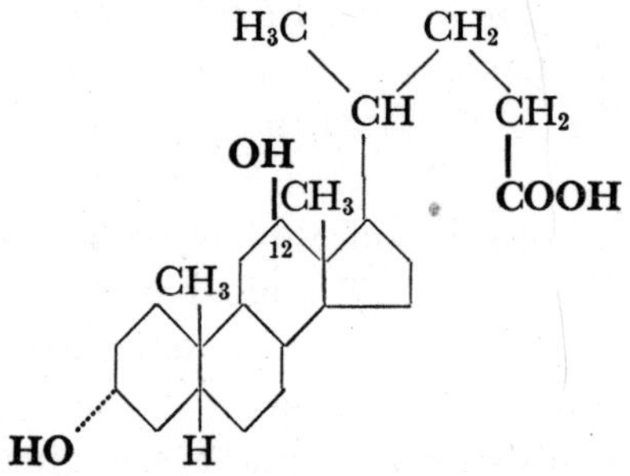

$$H_3C \quad CH_2$$
$$CH \quad CH_2$$
$$OH$$
$$CH_3$$
$$12$$
$$CH_3$$
$$COOH$$
$$HO \quad H$$

Desoxycholic acid contains two hydroxyl groups instead of three as in cholic acid. The parent substance without hydroxyl groups is *cholanic acid,* cholic acid being 3-7-12-trihydroxycholanic acid and desoxycholic acid 3-12-di-hydroxycholanic acid.

The origin of the bile acids is unknown, although studies with isotopes indicate that cholesterol or part of its molecule is a precursor of cholic acid. Feeding of large amounts of cholesterol does not increase the excretion of bilt salts in the bile. The fact that bile salts continue to be formed and excreted during prolonged periods of starvation indicates that they may be formed from other types of molecules.

SEX HORMONES

The sex hormones are steroids secreted by the gonads under stimulation of proteinoid hormones from the anterior hypophysis. They control development and secondary sex characteristics. In a broader sense they influence cellular development and maintenance and, therefore, may be classified as growth promoting substances.

The *estrogens* are capable of producing estrus in animals. The relative potency can be determined by bio-assays (Allen-Doisy) based on the cellular response to their administration as observed in vaginal smears from castrated females. In mice the effective dose has been found to be approximately 0.1 gamma, and this amount of pure, crystalline estrone is accepted as 1 *international unit* of estrogen.

Estrogenic activity promotes growth and proliferation of the functional uterine mucosa. In the human this effect is probably due entirely to *estradiol,* which is the only estrogenic hormone known to be produced naturally in the organism.

Estriol is a third estrogenic steroid hormone. Estrone and estriol are found together as excretory products in the urine and are probably not true hormones.

ESTRONE   ESTRADIOL   ESTRIOL

It will be observed that in the estrogenic hormones ring A has double bonds distributed as in the benzene ring, and therefore, is aromatic in character. The OH-group at C_3 is phenolic, which gives the estrogens the properties of weak acids. The aromatic nature of this ring makes impossible the occurrence of the methyl group at C_{10}. The weakly acid character is made use of in their separation from other urinary steroid constituents.

Urine is a much better source of estrogens than is ovarian tissue. Urine from pregnant women is processed commercially because of its content of estriol. Estriol is less potent as an estrogen than estrone, but it is a valuable therapeutic product as it exhibits its effect after oral administration in contrast to the other naturally occurring estrogens. The urine from pregnant mares contains large amounts of estrone which is extracted and converted commercially to estradiol, as the potency of estradiol is approximately 10 times that of estrone. Estradiol was prepared from estrone as the dihydro-derivative by reduction at the C_{17} carbon atom. Doisy in 1935 isolated estradiol from hog ovaries and showed it to be identical with the already known estradiol. The hormones found in the urine are partly free and partly conjugated as glucuronides or sulfate esters. To give a maximum yield the urines are, therefore, subjected to acid hydrolysis before the hormone fractions are extracted.

Children excrete small amounts of estrogen in the urine. In girls this amount increases at about 8 to 10 years of age. The urinary estrogen excretion shows variations during the reproductive period, having 2 maxima during each menstrual cycle. At the onset of menstruation the amount is small with gradual increase to a maximum at the midperiod. The second maximum occurs during the premenstrual phase, a sharp drop occurring just preceding the flow. This pattern of excretion may vary greatly in different individuals and it does not always repeat itself in the same person. The maximum excretion at the midperiod usually coincides with the peak of chorionic gonadotropins. During pregnancy the blood content of estrogen and the urinary excretion increases progressively to its highest value at term. During the first 12 weeks these values may not be higher than in the non-pregnant female. Beyond this period the blood levels usually exceed 125 I.U. per 100 cc. During the menopausal period urinary estrogen excretion tends to fall below the minimum values of the menstrual cycle.

Decrease in estrogen content of blood and excretion in the urine may be due to a primary pituitary or secondary ovarian deficiency. The differentiation is made by gonadotropin assays. Whether the cause is one or the other the estrogen deficiency may result in hypo- or amenorrhea and sexual infantilism, eunuchoidism and sterility. The deficiency eventually brings on the picture of a premature menopause. Abnormalities in the production of estrogen may be the cause of various types of functional bleeding.

Diabetic women tend to show a hormonal imbalance during pregnancy. White's observations indicate that this occurs in approximately 75 per cent of such cases. The blood level of estrogen is lower than in the normal pregnant subject, the urinary excretion of pregnanediol is less and associated with a rise in chorionic gonadotropins. By administration of estrogen (diethylstilbestrol) and progesterone White succeeded in raising the fetal survival from about 50 per cent to approximately 90 per cent.

Certain tumors may increase the production of estrogen but generally not to levels comparable to those found in pregnancy. Granulosa-cell tumors belong in this group, but the increased estrogen production may not be significantly higher than the peaks in the normal menstrual cycle. Nor may the clinical evidence of increased amounts of estrogens be established readily. The lower levels of production of estrogen before puberty and during the menopause make it easier to confirm the diagnosis both from the laboratory as well as from the clinical standpoint.

Endometrial hyperplasia may be associated with increased total production of estrogenic hormone without this increase necessarily being reflected in increased concentration in the blood.

The synthetic commercial production of the natural estrogens from available material, such as cholesterol, is an undertaking of major magnitude mainly because of the many isomers possible. A number of synthetic compounds are not steroids but exhibit estrogenic effect to a remarkable degree. One of these is *diethylstilbestrol* having the formula:

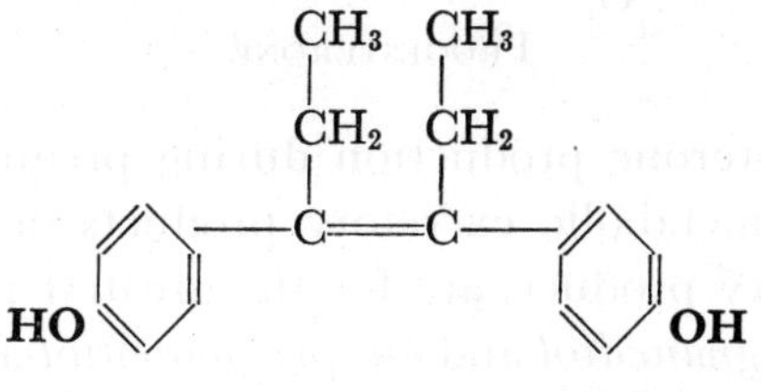

$$
\begin{array}{cc}
CH_3 & CH_3 \\
| & | \\
CH_2 & CH_2 \\
| & | \\
\end{array}
$$

HO — C = C — OH

This formula may be rewritten to give a superficial resemblance to the steroid structure.

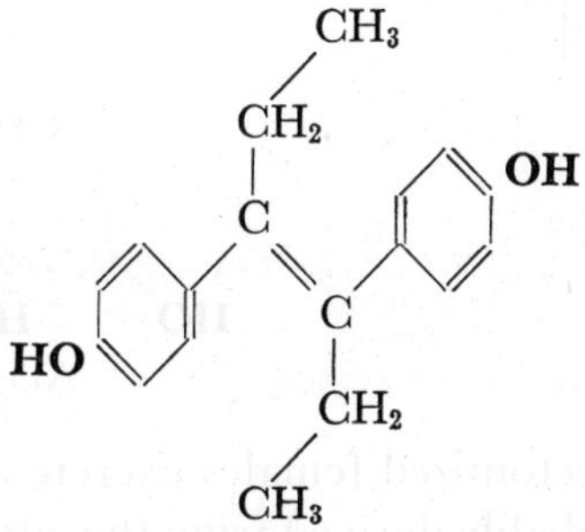

$$
\begin{array}{c}
CH_3 \\
CH_2 \\
C \\
C \\
CH_2 \\
CH_3
\end{array}
$$

HO   OH

Satisfactory explanation of the estrogenic effect of non-steroid substances might contribute to the understanding of structure in relation to biological activity. Estrogens having hydroxyl groups are more active than those having keto groups. The distances between groups in these molecules can be determined, and it is known that in estrogenic substances the optimum biological activity is associated with a distance of 8.55 Angstrom units between the hydroxyl or keto groups. The actual distance between the 2 OH-groups in diethylstilbestrol is equal to the distance between the OH-groups in the natural estrogens (OH- and keto group in estrone) and this may account for their similar physiological effect.

Progestational changes in the uterus are initiated by the ovarian estrogenic hormones. The secretory activity, which continues the change in the mucosa necessary for the implantation of the fertilized ovum and maintenance of pregnancy, is due to the action of *progesterone,* produced by the corpus luteum. Comparatively large amounts of progesterone are elaborated during pregnancy and, in replacement therapy the necessary dosage makes adequate treatment very expensive.

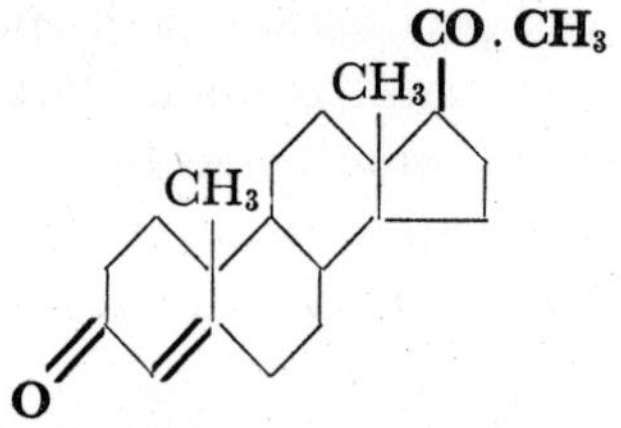

$$CO.CH_3$$

PROGESTERONE

The rate of progesterone production during pregnancy can be followed by determining the metabolic excretory products of this hormone in the urine. These excretory products are for the greatest part reduced alcoholic steroids, of which *pregnanediol* and *allopregnanediol* are the principal members:

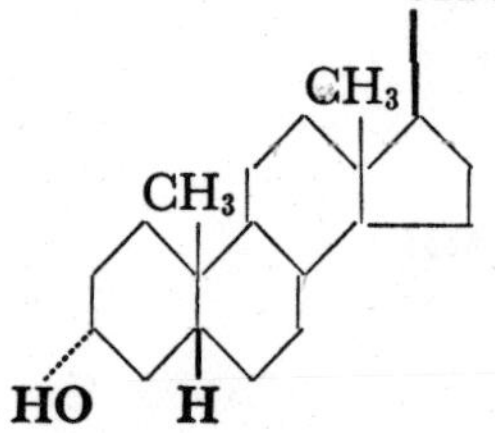

$$CHOH.CH_3 \qquad\qquad CHOH.CH_3$$

PREGNANEDIOL 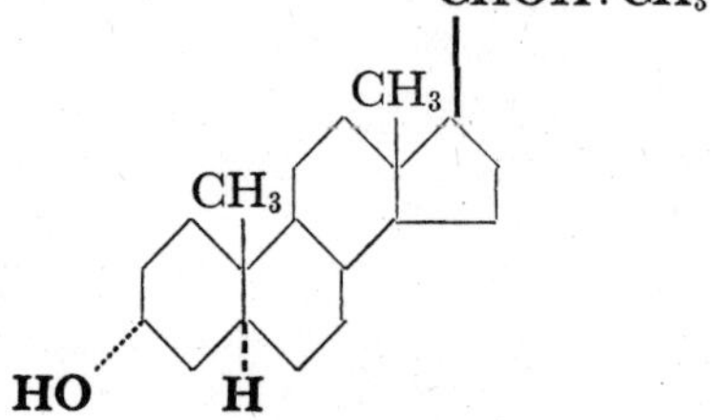   ALLOPREGNANEDIOL

Normal males and ovariectomized females excrete approximately 0.1 mg. of pregnanediol per day, probably derived from the adrenal cortex. The amount in the normal female varies with the menstrual cycle, being very small in the follicular phase. At the peak of the luteal phase the excretion may go up to 5 mg. per day. During pregnancy much larger amounts of pregnanediol are found in the urine. In the early months the daily excretion is approximately 10 mg. per day, but toward the end of pregnancy it increases to approximately 100 mg. per day. These figures are subject to wide variations.

While the female sex hormones can be classified according to the two phases of the menstrual cycle, the male sex hormones all have the same qualitative effect and they differ only in potency. The two main members of the male sex hormones are *testosterone* and *androsterone*.

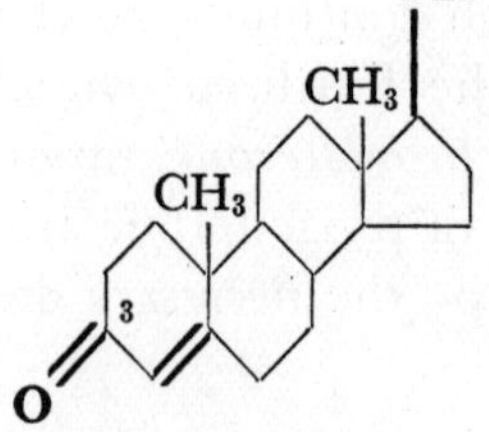

TESTOSTERONE 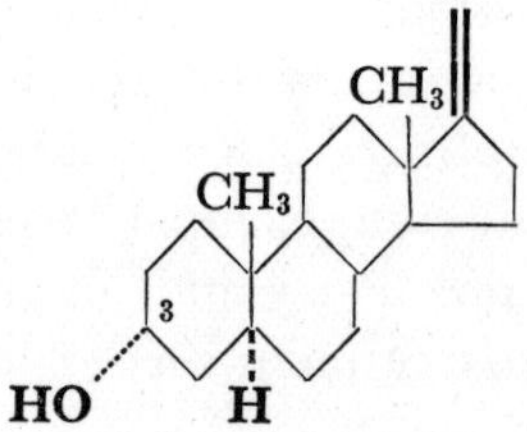   ANDROSTERONE

In androsterone the alcoholic OH-group at C_3 is in the α-position and androsterone is consequently not precipitated by digitonin. Testosterone is probably the only true testicular hormone. The androgenic effect can be measured either by the comb growth in capons (capon unit) or the stimulatory effect on the growth of the seminal vesicles in castrated male rodents.

The *urinary androgen fraction* is of considerable diagnostic importance in endocrine disorders. When the phenolic urinary estrogens are removed with alkali the remaining neutral mixture can be fractionated to give substances having a keto group. The ketonic fraction comprises the *17-ketosteroids*. These are derived from the metabolism of hormones both from the testes and from the adrenal cortex. Ovariectomy does not alter the quantitative excretion. It is not possible at present to separate the individual members of the 17-ketosteroids according to their origin, although it is likely that *isoandrosterone* is derived from testicular tissue and that *dehydroisoandrosterone* originates in the adrenal cortex. All 17-ketosteroids have an alcoholic OH-group at C_3, and they can be further subdivided into 3-α and 3-β-fractions according to their reaction with digitonin.

The average daily excretion of urinary 17-ketosteroids varies a good deal from person to person, and the clinical interpretation of excretion data is difficult. It is generally considered that the testes contribute about 5 mg. per day, and that the adrenocortical hormones produce approximately 9 mg. of 17-ketosteroids per day. In advanced Addison's disease there is presumably no cortical activity so that the excretion of 17-ketosteroids in such cases is zero in the female. Approximately 5 mg. per day could be produced by the testicular tissue and excreted in the male.

The principal 3-α-17-ketosteroids are:

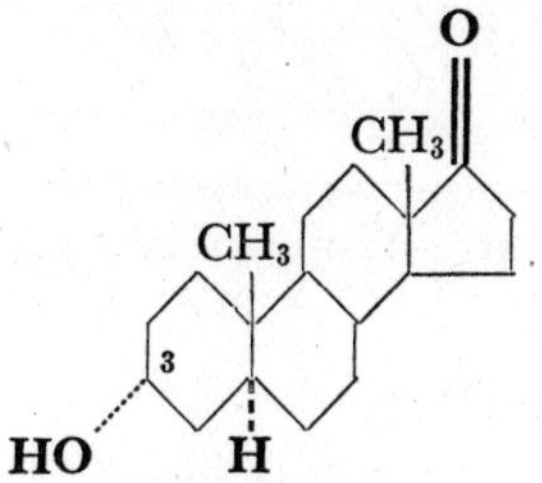

ANDROSTERONE

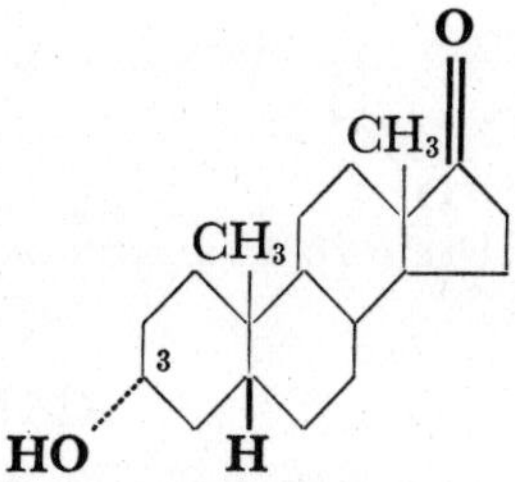

3-α-HYDROXYETIOCHOLANONE-17

Dehydroisoandrosterone is a representative of the β-fraction:

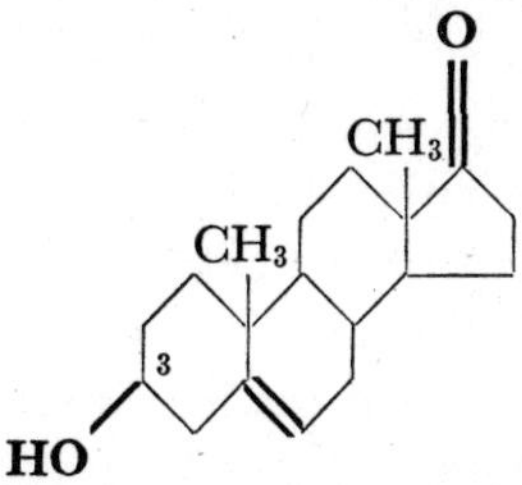

DEHYDROISOANDROSTERONE

CORTICAL HORMONES

Twenty-eight steroids have been isolated from the adrenal cortex. At present physiological activity can be correlated with structural characteristics fairly well, although the response to a cortical extract cannot be entirely duplicated by injections of a known mixture of hormones. This indicates that specific physiological properties must be ascribed to hormones not yet isolated.

Cortical steroids having specific activity all have a keto-group at C_3 resembling testosterone and progesterone. All of them have side chains at C_{17} and some of them have an oxygen atom or a hydroxyl group at C_{11}.

The cortical hormones in pure form exhibit characteristic activity in regard to electrolyte balance and carbohydrate metabolism. *Desoxycorticosterone* acts specifically to promote retention of sodium and chloride ions by the kidney. This substance is used therapeutically in the form of the acetate to maintain normal electrolyte balance in Addison's disease.

The compounds with an OH-group at C_{11} influence the conversion of protein to carbohydrate (gluconeogenesis), and this effect is presumably due to the oxygen as the effect is about equal whether the oxygen is in the keto or the hydroxyl form. *Kendall's compound E* (cortisone), 11-dehydro-17-hydroxycorticosterone, is typical of the steroids with specific gluconeogenic properties. Physiological properties of the cortical hormones will be discussed in greater detail in Chapter 15.

COCH₂OH$\qquad$COCH₂OH

DESOXYCORTICOSTERONE$\qquad$11-DEHYDRO-17-HYDROXYCORTICOSTERONE
(COMPOUND E)

CARDIAC GLYCOSIDES

These substances are complex structures containing the steroid configuration as part of their molecules. They are water-soluble principles found in various plants, particularly in digitalis, strophanthus and squill. The parotid glands of certain species of toads contain cardiac toxins of similar structure. The glycosides in general are hydroxy-compounds combined with a sugar and they can be broken down to their components by various hydrolytic means. The non-sugar part is called a *genin* or *aglycone*. Digitalis is the most important source of heart toxins and extensive fractionation and separation of the active principles have been made. There are three native glycosides known, namely, *digilanide A, B,* and *C.* Digitalis contains a hydrolytic enzyme *digilanidase,* and under the influence of this enzyme the original glycoside, digilanide A, splits off acetyl and glucose to form *digitoxin.* Digitoxin contains the aglycone, *digitoxigenin,* and a sugar called digitoxose, which can be removed from digitoxin by acid hydrolysis, yielding the pure aglycone.

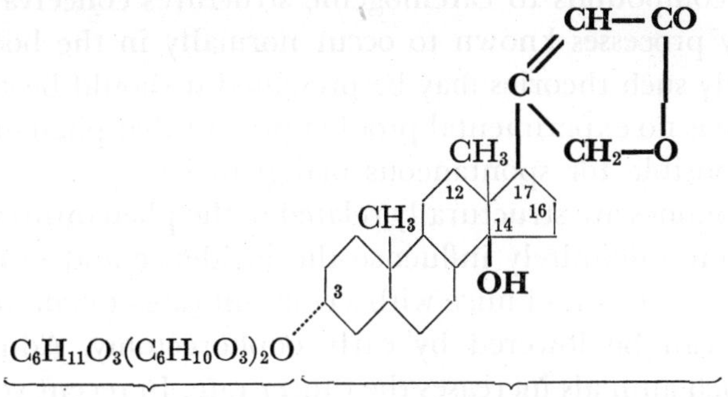

$$C_6H_{11}O_3(C_6H_{10}O_3)_2O$$

DIGITOXOSE   DIGITOXIGENIN

DIGITOXIN

Enzymic hydrolysis of digilanide B and C yields corresponding compounds. Digilanide B is converted to *gitoxin* which in turn liberates *gitoxigenin* if hydrolyzed in acid medium. In a similar manner *digoxin* is produced from digilanide C. The corresponding aglycone is called *digoxigenin.* The structures of these aglycones are very similar to that of digitoxigenin. Digoxigenin has an additional OH-group at C_{12} while in gitoxigenin the additional OH-group is found at C_{16}

The cardiac effect is associated with the ring structure at C_{17}. This ring is an unsaturated lactone and the double bond is important for the therapeutic effect as most of the cardiac activity is lost if the double bond is destroyed. There is evidence that the hydroxyl-group at C_{14} contributes to the action on the heart.

CARCINOGENS

A number of agents are able to produce cellular changes characteristic of malignant growth. Well-known physical entities with this power include radiation from radium, x-rays and ultraviolet radiation. Many chemical irritants are capable of producing cancerous changes if they are applied over a long enough period of time. In more recent years considerable attention has been paid to viruses which upon transfer from animal to animal produce neoplasms. Generally the viruses initiate tumor growths with cellular characteristics depending on the particular virus. The chemical agents with carcinogenic power produce neoplastic changes in the original cells exposed to the chemical regardless of the specific chemical used. The carcinogenic chemicals are not confined to phenanthrene derivatives, but this group has been studied most extensively. Many theoretical speculations have been made that cancerous growths in some way are initiated and sustained by products resulting from abnormal derivatives from the normal sterol metabolism. Some of the carcinogenic phenanthrene derivatives have a great resemblance to naturally occurring steroids, such as the bile acids, and the conversion of these normal compounds to carcinogenic structures conceivably can be accomplished by processes known to occur normally in the body. No matter how attractively such theories may be presented it should be stated emphatically that there is no experimental proof at present that phenanthrene derivatives are responsible for spontaneous malignancies.

The sex hormones are structurally related to the phenanthrene carcinogens and sex hormones definitely influence the incidence and rate of growth of certain tumors. In strains of mice with a constant rate of mammary carcinoma the incidence can be lowered by early oophorectomy. Administration of estrogens to such animals increases the cancer rate. In recent years it has been standard treatment to remove the testes and to give female sex hormones to males with metastatic carcinoma of the prostate. Beneficial effects have been observed also in females with carcinoma of the breast following administration of male sex hormones. Although such therapy does not constitute a cure, the benefits obtained demonstrate adequately the relationship of the growth of these types of cancer to the sex hormones. Recent observations on the effect of adrenal steroid hormones and adrenocorticotropic hormone (ACTH) in persons with various malignancies and in the leukemias indicate new fields of chemotherapy in cancer.

The studies on carcinogenic properties of chemicals began with the observation that certain factory workers developed skin cancers following exposure to coal tar. It was also observed that the incidence of bladder tumors was higher than normal in aniline plants. The first experimental cancers from coal tar were produced in Japan in 1915. In 1930 it was found in London that *1,2,5,6-dibenzanthracene* in pure form could produce cancer experimentally. Three years later a potent carcinogenic agent, *3,4-benzpyrene*, was isolated from coal tar.

1,2,5,6-Dibenzanthracene   3,4-Benzpyrene

Desoxycholic acid has been degraded in various steps to an aromatic hydrocarbon, called *methylcholanthrene*. If the formula for desoxycholic acid is rearranged as indicated below the possibility is apparent that the terminal carboxyl may condense with the OH-group at C_{12} and the open chain thus forms a closed ring structure.

DESOXYCHOLIC ACID   METHYLCHOLANTHRENE

Methylcholanthrene is the most potent of the known carcinogenic substances. Apparently the CH_3-group has little or no carcinogenic effect. There is no explanation available of the actual mechanism whereby the carcinogens incite malignant growth. In general the aromatic hydrocarbons are quite inert substances chemically but many of the carcinogenic hydrocarbons exhibit a much higher degree of reactivity than the group as a whole. However, this higher degree of reactivity is not always correlated to carcinogenic power.

SUPPLEMENTARY READING

BLOOR, W. R.: *Biochemistry of the Fatty Acids.* Reinhold Publishing Corp., 1943.

CHAIKOFF, I. L., and SOSKIN, S.: The utilization of acetoacetic acid by normal and diabetic dogs before and after evisceration. *Am. J. Physiol., 87:*58, 1928.

COHEN, P. P.: Studies in ketogenesis. *J. Biol. Chem., 119:*333, 1937.

FIESER, L. F. and FIESER, M.: *Natural Products Related to Phenanthrene.* Reinhold Publishing Corp., 1949.

FRIEDGOOD, H. B. Concerning the biochemistry and the physiological and clinical significance of the sex hormones and 17-ketosteroids. The Chemistry and Physiology of the Hormones, p. 195, *Am. A. Adv. Sc.,* 1944.

HANSEN, A. E., and BURR, G. O.: Essential fatty acids and human nutrition. *J.A.M.A., 132:*855, 1946.

JUKES, T. H.: Lipotropic factors. *Ann Rev. Biochem., 16:*205, 1947.

MACKAY, E. M., WICK, A. N., and BARNUM, C. P.: Ketogenic action of odd-numbered carbon fatty acids. *J. Biol. Chem., 136:*503, 1940.

MEDES, G., WEINHOUSE, S., and FLOYD, N. F.: Ketone body formation from acetate in kidney, with isotopic carbon as a tracer. *J. Biol. Chem., 157:*751, 1945.

MIRSKY, I. A., and BROH-KAHN, R. H.: The influence of dextrose administration on the utilization of beta-hydroxybutyric acid by the normal and eviscerated rabbit. *Am. J. Physiol., 119:*734, 1937.

SCHOENHEIMER, R.: *The Dynamic State of Body Constituents.* Harvard University Press, 1946.

SOBOTKA, H.: *Physiological Chemistry of the Bile.* The Williams and Wilkins Co., 1937.

SOSKIN, S., and LEVINE, R.: Origin of ketone bodies from fats and their regulation. *Arch. Int. Med., 68:*674, 1941.

STADIE, W. C., ZAPP, J. A., JR., and LUKENS, F. D. W.: The effect of insulin upon the ketone metabolism of normal and diabetic cats. *J. Biol. Chem., 132:*423, 1940.

STADIE, W. C., ZAPP, J. A., JR., and LUKENS, F. D. W.: The non-formation of acetic acid and the ratio of ketone-body increase to fatty acid decrease in livers of diabetic animals. *J. Biol. Chem., 137:*75, 1941.

STADIE, W. C.: The intermediary metabolism of fatty acids. *Physiol. Rev., 25:*395, 1945.

STETTEN, DEW., and SALCEDO, J., JR.: The source of the extra liver fat in various types of fatty liver. *J. Biol. Chem., 156:*27, 1944.

Symposium on the Adrenal Glands: *Am. J. Med.,* May, 1951.

Symposium on Steroids in Experimental and Clinical Practice. The Blakiston Company, 1951.

THANNHAUSER, S. J., BENOTTI, J., WALCOTT, A., and REINSTEIN, H. J.: The lecithin, cephalin, and sphingomyelin content of normal human organs. *J. Biol. Chem., 129:*717, 1939.

WEINHOUSE, S., MEDES, G., and FLOYD, N., Ketone body formation from fatty acids using heavy carbon as a tracer. *Am. J. Med. Sc., 207:*812, 1944.

Chapter 7

PROTEINS

COMPOSITION

Pʀᴏᴛᴇɪɴs are of key importance in all living tissues. They are of high molecular weight and have complicated chemical structures which in all instances have defied attempts to define them accurately by use of analytical methods. Their elementary composition sets them apart from other food materials, for in addition to carbon, hydrogen, and oxygen, they contain nitrogen. Sulfur is present in practically all proteins and phosphorus is a common constituent. The nitrogen content of proteins is approximately 16 per cent or 1/6.25 of the total, and is subject to minor variations in different proteins. Therefore, total protein can be calculated to be about 6.25 times the nitrogen content as determined by analysis.

Proteins are built up of a very large number of amino acid molecules. These amino acids can be obtained after hydrolyzing the proteins by chemical means or by the action of proteolytic enzymes. The total number of individual amino acids found in protein hydrolysates is about 23 and it is not likely that many more will be found.

ANALYTICAL IDENTIFICATION

As already mentioned the analytical approach to the study of protein structures is extremely difficult. The protein can be separated into fractions which are thought to represent pure substances, and some of them can be crystallized in characteristic patterns. It is not always easy to be sure that the isolated material is pure in the sense that it consists only of identical molecules. It is quite likely that many so-called pure proteins are present in living tissue in complexes of various related structures in equilibrium. Equilibria of such nature are apt to be destroyed during isolation procedures, and fractionation by usual chemical means cannot be done with assurance that the isolated entities are identical with the original molecular structures.

The sensitivity of proteins to environmental factors is well demonstrated in the process of *denaturation*. The denaturation of proteins can be accomplished by exposure to heat, light, chemicals, and even by physical force such as shaking. The process is usually irreversible, but milder forms of denaturation may be reversible. Denaturation always results in a decrease in solubility. Changes in physiological behaviour after denaturation point to chemical alterations in the molecule. Immunological specificity disappears and enzymic and hormonal functions are destroyed. Certain native proteins, stable to the proteolytic enzymes, become digestible after denaturation.

Molecular weights of proteins vary over a wide range. Egg albumin is estimated to be approximately 40,000 while the tobacco mosaic virus is probably over 15,000,000. Proteins do not have *melting points* and undergo destruction at rather low temperatures. Separation of individual components in protein mixtures can be accomplished by subjecting them to an electrical field. This principle is employed in the *Tiselius electrophoresis apparatus.* The rate of motion of the molecules across a constant electrical field is determined by their size and shape and the characteristics of the field. Therefore, the molecules tend to separate as they move along in the field. This separation can be recorded by optical means on photographic plates, and the electrophoretic patterns thus obtained give valuable information as to the number of individual proteins present and their relative concentration. Changes in protein composition of plasma have been demonstrated to be related to various diseases, and electrophoretic patterns have been used to determine the optimum production of certain antibody fractions in animals to obtain the most potent sera.

Due to the characteristic structure of the amino acids the proteins behave like amphoteric compounds which means that they can react both as acids and bases. This is due to their content of carboxyl groups, as well as amino groups. If the acidic and basic ionizations are equal the corresponding pH is called the *isoelectric point.* This is a characteristic constant for each individual protein or amino acid. The solubility is minimal at this point.

CLASSIFICATION

Because of their complexity the chemical composition of proteins cannot be made the basis for their classification. It is common practice to refer to an arbitrary system of classification which divides the proteins into groups mainly on the basis of physical properties such as dispersibility in various media. It would not serve the purpose of this book to go into details of this classification. Suffice it to say that there are 3 main groups:

A. Simple proteins
B. Conjugated proteins
C. Derived proteins

Group B consists of proteins in combination with non-protein groups such as nucleoproteins, glycoproteins, etc. The non-protein part of the molecule is frequently referred to as a prosthetic group. Derived proteins include the structures formed from other proteins by various physical and chemical agents. The intermediate breakdown products of protein metabolism belong in this group.

From a functional standpoint it is convenient to divide the simple proteins into two types, fibrous and globular. The fibrous proteins are thought to be of elongated molecular structure, with elastic properties due to folding and unfolding of the polypeptide chains. The globular proteins are soluble and they are probably made up of molecules arranged in compact globular shape.

The globular proteins are dealt with extensively in physiological chemistry. They can be subclassified as follows:

a. Albumins: Soluble in pure water.
b. Globulins: Insoluble in pure water. Soluble in salt solutions.
c. Glutelins: Soluble in dilute acids and alkalis.
d. Prolamines: Soluble in 80 per cent alcohol.
e. Histones: Strongly basic substances soluble in dilute acids.
f. Protamines: Strongly basic substances soluble in water.

AMINO ACIDS

The amino acids obtained from proteins are organic acids with an amino group (NH_2) substituted for one of the hydrogen atoms at the carbon atom adjacent to the carboxyl group. They are, therefore, α-amino acids. In two of them, proline and hydroxyproline, the α-amino group is modified as it takes part in the formation of a ring structure. The amino acids with the exception of glycine have either one or two asymmetric carbon atoms. The natural amino acids have the L-configuration regardless of the actual specific optical rotation. D-amino acids with a few exceptions cannot be substituted for the natural acids in metabolic processes. Amino acids have the general formula:

$$RCH(NH_2)COOH$$

The structures of some of the commonly occurring amino acids are shown below:

GLYCINE: $CH_2(NH_2)COOH$
ALANINE: $CH_3CH(NH_2)COOH$
CYSTINE: $COOH(NH_2)CHCH_2S—SCH_2CH(NH_2)COOH$
METHIONINE: $CH_3S(CH_2)_2CH(NH_2)COOH$
TYROSINE: $HO\!\!\bigcirc\!\!CH_2CH(NH_2)COOH$
TRYPTOPHAN:

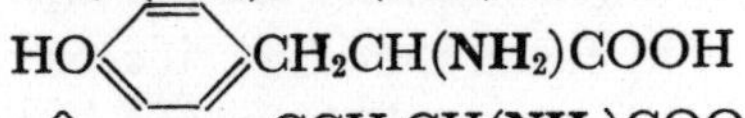

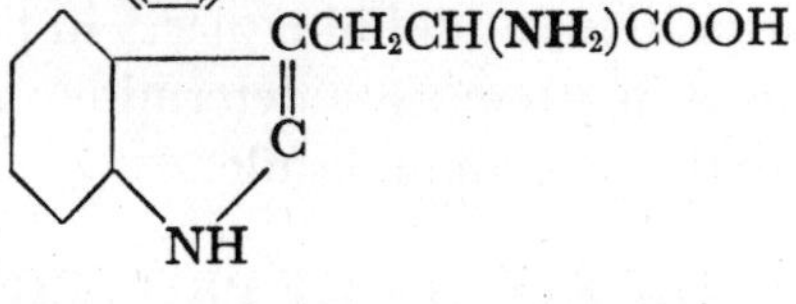

Certain amino acids can be synthesized by the animal organism and others cannot. Those that cannot be synthesized must be supplied in the food for normal growth and tissue maintenance, and therefore, they are called *essential amino acids*. By using mixtures of pure amino acids in feeding experiments on white rats, the following have been found to be essential:

leucine, isoleucine, valine, threonine, methionine, phenylalanine, tryptophan, histidine, lysine, and arginine. They may not all be essential in man.

Proteins contain very few free amino and carboxyl groups which is in
contrast to the large number of these groups present in their hydrolysates.
When proteins are hydrolyzed they yield equal numbers of the two groups.
The theory of *peptide linkage* presented independently by Hofmeister and
Fischer in 1902 is developed on the basis of this observation.

"Peptide linkage" implies that two amino acids unite through the amino
group of one with the carboxyl group of the other. The process may be
pictured as follows:

$$\underset{\text{Amino Acid}}{H_2N-\underset{\overset{|}{R_1}}{C}H-COOH} + \underset{\text{Amino Acid}}{H_2NCHCOOH} \rightarrow \underset{\text{Dipeptide}}{H_2N\underset{\overset{|}{R_1}}{C}HCO-NH\underset{\overset{|}{R_2}}{C}HCOOH} + H_2O$$

The resulting *dipeptide* has a free amino acid group at one end of the molecule and a free carboxyl group at the other end. Therefore, it is able to react
again with other amino acids at each end of its molecule and this process
can be imagined to go on repeatedly. This is the mechanism by which proteins of large molecular size seem to be synthesized in nature.

The natural synthesis of proteins is controlled by enzymes. Bergmann in
1937 demonstrated that these enzymes are also responsible for the hydrolytic
breakdown of proteins. Originally the specific action of the proteolytic
enzymes, the *proteinases*, argued against the acceptance of the peptide structure because they do not hydrolyze all short-chain peptides. It has been
shown, however, that each of the proteinases has its own specific action at
certain loci in the peptide chains and that the various groupings of amino
acids constitute the substrates for which the individual enzymes are specific.
When a new amino acid is added to a peptide structure the resulting complex
represents a different substrate requiring another enzyme for further synthetic reactions. This concept explains why proteins apparently are built up
of amino acids in an ordered sequence rather than in the random fashion
which would be expected from a non-specific enzymic action. Conversely,
specific enzymes split proteins at definite places in the amino acid chain, and
this action is being used in attempts to determine the relative position of the
various amino acids in the protein molecule.

DIGESTION OF PROTEINS

Food proteins are not used as such by the body. It is possible that minute
amounts are absorbed from the intestinal tract, but practically all of the
protein is broken down into a mixture of individual amino acids and these
are absorbed by the intestinal mucosa. The body's need for protein replacement of tissue is supplied by the process of resynthesis from the absorbed

amino acids as selected for the particular need. Schoenheimer and his associates used isotopic nitrogen to demonstrate that a continuous, rapid exchange of amino acids in the tissue proteins takes place in a manner comparable to the exchange of depot fat as described in Chapter 6. The ingested protein nitrogen is sufficient for the metabolic needs under ordinary dietary conditions and, therefore, is equal to the total nitrogen excretion. Animals in such a state are said to be in *nitrogen equilibrium.*

The ingested protein is first subjected to hydrolytic breakdown in the stomach through the action of *pepsin.* This enzyme is derived from a precursor substance, *pepsinogen,* which is elaborated by the gastric mucosa and transformed by the pH of gastric juice into pepsin. The dietary proteins are converted into *proteoses* and *peptones,* and these reactions proceed rapidly at the pH of the gastric juice (approximately two). *Rennin* is an important enzyme in young mammals because it is a specific proteinase which hydrolyzes the casein in the milk. The optimal pH for digestion of casein by rennin is 5.4, and this corresponds approximately to the hydrogen ion concentration of the gastric juice in infants.

The pancreatic juice contains *trypsinogen* which in the presence of *enterokinase* in the intestinal tract is converted to *trypsin.* Trypsin carries on the protein digestion initiated by the pepsin. This action results in peptides. The tryptic digestion takes place simultaneously with the action of a number of other specific enzymes partly contained in the pancreatic juice and partly in the *succus entericus.* Peptidases complete the hydrolysis of the various intermediary digestion products to a mixture of amino acids ready for absorption by the mucosa.

Most of the amino acids are absorbed before the intestinal contents reach the colon. A part of the nitrogen content of the feces is of epithelial or secretory origin; the portion derived from food normally constitutes only a small percentage of the total nitrogen ingested. In pancreatic disease attended by deficiency in the secretion of digestive enzymes the nitrogen content of the feces may increase considerably due to incomplete protein digestion.

The amino acids in blood are usually estimated from the determination of the content of α-amino nitrogen. In plasma this figure is between 5 and 7 mg. per 100 cc. in the fasting state. In the postprandial phase this nitrogen content is increased over a period of up to seven hours with the maximal increase at the 4th hour. The increase is generally from 2 to 4 mg. per 100 cc. and the largest part of it is found in the plasma.

DEAMINATION

Removal of the amino group in the metabolism of amino acids results ultimately in the formation of urea as the main excretory product containing nitrogen. This process is one of the functions of the liver. In experiments on dogs, Mann and his associates have failed to show extrahepatic formation of urea. Rabinowitch observed in a case of acute yellow atrophy of the liver, associated with extensive renal damage, that the blood urea nitrogen did not increase in spite of the failure of the kidneys. When the function of the liver is abolished as in cases of acute yellow atrophy, there is a decrease of the urea concentration in the blood and a concomitant increase of the amino acid content. Crystals of leucine and tyrosine are frequently observed in the urine of such patients and their presence has been interpreted as characteristic of destruction of liver tissue. These two amino acids are rather insoluble and they may simply represent easily detectable components of the urinary amino acids which the liver has failed to deaminize.

It is believed that oxidation at the α-carbon atom to which the amino group is attached is the initial step in the deamination process. This results in the production of an α-keto acid and ammonia:

$$RCH_2CHNH_2COOH + O \rightarrow RCH_2COCOOH + NH_3$$
$$\text{α-Amino Acid} \qquad \text{α-Keto Acid} \quad \text{Ammonia}$$

In mammals the ammonia is transformed to urea by a series of complicated reactions. One of the amino acids, *arginine*, can be hydrolyzed by *arginase* to form urea directly, another amino acid, ornithine, being produced at the same time. Krebs found that the amino acids *ornithine* and *citrulline* accelerate the formation of urea, and he suggested that citrulline is formed from ornithine by combination with carbon dioxide and ammonia. Citrulline in turn is converted to arginine by adding more ammonia, and the arginine molecule then liberates urea by the action of arginase. As ornithine is formed, the process is ready to be repeated and ornithine appears to serve the function of a catalyst. Urea can also be formed from certain compounds in the absence of ornithine, so that the ornithine-arginine cycle is not necessarily the only mechanism operating to produce urea. The reactions involved in the ornithine-arginine cycle may be presented as follows:

$$NH_2(CH_2)_3CH(NH_2)COOH \qquad \text{Ornithine}$$
$$+CO_2 \downarrow +NH_3$$
$$NH_2CONH(CH_2)_3CH(NH_2)COOH + H_2O \qquad \text{Citrulline}$$
$$\downarrow +NH_3$$
$$NH_2C(=NH)NH(CH_2)_3CH(NH_2)COOH + H_2O \qquad \text{Arginine}$$
$$+H_2O \downarrow +\text{Arginase}$$
$$NH_2CONH_2 + NH_2(CH_2)_3CH(NH_2)COOH \qquad \text{Urea} + \text{Ornithine}$$

GLUCONEOGENESIS

The deaminized acids may be oxidized completely and thus contribute to the general supply of energy to the body. Some of them may be converted to glucose or fat and stored as such. The term gluconeogenesis is applied to the formation of carbohydrate in the body from non-carbohydrate material. Failure of the organism to form carbohydrate from protein is an important feature in Addison's disease as this process of gluconeogenesis is under control of certain adrenocortical hormones (see Chapters 6 and 15).

The amino acids which may be converted to carbohydrate are glycine, alanine, glutamic acid, aspartic acid, serine, cystine, arginine, proline, valine, and probably others. Some amino acids are potentially glucogenic through their conversion to one of the above acids.

The glucose-forming amino acids contained in the average food are sufficient in amount to produce approximately 58 grams of glucose per 100 grams of protein. Therefore, the diabetic organism may be able to obtain that much carbohydrate from ingested protein. It is likely that gluconeogenesis from protein takes place in the normal individual, and it seems reasonable to assume that the percentage of glucose-forming amino acids converted to sugar depends on the amount of glucose otherwise available from ingested carbohydrates.

TRANSAMINATION

Von Euler demonstrated that α-ketoglutaric acid and ammonia can combine to form glutamic acid in an enzyme-controlled reaction. Some essential amino acids may participate in similar reactions because the corresponding α-keto or α-hydroxy acids can be substituted for them in the diet of experimental animals. Schoenheimer used amino acids tagged with isotopic nitrogen in the amino group and established the fact that such amino groups are freely interchanged between the amino acids, because in a short period of time the isotopic nitrogen appeared in practically all the amino acids.

At the present time it is assumed that one of the components in the reaction must be a dicarboxylic acid, either amino or keto acid. This transfer of amino groups from one amino acid for the synthesis in vivo of another amino acid is called transamination. Ammonia appears to be an intermediate in the process of transamination because isotopic nitrogen was found by Schoenheimer to be present in the amino acids of the tissues when tagged ammonium citrate was fed to the animals. Lysine behaves exceptionally as it does not take up the tagged nitrogen in feeding experiments, indicating that the deamination of this amino acid is an irreversible process.

The general process of transamination can be illustrated as follows:

$$
\begin{array}{ccccc}
\mathrm{R_1} & & \mathrm{R_2} & \mathrm{R_1} & \mathrm{R_2} \\
| & & | & | & | \\
\mathrm{CHNH_2} + & \mathrm{CO} & \rightleftarrows & \mathrm{CO} + & \mathrm{CHNH_2} \\
| & & | & | & | \\
\mathrm{COOH} & \mathrm{COOH} & & \mathrm{COOH} & \mathrm{COOH} \\
\text{Amino Acid} & \alpha\text{-Keto Acid} & & \alpha\text{-Keto Acid} & \text{Amino Acid}
\end{array}
$$

Transamination may bring about an interconversion between intermediates of protein and carbohydrate metabolism. For instance alanine can be formed by transfer of the amino group from glutamic acid to pyruvic acid which is an intermediary product of glucose metabolism.

$$
\begin{array}{c}
\text{COOH} \\
| \\
\text{(CH}_2)_2 \\
| \\
\text{CHNH}_2 \\
| \\
\text{COOH}
\end{array}
\;+\;
\begin{array}{c}
\\
\text{CH}_3 \\
| \\
\text{CO} \\
| \\
\text{COOH}
\end{array}
\;\rightleftarrows\;
\begin{array}{c}
\text{COOH} \\
| \\
\text{(CH}_2)_2 \\
| \\
\text{CO} \\
| \\
\text{COOH}
\end{array}
\;+\;
\begin{array}{c}
\\
\text{CH}_3 \\
| \\
\text{CHNH}_2 \\
| \\
\text{COOH}
\end{array}
$$

GLUTAMIC   PYRUVIC   α-KETOGLUTARIC   ALANINE
ACID   ACID   ACID

DECARBOXYLATION

Certain microorganisms in the intestinal tract can decarboxylate amino acids to form amines. This process also takes place in the body tissues to a limited extent. Some of the amines formed have known specific functions which are performed by their presence even in very small amounts.

Histidine is decarboxylated to *histamine*:

$$
\begin{array}{c}
\text{CH}=\!=\!\text{CCH}_2\textbf{CHNH}_2\textbf{COOH} \\
| \qquad\quad | \\
\text{N} \qquad\;\; \text{NH} \\
\diagdown \quad \diagup \\
\text{CH}
\end{array}
\qquad \rightarrow \qquad
\begin{array}{c}
\text{CH}=\!=\!\text{CCH}_2\text{CH}_2\text{NH}_2 \\
| \qquad\quad | \\
\text{N} \qquad\;\; \text{NH} \\
\diagdown \quad \diagup \\
\text{CH}
\end{array}
$$

HISTIDINE   HISTAMINE

In animals histamine induces manifestations which are very similar to those of anaphylactic shock. Some of the symptoms of allergic reactions may be accounted for by assuming a release of histamine in the tissues upon contact with the specific allergen. Best and his associates demonstrated that in traces histamine is a normal constituent of many tissues, and also that certain tissues contain an enzyme, *histaminase,* capable of destroying histamine. While this enzyme action is easily observed in vitro, the administration of histaminase to animals does not prevent or influence anaphylaxis. A number of drugs with antihistamine actions are used to relieve the symptoms of allergy. Most of them are amines and it is generally thought that they counteract the effect of histamine by competing with this substance for attachment to cell receptors.

Tyrosine can be converted to *tyramine* as can be demonstrated by kidney slice experiments. Experiments with isotopes prove that phenylalanine is a precursor of *epinephrine* presumably through tyrosine and tyramine.

$$
\begin{array}{c}
\text{OH} \\
\bigcirc \\
| \\
\text{CH}_2 \\
| \\
\textbf{CHNH}_2 \\
| \\
\textbf{COOH}
\end{array}
\;\longrightarrow\;
\begin{array}{c}
\text{OH} \\
\bigcirc \\
| \\
\text{CH}_2 \\
| \\
\textbf{CH}_2\textbf{NH}_2
\end{array}
\;\overset{(?)}{\longrightarrow}\;
\begin{array}{c}
\text{OH} \\
\bigcirc\,\textbf{OH} \\
| \\
\textbf{CHOH} \\
| \\
\textbf{CH}_2\textbf{NHCH}_3
\end{array}
$$

TYROSINE   TYRAMINE   EPINEPHRINE

Skatole and *indole* are found in feces and are produced by the degradation of tryptophan. The *ptomaines, putrescine* and *cadaverine,* are formed by decarboxylation of ornithine and lysine respectively. They are found in decomposing tissues. Pharmacologically they induce a fall in blood pressure. The simple monoamines have sympathomimetic properties. Their physiological action increases as the carbon chain is lengthened.

METHYLATION

It may be noted in the proposed mechanism of production of epinephrine that a methyl group (CH_3) is attached to the amino nitrogen. The organism is probably unable to synthesize methyl groups, and it is likely that all CH_3 radicals are obtained from methyl carriers such as *choline* or *methionine.* The process whereby the methyl group is transferred from these substances is called *transmethylation.*

CREATINE AND CREATININE

Of the creatine content in the body about 98 per cent is contained in the muscle and 1.5 per cent in the nervous system. Skeletal and cardiac muscles are much richer in creatine than smooth muscle. Four-fifths of the creatine is combined with phosphoric acid as phosphocreatine which is an important element in the energy system of muscle. Phosphocreatine is believed to supply phosphate for the conversion of adenylic acid to adenosine triphosphate. The subsequent breakdown of the adenosine triphosphate liberates the energy necessary for the work performed during muscular contraction.

Some creatine is lost in the urine. In well developed adult males this loss is negligible but children and adult females eliminate various amounts. As creatinine is derived from creatine and is excreted as a waste product it is possible that creatinuria occurs when the liberation of creatine exceeds its normal rate of conversion to creatinine. This viewpoint is in agreement with the observations on conditions in which catabolism of muscle tissue is accelerated. Thus, creatinuria occurs in starvation, uncontrolled diabetes, hyperthyroidism, and debilitating diseases. In the muscular dystrophies the muscles are defective in their ability to retain creatine. The large and rather inactive mass of uterine muscle during pregnancy may account for the creatinuria commonly observed in this condition, although it has been shown that the postpartum excretion of creatine may be above the normal value for the individual after hysterectomy. The elimination of creatine is often increased further during the first few weeks following delivery.

Creatine is synthesized readily in the body, and there is no evidence to indicate that the organism utilizes the creatine contained in the diet. The production of creatine and its transformation to creatinine takes place in the muscles. Hepatectomy does not change the rate of creatinine excretion.

Brand and his associates demonstrated increases in the elimination of creatine in patients with muscular dystrophies if they were fed glycine, arginine or guanidoacetic acid. Bloch and Schoenheimer demonstrated the synthesis of creatine from glycine and arginine by tagging these two amino acids with isotopic nitrogen. Borsook and Dubnoff and du Vigneaud showed that the methyl group in creatine originated from methionine. The mechanism of these reactions is indicated in the following:

$$
\begin{array}{ccc}
\text{NH}_2 & \text{NH}_2 & \text{NH}_2 \\
| & | & | \\
\text{CH}_2\text{COOH} \quad + & \text{C}\!\!=\!\!\text{NH} & \text{C}\!\!=\!\!\text{NH} \\
& | & | \\
& \text{NH} \quad\rightarrow & \text{NH} \\
& | & | \\
& (\text{CH}_2)_3 & \text{CH}_2\text{COOH} \\
& | & \\
& \text{CHNH}_2 & \\
& | & \\
& \text{COOH} & \\
\text{GLYCINE} & \text{ARGININE} & \text{GUANIDOACETIC ACID} \\
& & (\text{GLYCOCYAMINE})
\end{array}
$$

The nitrogen of the glycocyamine is then methylated to form creatine:

$$
\begin{array}{ccc}
\text{NH}_2 & & \text{NH} \\
| & & \| \\
\text{C}\!\!=\!\!\text{NH} & & \text{C} \\
| & \xrightarrow{\text{Dehydration}} & / \quad \backslash \\
\text{N}\!\!-\!\!- & & \text{HN} \quad\quad \text{NCH}_3 \\
| & & | \quad\quad\quad | \\
\text{CH}_2\text{COOH} & & \text{OC}\!\!-\!\!-\!\!-\!\!\text{CH}_2 \\
\text{CREATINE} & & \text{CREATININE}
\end{array}
$$

Whole blood normally contains from 3.5 to 5 mg. of creatine and approximately 2.5 mg. of creatinine per 100 cc. Practically all the creatine is contained in the erythrocytes. Creatinine is a diffusible substance and it is distributed quite evenly between plasma and cells.

ABNORMAL AMINO ACID METABOLISM

Alcaptonuria is a rare, inborn condition usually present throughout life of the individual. It is characterized chemically by the excretion in the urine of considerable quantities of *homogentisic* acid which is an intermediate of tyrosine and phenylalanine metabolism. The excretion of homogentisic acid is increased if the patient is fed additional tyrosine or phenylalanine. The latter is at least partly converted to tyrosine during its metabolism. Phenylalanine and tyrosine probably constitute the main supply of benzene rings for the body which cannot synthesize them. The structure of homogentisic acid is as follows:

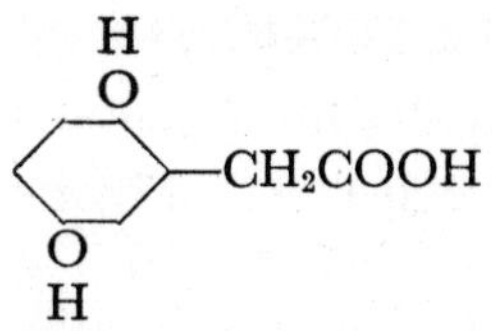

$$\text{(structure: benzene ring with OH at top and bottom positions)} \quad \text{—CH}_2\text{COOH}$$

Guinea pigs deprived of ascorbic acid can be made alcaptonuric. This vitamin has no effect on the disorder in the human. p-Hydroxyphenylpyruvic acid is another possible intermediate in tyrosine metabolism. It is found together with homogentisic acid in the urine of alcaptonuric guinea pigs.

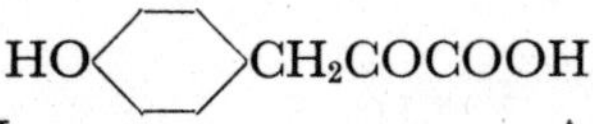

$$HO\text{—}\bigcirc\text{—}CH_2COCOOH$$

p-Hydroxyphenylpyruvic Acid

Tyrosine is believed to be the precursor of *melanin,* the dark pigment of hair, skin, retina, etc. It can be formed readily from tyrosine by oxidation with tyrosinase. The composition of melanin is not known but some of the intermediate reaction products have been isolated and studied as clues to the formation of the pigment. Quite a number of steps are involved. Melanin contains another aromatic ring besides the benzene ring in the tyrosine molecule. This extra ring is formed from the straight carbon chain part in tyrosine:

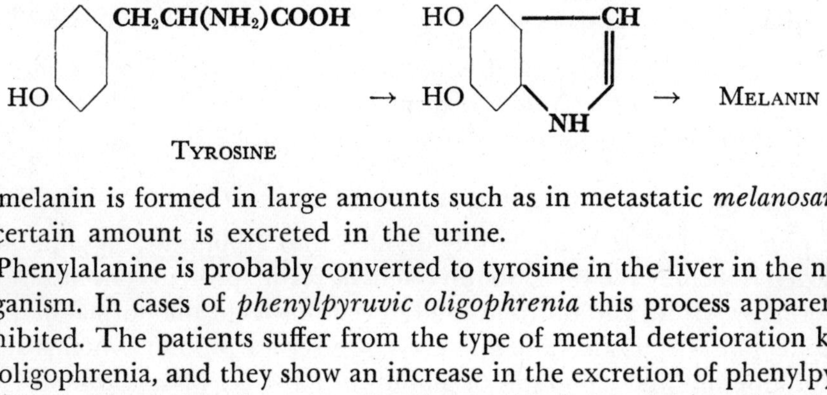

$$HO\text{—}\bigcirc\text{—}CH_2CH(NH_2)COOH \quad \rightarrow \quad HO\text{—(ring)—}NH \quad \rightarrow \quad \text{Melanin}$$

Tyrosine

If melanin is formed in large amounts such as in metastatic *melanosarcoma* a certain amount is excreted in the urine.

Phenylalanine is probably converted to tyrosine in the liver in the normal organism. In cases of *phenylpyruvic oligophrenia* this process apparently is inhibited. The patients suffer from the type of mental deterioration known as oligophrenia, and they show an increase in the excretion of phenylpyruvic acid. The blood contains an increased amount of phenylalanine but the content of phenylpyruvic acid is normal. This points to an inhibition of the normal rate of metabolism of phenylalanine through tyrosine. The patients can metabolize tyrosine and homogentisic acid normally.

Cystinuria is a hereditary condition characterized by the excretion of abnormal amounts of cystine in the urine. When cystine is administered to cystinuric patients it is metabolized normally and its sulfur is excreted as sulfate. If methionine or cysteine is given the cystine excretion increases. It appears that cysteine is carried to the kidneys where the oxidation to cystine takes place. Cystine tends to precipitate to form renal calculi.

DETOXICATION

The body absorbs through the intestinal wall certain amounts of highly toxic substances. These may be disposed of by rapid oxidation or occasionally by reduction. Substances that are not readily susceptible to oxidation may conjugate with other structures to form less toxic products. Sulfuric and glucuronic acids enter into such processes quite commonly. *Indole* from tryptophan is partly eliminated in the feces and partly detoxified and excreted in the urine as *indican:*

$$+O \qquad OH + KSO_4^- \qquad OSO_3K$$

INDOLE	INDOXYL	INDICAN
NH	NH	NH

Acylation is a common method of detoxication. The conjugation occurs by combination between amino radicals and carboxyl groups of various acids. The sulfonamides and p-aminobenzoic acid are excreted largely as acetyl derivatives such as:

COOH   SO$_2$NH$_2$

NH**COCH**$_3$ NH**COCH**$_3$

p-Acetylaminobenzoic Acid   p-Acetylaminobenzenesulfonamide

The detoxication of benzoic acid is particularly interesting because it conjugates in the liver with glycine to form *hippuric acid.* The ability of the liver to perform this process is used as a test of hepatic function.

BLOOD PROTEINS

The proteins of plasma are mainly divided into albumins and globulins, Fibrinogen is included in the globulin fraction. Serum protein concentrations vary normally within certain limits and deviations from the normal may be of considerable diagnostic value. The average serum protein content is 4.6 grams of albumin and 2.6 grams of globulin in 100 cc. Plasma contains approximately 0.3 to 0.6 grams of fibrinogen per 100 cc. The normal limits of serum proteins may be stated as follows:

Total protein:	7 ± 1.0 grams per 100 cc.
Albumin:	4.5 ± 0.5 grams per 100 cc.
Globulin:	2.2 ± 0.8 grams per 100 cc.

The clinician is so much in the habit of stating concentrations of blood constituents in mg. per 100 cc. that he occasionally applies the same unit inadvertently to protein values. It should be recalled that these figures are expressed in grams per 100 cc. It is also an unfortunate habit among clinicians

to interpret ratios of the albumin-globulin fractions without adequate attention to deviations of the two individual figures from the normal. If the value
of each is considered, abnormalities encountered in disease can be correlated
much better with the actual underlying pathological process. For instance
reversal of the ratio may occur as the result of a marked reduction in albumin
without any changes in the globulin concentration. Similar reversals of ratio
are seen clinically when there is an extreme increase in the globulin fraction
without any associated change in the albumin. Interpretations in these two
cases, of course, would be entirely different.

The *origin* of the protein constituents of plasma is not very clear at present. Changes in the concentration of fibrinogen are definitely associated with
pathological conditions of the liver, and some diseases in this organ are attended by increases in globulin. Disintegration of white blood cells undoubtedly supply a certain amount of plasma proteins. The general tissue
cells may be a source and special fractions may arise from reticulo-endothelial
cells of lymphocytic tissue.

Plasma proteins fulfill a number of *functions*. They constitute a reserve
upon which the organism may be able to draw during periods of dietary
deprivation. The plasma proteins also are factors in the maintenance of
normal rate of flow throughout the vascular systems as they influence blood
viscosity and thus aid in maintaining normal differences in systolic and di-
astolic blood pressures. Some of the plasma protein constituents have specific functions. Fibrinogen is a participant in the clotting mechanism and
immune bodies are found in certain fractions of the globulins. Proteins are
of major importance in the osmotic equilibrium between plasma and interstitial fluid. Edema usually appears below a critical level of total protein
which is approximately 5 grams per 100 cc. It should be kept in mind, however, that osmotic pressure is determined by the actual number of particles
(molecular or ions) present in a given volume. Because of the smaller
molecular weight of albumin the osmotic activity is approximately 2.5 times
that of an equal weight of globulin. Therefore, a decrease of albumin in
plasma causes a critical edema level to be reached sooner than if the same decrease applies to the globulin. Serum albumin concentrations of less than
2.5 grams per 100 cc. usually produce edema.

Hypoproteinemia commonly results from long-continued albuminuria.
Actually the term proteinuria is more appropriate as there is some escape of
all the plasma proteins, but albumin predominates because of its smaller
molecular size. The organism is able to synthesize plasma albumin at a
rapid rate but this ability becomes diminished gradually if the loss is continued over a long period of time. Dietary deficiencies become reflected in
decreases in the plasma protein concentration which eventually result in
nutritional edema. Depression of albumin synthesis is observed in chronic

hepatic disease and also occasionally in acute disorders of the liver. Diversion of some of the protein to ascitic fluid in these diseases may partly account for the decreased plasma protein concentration.

Pregnancy is often associated with decreases in plasma proteins. A further reduction may be seen in the toxemias of this condition. Low protein levels during lactation may be explained on the basis of rapid utilization of blood proteins for the formation of milk proteins.

Hypoproteinemia may occasionally be concealed by a temporary concentration of the blood due to dehydration. When the volume of the blood is brought back to normal the true condition becomes apparent. The so-called 'insulin edema' may well be due to this phenomenon because it is seen when patients recover from diabetic coma.

Hyperproteinemia is observed as the result of dehydration or elevation of one of the fractions, usually the globulin. Increases in the globulin concentration are frequently associated with certain disorders such as fever and various malignancies. Specific diseases which often exhibit hyperglobulinemia are: multiple myeloma, syphilis, kala azar, lymphogranuloma inguinale, and lupus erythematosis.

NUCLEOPROTEINS

The nucleoproteins are ingested in meat and fish. They are proteins conjugated with nucleic acid, but the conjugates are not in equimolecular proportion because they split off an excess of protein in their initial hydrolysis to form *nuclein*. This substance is also a conjugate of nucleic acid and protein. Further hydrolysis of nucleins occurs in the intestinal tract and the protein part of the molecule follows the same metabolic pathways as other dietary proteins. Nucleic acid can be hydrolyzed into phosphoric acid pentoses, and nitrogenous compounds, the latter composed of purines and *pyrimidines*. There are two known varieties of nucleic acid, yeast and thymus nucleic acid. Both of them occur in animal and plant tissues.

In addition to phosphoric acid the two types of nucleic acid give the following pentoses and nitrogenous compounds on hydrolysis:

	Yeast Nucleic Acid	Thymus Nucleic Acid
Pentoses	D-Ribose	D-2-Desoxyribose
Purines	Adenine Guanine	Adenine Guanine
Pyrimidines	Cytosine Uracil	Cytosine Thymine

Yeast nucleic acid is also called *ribose nucleic acid* or *plasmonucleic acid* because it is found in the cystoplasm and nucleolus. Thymus nucleic acid similarly is called *desoxyribose nucleic acid* or *chromonucleic acid* due to its presence in the chromatin of the cell nucleus. Purines and pyrimidines have the pyrimidine ring in common. The atoms forming the rings are numbered for convenience in designating substitutions:

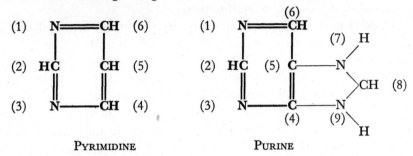

PYRIMIDINE   PURINE

Nucleic acid contains four *nucleotide units,* and each nucleotide is composed of phosphoric acid and a *nucleoside* consisting of a pentose and a purine or pyrimidine:

$$H_3PO_4\text{—Pentose—Pyrimidine}$$
$$H_3PO_4\text{—Pentose—Purine}$$
$$H_3PO_4\text{—Pentose—Pyrimidine}$$
$$H_3PO_4\text{—Pentose—Purine}$$

Nucleoside

Nucleotide

NUCLEIC ACID

The two purine nucleotides are *adenylic acid* and *guanylic acid* and the corresponding nucleosides are *adenosine* and *guanosine*. Nucleotides occur free in nature, that is, they are not bound to other nucleotides as in nucleic acid, but they combine easily with protein. *Adenosinetriphosphate* is such a nucleotide combined with two additional molecules of phosphoric acid. *Inosinic acid* is found in muscle together with adenosinetriphosphate. The latter is converted to the former through the action of a specific deaminase and the simultaneous loss of two molecules of phosphoric acid.

PURINE AND PYRIMIDINE END PRODUCTS

Uric acid is the end product of purine metabolism in man. Adenine contains an amino group at C_6, while the amino group in guanine is at C_2 and an oxygen atom is substituted at C_6. In their degradation they are both deaminized and oxidized by special enzymes. Adenine forms *hypoxanthine,* guanine forms *xanthine,* and these two metabolites are both converted to uric acid. In most mammals uric acid is further converted into *allantoin* as the final excretion product. In man, anthropoid apes, the Dalmatian dog, birds, and certain reptiles, uric acid is the final excretion product although the excreted uric acid does not represent the entire amount of purine metabolized as part of it is destroyed in the liver.

The urinary excretion of uric acid varies with the intake of purines in the diet. Uric acid in the urine is in the free form or as urates of sodium, potassium, or ammonium. The daily excretion is approximately 0.5 to 1 gram of which the endogenous amount may be about 0.3 grams. On a purine free diet a person approaches this figure for his uric acid excretion in 24 hours. Intermediate metabolites of the uric acid destroyed in the body are largely unknown. Man excretes only about 30 mg. of allantoin daily and this may be from exogenous sources. Small amounts of purines other than uric acid are excreted in the urine. Some of these are obtained from beverages containing

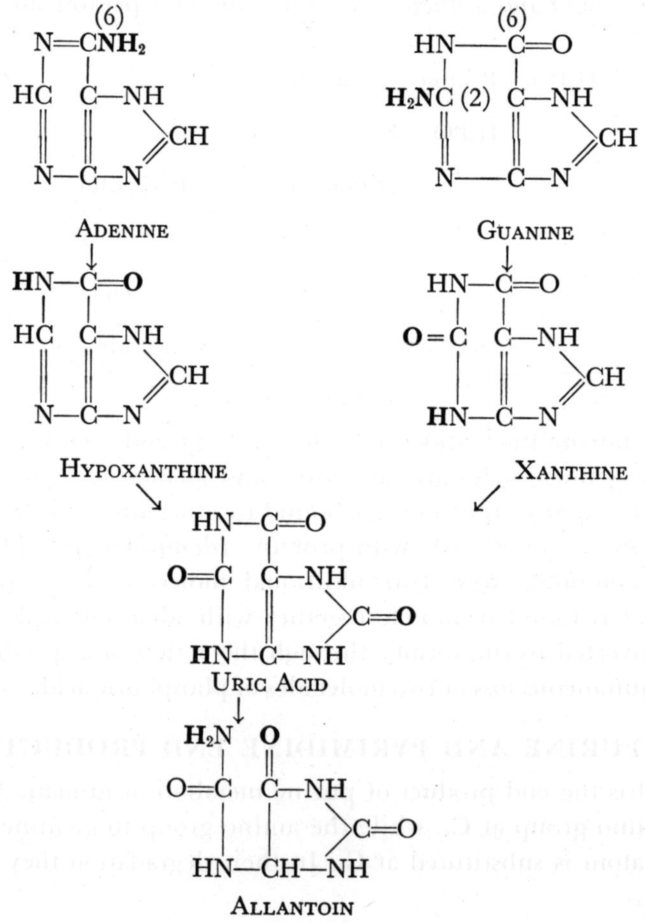

$$
\begin{array}{cc}
\overset{(6)}{N=CNH_2} & \overset{(6)}{HN\!-\!\!C=O} \\
\text{ADENINE} & \text{GUANINE} \\
\\
HN\!-\!C=O & HN\!-\!C=O \\
\text{HYPOXANTHINE} & \text{XANTHINE} \\
\\
& HN\!-\!C=O \\
& \text{URIC ACID} \\
\\
& H_2N\quad O \\
& \text{ALLANTOIN}
\end{array}
$$

caffeine, theobromine, and theophylline, as these are methylated purines.

Little is known concerning the intermediate steps in the catabolism of the pyrimidines. They are almost completely oxidized urea being the final excretion product. Thiamine and riboflavine are pyrimidine derivatives.

HYPERURICEMIA

Normal blood contains from 2 to 4 mg. of uric acid per 100 cc. The plasma concentration is relatively higher than that of the cells so that the plasma uric acid concentration is approximately 3 to 5 mg. per 100 cc. Uric acid in blood increases along with other waste products in renal failure. In *eclampsia* the increase may be independent of retention of urea and creatinine. The elevated uric acid level in blood observed in *polycythemia,* *leukemia,* and occasionally in *multiple myeloma* may be the result of increase in the endogenous nucleoprotein metabolism. Higher uric acid levels in the blood may be seen during remissions in pernicious anemia.

Gout is associated with elevated blood uric acid levels and deposits of urates in the form of tophi in cartilaginous tissues mostly involving the joints of the fingers and toes. The etiology remains undetermined, the retention of uric acid as such does not precipitate attacks of gout as the condition is not seen in other diseases causing elevated blood uric acid levels. Therapeutic measures directed toward reduction of the uric acid concentration exert a beneficial effect. These measures consist of limitations in the purine intake and administration of certain drugs. Salicylates facilitate the elimination of uric acid. The same effect has been observed after the administration of adrenocorticotropic hormone (ACTH). Colchicine causes a lowering of the concentration of uric acid in the blood without a perceptible increase in the amount excreted in the urine.

ANTIGEN-ANTIBODY REACTIONS

The antigen-antibody reaction is, broadly speaking, the basis for the laboratory science of immunology. In all its various forms the reaction expresses the basic principle that by physical observation it can be determined that an interaction takes place between systems containing antigens and the corresponding antibodies. Observations of such nature do not involve any explanation of the mechanism whereby the reactions are brought about, and the situation is quite comparable to a chemist observing that a reaction between chemicals in a test tube takes place without further attempt to explain the chemical background. In most of the common antigen-antibody reactions the substances involved are of a very incompletely understood chemical nature, so that the chemist is of limited help to the immunologist. The feature of antigen-antibody reactions of the greatest usefulness to the immunologist is the high degree of specificity that these reactions exhibit.

Methods of observation in immunology are usually simple and very imperfect, but again the high degree of specificity and the sensitivity of the reactions involved makes it possible to observe phenomena by uncomplicated laboratory procedures, and indeed the sensitivity of serological reactions, in spite of these simple methods of observations, frequently go far beyond anything that the chemist can demonstrate by much more complicated working methods.

Results of immunological reactions are often observed by precipitation or agglutination reactions or by such indirect methods as inhibition of agglutination reactions. Whether or not a reaction is of such magnitude that it can be observed depends on certain factors of physical nature, such as the size of the molecules involved, the polarity and reactivity of the molecule, the medium used, temperature, hydrogen ion concentration, etc. As in all other sciences, negative results may at times only mean that methods of observations are not sensitive enough.

An antigen is a substance capable of producing and combining with antibodies. Most antigens are proteins, but antigenic activity is not confined to proteins and may be exhibited by a wide range of chemical entities, even fairly simple ones. It is possible, that, at least in some cases, simple chemicals exhibiting antigenic properties may do so through combination with proteins.

The high degree of specificity in serological reactions is almost certainly chemical in nature and, of course, it is desirable to analyze specificity in relation to definite chemical components. The chemical knowledge of the structure of the proteins is inadequate. Many minor structural differences in proteins can only be surmised and not determined with analytical accuracy. Spatial arrangements of atoms in the protein structure tend to complicate matters further. At present, it is in most cases a hopeless task to attempt to correlate immunological specificity with chemical structure. There is, however, some promise of correlations being made of split proteins and artificial antigens, particularly azo-proteins containing peptides of known structure. This will be discussed later.

Several theories as to the role of proteins in serological reactions may be advanced. They may be contaminating substances or carrier substances of non-specific nature. Ehrlich's original idea, however, is almost conclusively correct, namely, that specificity depends entirely on the chemical constitution of a protein. Considerable work has been done on plant protein specificity; for example, alcohol-soluble proteins, gliadins, from wheat and rye behave alike from both the chemical and anaphylactic standpoint. Hordein of barley which differs slightly in composition is serologically related but distinguishable from the others.

In the study of proteins a given protein is first analyzed for its amino acid constituents. It is evident that the small number of known individual amino acids cannot in any way be responsible for the tremendous number of specific reactions known. As a matter of fact, constellations of amino acids and simple amino acid groups as we know them cannot contribute to any explanation because the number of mathematical possibilities is entirely too few.

It should be remembered that classification of proteins is quite arbitrary and is based largely upon physical properties. It must be assumed, however, that there is some structural correspondence which gives protein groups their individual chemical characteristics; for example, the globins show common characteristics although there is a definite serological variant of the globins in each species. It is entirely inexplicable from present chemical knowledge that the various proteins of one species of animal have common species specific serological properties, and that proteins from an animal show specificities attributable even to a definite organ.

In order to correlate chemical composition with serological specificity, cross reactions observed between precipitin sera with proteins of related animal species must be accounted for. The theory has been advanced that the immunization reactions to the protein of one species are actually multiple reactions in respect to one principal and several minor antigens. The minor antigens would be responsible for the reactions common to the related animal species. From this viewpoint the conclusion could be drawn that normal serum contains numerous proteins respectively identical with those of other species and, therefore, the quantitative distribution of these proteins may be an expression of zoological relationship. Chemically there is little to substantiate such a theory. For instance, hemoglobin from various sources shows definite species specificity. The hemoglobins from these various sources, however, do not crystallize in a number of different forms as one might expect from the theory. In general this concept leads to many unlikely conclusions. It is much simpler to assume that antibodies react with substances chemically similar to the homologous antigens.

It is apparent that serological specificity must be referable to complicated chemical structures, and it is possible that several affinities must be satisfied before a visible reaction can take place. For example, it can be demonstrated that antibodies for iodized protein will precipitate any iodoprotein, and this effect is due to the specific reaction of diiodotyrosine in the protein molecule. However, this precipitation reaction is much stronger if it is performed with the iodoprotein originally used for the immunization.

When proteins are studied from the immunochemical standpoint it is difficult to be sure when the substance is homologous. Frequently a protein, previously considered homologous, can be separated into various fractions which individually can be expected to exhibit the same species specific reactions. Sorenson advanced the concept that proteins may be mixtures of complexes in equilibrium and that environmental factors shift this equilibrium reversibly. Therefore, the serological specificity of a protein probably resides in the smallest unit of such reversible reactions. Delicate equilibria of this nature would presumably be displaced by most isolation procedures and protein fractions as they are obtained for study are probably different from the protein in its native state.

The discovery that polysaccharides in certain bacteria determine the specific type raises the question if carbohydrates, often contained in proteins, might be responsible for protein specificity. In some cases the carbohydrate complexes contained in proteins may participate in the reactions determining the serological protein specificity, but on the other hand, there are many proteins that do not contain carbohydrate. As an example of a protein lacking a carbohydrate complex hemoglobin may be cited again. It has also been found that chemically identical carbohydrates may be isolated from proteins of widely scattered origin and having no serological relationship.

The blood group specific substances A and B are complex, high-molecular weight carbohydrates which determine the typing characteristics of the four major human blood groups. In themselves and without any protein combination they may exhibit antigenic activity within a limited meaning of the word. For instance, they will markedly increase the isoagglutinin titer in human plasma following their injection. They serve as good examples of non-protein substances with specific serological properties.

A fruitful line of attack in studying the specificity of serological reactions consists of the introduction of simpler chemical compounds into the protein molecule. Certain chemical reactions, such as oxidations, iodination, etc., do not destroy the antigenic properties of a protein, while other types of reactions, as exemplified by hydrolysis with enzymes or alkalis, apparently attack structural parts essential for the antigenic function. From the experimental standpoint, artificially modified antigens have the great advantage of containing components of known structure.

Landsteiner and his co-workers prepared a number of artificially conjugated antigens by introduction of various groups into proteins. It was shown that these groups produced alterations in the antigenic specificity and that the serological differentiation was fairly sharp. Individual complexes introduced into protein molecules as described might alter the antigenic specificity through their own chemical characteristics, or possibly through characteristics defined by complexes formed by them with neighboring structures in the protein molecule. Light was shed on this part of the problem of specificity by using proteins coupled with diazonium salts. These artificial conjugates are particularly suited for the purpose because they permit further introduction of chemical groups through the nitrogen-bridge and should lead to correlation of the serological specificity down to minor units of the artificial complex.

Proteins coupled with diazonium compounds are colored substances called azoproteins. Frequently the azoproteins will give only weak reactions with the immune sera for the unchanged protein. They are capable of producing antibodies in animals even if prepared from protein from the same animal. It can be demonstrated by use of azoproteins that groups attached to proteins can react as such with antibodies. Reactions can be obtained in experiments where the aromatic groups are conjugated with heterologous proteins. In such experiments the specific reaction must be ascribed to the introduced group alone even if the protein is necessary for antigenicity and, also, necessary for its physicochemical properties in producing an observable reaction. The artificial complexes introduced are not limited to aromatic organic structures because aliphatic complexes can be added through the nitrogen bridge. Many experiments have been performed in a manner similar to those with the diazonium compounds but using other substances, such as quinones, aldehydes, phenols, etc.

Spatial arrangement in the antigenic molecule is reflected in specific antibody response. This is particularly interesting as it adds to our understanding of the practically endless number of possibilities which unquestionably exist in nature. Landsteiner used the d- and l- forms of para-aminobenzoyl-phenylaminoacetic acid to show that these two forms could be differentiated serologically. Similar experiments have been carried out with many other groups of isomers.

d- AND l- PARA-AMINOBENZOYL-PHENYLAMINOACETIC ACIDS

SUPPLEMENTARY READING

ALBANESE, A. A., and WANGERIN, D. M.: The creatine and creatinine excretion of normal adult males. *Science, 100:*58, 1944.

BARNES, F. W., JR., and SCHOENHEIMER, R.: On the biological synthesis of purines and pyrimidines. *J. Biol. Chem., 151:*123, 1943.

BLOCH, K., and SCHOENHEIMER, R.: The biological formation of creatine. *J. Biol. Chem., 133:*633, 1940.

BOYD, W. C.: *Fundamentals of Immunology.* Interscience Publishers, Inc., 1947.

CLARKE, H. T.: Natural amino acids. Gilman: *Organic Chemistry* Chapter 14, p. 1079., John Wiley and Sons, 1943.

COHEN, P. P.: Transamination with purified enzyme preparations (transaminase). *J. Biol. Chem., 136:*565, 1940.

CRAMER, F. B., JR., and WINNICK, T.: Amino acid nitrogen of normal human plasma. *J. Biol. Chem., 150:*259, 1943.

GORNALL, A. G., and HUNTER, A.: The synthesis of urea in the liver, with special reference to citrulline as an intermediary in the ornithine cycle. *J. Biol. Chem., 147:*593, 1943.

HEIDELBERGER, M.: Immunochemistry. In Green, D. E., *Currents in Biochemical Research.* Interscience Publishers. Inc., 1946.

HERBST, R. M.: The transamination reaction. *Adv. in Enzymol., 4:*75, 1944.

KABAT, E. A., and MAYER, M. M.: *Experimental Immunochemistry.* Charles C Thomas, Publisher, 1948.

LANDSTEINER, K.: *The Specificity of Serological Reactions.* Harvard University Press, 1945.

RABINOWITCH, I. M.: The origin of urinary ammonia. *Arch. Int. Med., 33:*394, 1924.

SCHOENHEIMER, R.: *The Dynamic State of Body Constituents.* Harvard University Press, 1946.

SIMMONDS, S., and VIGNEAUD, V. DU.: Transmethylation as a metabolic process in man. *J. Biol. Chem., 146:*685, 1942.

TALBOTT, J. H., and COOMBS, F. S.: Metabolic studies on patients with gout. *J.A.M.A., 110:*1977, 1938.

VIGNEAUD, V. DU., COHN, M., CHANDLER, J. P., SCHENCK, J. R., and SIMMONDS, S., The utilization of the methyl group of methionine in the biological synthesis of choline and creatine. *J. Biol. Chem., 140:*625, 1941.

Chapter 8

CARBOHYDRATES

CARBOHYDRATES are distributed abundantly among animals and plants. They are the source of a large part of the energy required in the animal organism and, as they furnish most of the material for the synthesis of proteins and fats by plants, they may be considered as the major ultimate organic origin of energy. In plants the higher carbohydrates constitute an essential part of the supporting structures in a manner corresponding to the role of proteins in animal tissues.

Most carbohydrates contain carbon, hydrogen, and oxygen only, however, a small number of them include another element, usually nitrogen, and some of these more complex carbohydrates exhibit specific biological properties. The name 'carbohydrate' was applied by French workers because hydrogen and oxygen were observed to be present in many sugars in the same proportion as in water, the term is used now as a matter of convenience without any implications in regard to molecular structure.

Molecular weights of carbohydrates vary over a wide range. The larger molecules are built up from simple structural units to which they can usually be broken down by hydrolysis. When large molecules are constructed from smaller units by an orderly sequence of union between these units without causing any fundamental change in their constitution, the product is a *polymer* and the process is *polymerization*. Cellulose, gums, pectins, etc., are typical carbohydrate polymers.

The *monosaccharides* are the simplest carbohydrates and they are subdivided into *dioses, trioses, tetroses, pentoses, hexoses,* and *heptoses* according to the number of carbon atoms in the molecule. The monosaccharides are also divided into *aldoses* and *ketoses* according to the presence of potential aldehyde or ketone groups respectively.

Higher carbohydrates are named so as to indicate the approximate number of monosaccharide molecules from which they are derived. *Oligosaccharides* include the *di-, tri-, and tetrasaccharides* while more than 4 monosaccharide units in the molecule classifies the carbohydrate as a polysaccharide.

Simple polysaccharides are divided into *pentosans* which are polymers of anhydropentoses and *hexosans* which are polymers of anhydrohexoses. The complex polysaccharides include cellulose, gums, pectins, prosthetic polysaccharide groups of certain proteins, etc.

Certain carbohydrates such as those containing amino groups require special classification. This also applies to derivatives of monosaccharides comprising sugar alcohols, sugar acids, sugar esters, and ethers, and glucosides.

CHEMICAL STRUCTURE OF CARBOHYDRATES

Glucose is the most important of the sugars from a biochemical standpoint. Its formula is $C_6H_{12}O_6$. Early studies on the spatial arrangement of the atoms in glucose led to the conclusion that the six carbon atoms are joined in a normal or unbranched chain, and that it contains five hydroxyl groups and one aldehyde group. In organic compounds it is rare to find more than one hydroxyl group attached to one carbon atom and the following formula is, therefore, an expression of the atomic arrangement to be expected:

$$(1) \quad (2) \quad\;\; (3) \quad\;\; (4) \quad\;\; (5) \quad\;\; (6)$$
$$CHO.CHOH.CHOH.CHOH.CHOH.CH_2OH$$

The 4 carbon atoms, emphasized in the formula, are asymmetric and the various atoms and groups can be arranged in space to represent 16 possible isomeric aldohexoses. All of these are known. In discussions of the monosaccharide structures it is conventional to refer to the carbon atoms as numbered from 1 to 6 beginning with the carbon atom in the aldehyde group.

The trioses are of special interest because aldotriose contains 1 asymmetric carbon atom and it thus may occur in two isomeric modifications designated by the following formulas:

<pre>
        CHO   CHO
         | |
    H—C—OH   HO—C—H
         | |
       CH₂OH   CH₂OH
   D-GLYCERALDEHYDE   L-GLYCERALDEHYDE
</pre>

The arrangement of these formulas is used in the nomenclature of other carbohydrate structures. All monosaccharides belong to the d-series if they have the d-glyceraldehyde configuration of the asymmetric carbon atom farthest from the ketone or aldehyde group. This prefix is used regardless of the optical rotation of the sugar. Dextro- and levo-rotation may be indicated by following the d or the l with a plus or minus sign in parentheses. Thus a levorotatory sugar, belonging to the d-series, is designated d (-)-. Occasionally a prime is put on the d (d′) to signify levo-rotation and conversely. The Committee on Carbohydrate Nomenclature of the American Chemical Society has advanced the use of small capital letters in place of d and l to avoid confusion.

The optical behaviour of D-glucose gives further clues as to the spatial arrangement of its molecule. D-Glucose can be crystallized as a monohydrate exhibiting +106° specific rotation of plane polarized light at 20° C. This value spontaneously changes and becomes constant at +53°. Anhydrous D-glucose, crystallized from acetic acid, shows +19.8° initial rotation in its solution in water and this value also undergoes gradual change until $+53°$ at $20°$ C. is reached. The phenomenon is called *mutarotation*.

The optical properties of D-glucose must have their explanation in differences in molecular structure and the simplest assumption is that the compound with constant optical rotation $\alpha_D = +53°$ is a mixture of 2 isomeric forms in equilibrium.

The usual method of writing structural formulas, as for instance the straight chain carbon atoms in a hexose, gives quite an erroneous impression of the actual spatial arrangement of the atoms. In reality C_1 and C_5 are only a short distance apart because of the tetrahedral angle of the carbon bonds, and an oxygen bridge is easily established between these two carbon atoms. The result is a cyclic structure consisting of five carbon and one oxygen atoms, the carbon atom of the aldehyde group becoming asymmetric, yielding two stereoisomeric possibilities. These are the two forms exhibiting specific rotations of $+106°$ and $+19.8°$ respectively. Besides these two forms of glucose there is present a small amount of the aldehyde form, i.e., the structure without an oxygen bridge. These quantitative relations between the various structural forms account for the slow velocities of certain reactions involving the aldehyde group because the cyclic configurations must be converted to the free aldehyde form before the reaction occurs. The two cyclic forms of D-glucose are designated α and β, α being chosen arbitrarily to designate the form having the greater positive rotatory power. The three forms of D-glucose may be written as below:

	α-D-Glucose	Aldehyde Form	β-D-Glucose
(1)	H—C—OH	H—C=O	HO—C—H
(2)	H—C—OH	H—C—OH	H—C—OH
(3)	HO—C—H	HO—C—H	HO—C—H
(4)	H—C—OH	H—C—OH	H—C—OH
(5)	H—C	H—C—OH	H—C
(6)	CH_2OH	CH_2OH	CH_2OH

The postulated bridges of α-D- and β-D-glucose participate in a ring structure containing five carbon atoms and these forms of glucose are therefore referred to as *amylene oxide forms*. There are other, less stable, *butylene oxide forms* of D-glucose in which the oxygen bridge is formed between C_1 and C_4. The rings in the butylene and amylene oxide configurations resemble those of the cyclic compounds furan and pyran respectively and the corresponding sugar structures are designated *furanose* and *pyranose*.

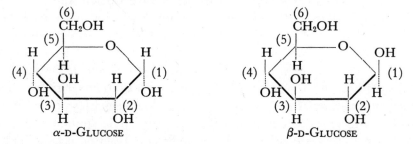

FURAN   PYRAN

All aldohexoses exist in both the α- and β- furanose and pyranose forms of which the pyranoses are the most stable.

Haworth has introduced perspective formulas for carbohydrate ring structures. For example α- and β-D-glucose may be written thus:

α-D-GLUCOSE   β-D-GLUCOSE

In these configurations the carbon atoms are numbered as in the previous formulas for glucose and if the two systems are compared it may readily be seen that they both indicate the presence of the OH groups attached to C_1 and C_2, on the same side of the plane of the molecule in the α-form while they are on alternate sides in the β-form.

It is interesting that enzymes may be specific toward one configuration in α- and β-mixtures. For instance, in glucosides containing both configurations one may be obtained pure by destroying the other with a hydrolytic enzyme which reacts specifically upon this other form.

ANALYTICAL METHODS

The clinician is particularly interested in the micromethods employed to determine sugar concentrations in biological fluids. Most of these methods are based upon the ability of glucose, and occasionally other monosaccharides, to reduce certain reagents. The reducing carbohydrates contain free or potentially free aldehyde or ketone radicals. Alkaline copper solutions are used most widely, their use depending upon the reduction of the copper to cuprous oxide. *Fehling's solution* consists of copper sulfate in the presence of alkaline tartrates which form a soluble blue complex containing cupric ions. This complex is converted to the insoluble cuprous oxide by interaction with reducing sugars. All free aldehyde groups and also many other organic compounds reduce Fehling's solution. Various additions to the copper reagent, such as citric acid, modify the rate of precipitation so that the reducing power of an unknown solution can be estimated semi-quantitatively according to the color of the precipitate in terms of one plus (+) to four plus (+ + + +). *Benedict's qualitative reagent* is a solution of the same type containing citrate rather than tartrate.

Several copper-reducing reactions are used for quantitative blood glucose analyses. In the *Folin-Wu* and the *Shaffer-Hartman* methods the glucose is determined as being equivalent to the reduced copper formed which may be estimated either by titration or by colorimetry. In the colorimetric procedure the reduced copper is made to form a soluble blue complex with phosphomolybdic acid. In the *Hagedorn-Jensen* method ferricyanide is used instead of copper as the oxidizing agent.

The *Meyer-Benedict* method is a simpler but less accurate procedure which depends upon the reduction of picric acid to the deep red picramic acid which may be determined colorimetrically.

The greatest error inherent in most simple clinical methods springs from the fact that they determine not glucose specifically but total reducing power in body fluids. Mosenthal has shown that the non-glucose reducing substances in blood vary greatly and that their concentration occasionally may be high enough to cause erroneous interpretations of blood glucose values if the commonly accepted criteria for normal limits are applied. The total non-specific reducing value may be found by destroying the glucose through fermentation with yeast, and subsequently determining the residual reducing power.

Many tests are employed for the qualitative analysis of carbohydrates. The *Molisch Test* which is given by practically all carbohydrates, depends upon the formation of a red or violet color due to furfural derivatives from the sugar reacting with α-naphthol in the presence of concentrated sulfuric acid. *Phenylosazones* or *oximes* of reducing sugars are useful in their identification because of their characteristic crystal forms, optical properties, melting points, etc.

DIGESTION OF CARBOHYDRATES

Ingested carbohydrates must be hydrolyzed to monosaccharides in order to be absorbable by the intestinal mucosa. Digestion begins in the mouth because the secretions of the parotid gland contain an amylase, *ptyalin*. The action of this enzyme is of minor importance, however, as it stops when the food is mixed with hydrochloric acid in the stomach. The digestive juices of the stomach do not contain amylases but the acidity contributes to the hydrolysis of ingested carbohydrates. The hydrolysis of the sugars is completed in the small intestine through the action of enzymes in the pancreatic and intestinal secretions. *Amylopsin* in the pancreatic juice breaks down the larger carbohydrate molecules and *maltase, lactase,* and *invertase* carry the hydrolytic process to the monosaccharide stage. Cellulose, pectins, gums, etc. are not hydrolyzed by carbohydrate enzymes in mammals. They may undergo partial hydrolysis by bacterial action in the large intestine, but the amounts of monosaccharides formed and absorbed in this way are not of significance from a metabolic standpoint.

ABSORPTION

All monosaccharides may be absorbed from the small intestine by a rather slow process of diffusion. In addition, glucose, fructose, and galactose are assimilated by a much more rapid process involving esterification of the sugar molecule with phosphate (phosphorylation) to form a hexose phosphate. The monosaccharide is liberated from the phosphate radical through the action of phosphatase before it enters the portal circulation. The absorption rates of the three monosaccharides which undergo phosphorylation vary, that of galactose being the most rapid, that for glucose slightly less, and that for fructose being approximately $\frac{1}{2}$ of the rate for glucose. These values were determined on experimental animals and may not apply to humans.

Many factors affect absorption of monosaccharides even from a normal intestine. Rate of entry, concentration, physical and chemical composition of the food mixture, etc., are of significance. Endocrine dysfunctions involving the anterior pituitary and thyroid glands, and the adrenal cortex may change absorption rates. Althausen and his associates have used the apparent rate of absorption of galactose as measured by blood galactose levels to estimate the activity of the thyroid gland (see Chapter 13). Dietary deficiency of several of the members of the vitamin B complex results in diminished absorption of the monosaccharides.

PHOSPHORYLATION

It has already been mentioned that the specific absorption of glucose, fructose, and galactose involves coupling of their molecules with phosphate. Phosphorylation is an essential part of the mechanism of many phases of carbohydrate metabolism, and the utilization of available energy from carbohydrate in the organism is intimately related to the nature of various phosphate combinations.

Before glucose can enter into the series of reactions whereby it is ultimately oxidized to carbon dioxide and water, it adds phosphate to carbon atom number six. Activation of the glucose molecule is initiated by an enzyme system for which adenosine triphosphate (ATP) serves as a coenzyme. ATP contains three phosphate groups of which two can be split off successively to form adenosine diphosphate (ADP) and adenylic acid (AA) respectively. ATP is present in minute amounts only and it must be regenerated continuously and rapidly to serve as a steady source of supply of phosphate groups. Therefore, the adenylic acid system constitutes a phosphate transfer mechanism, phosphate ions being donated to it by phosphorylated carbohydrate intermediates such as phosphopyruvic acid and acetyl phosphate, or by phosphocreatine. The adenylic acid system in turn donates phosphate to glucose, or to hexose-6-phosphate, phosphoglyceraldehyde, or to creatine.

Kalckar and Lipmann have suggested that phosphate may be bound either to alcohol or aldehyde in an ester linkage, or to nitrogen, phosphorus (in another phosphate group), or carboxyl. Both authors believe that the hydrolysis of the ester linkage results in the liberation of only a negligible amount of energy while the disruption of the second or anhydride type of phosphate bond releases much larger amounts. The latter group is classified by Lipmann as compounds with *energy rich phosphate bonds*. Both Kalckar and Lipmann theorize that the energy-rich phosphate bonds are the organism's means of storing the energy liberated by oxidation of metabolites, and the means of utilizing the energy by breaking the bond.

When creatine phosphate reacts with ADP it forms free creatine and ATP. It was formerly thought that the splitting of creatine phosphate provided the necessary energy for muscular work but the reaction with the adenylic acid system, which is reversible, actually transfers energy to ATP and the free energy change is small. It is the breakdown of ATP which liberates the energy used in muscular work. The conversion of ATP to ADP involves an enzymic hydrolysis and it has been shown that *myosin,* the contractile protein of muscle, possesses this enzymic property. It appears therefore that the enzyme in this case utilizes the energy obtained from its substrate and that chemical energy is converted directly into work.

Additional evidence that the splitting of the creatine phosphate bond does not furnish energy directly is found in the fact that a muscle enzyme capable of catalyzing such a reaction has not been found after intensive search. The resynthesis of creatine phosphate, which must occur if its store is not to be depleted, takes place by reversal of the reaction

$$\text{PHOSPHOCREATINE} + \text{ADP} \rightarrow \text{CREATINE} + \text{ATP}$$

The necessary reservoir of energy as represented by ATP is maintained by its synthesis from energy-rich phosphorylated intermediary compounds of the glycolytic and oxidative processes of carbohydrates, certain amino acids, and possibly fats. Negelein and Bromel, Warburg and Christian have shown that phosphoglyceraldehyde will couple with inorganic phosphate in the presence of coenzyme I and that the diphosphoglyceric acid formed will in turn react with ADP to form phosphoglyceric acid and ATP.

Creatine phosphate appears to be the ideal system for storage of energy because it does not dissipate it in the form of heat through non-specific hydrolytic processes, but retains it as available energy for the adenylic acid system when needed.

GLYCOGEN

Glucose is stored in the form of glycogen in the liver, and, to a lesser extent, in muscles. Breakdown of glycogen supplies the glucose necessary to maintain its concentration in blood within normal limits. Removal of the liver in experimental animals rapidly results in hypoglycemia and death unless glucose is administered.

Glycogen is a glucose polymer in which the glucose molecules are united through glucosidic (C-O-C) linkages between C_1 and C_4 or between C_1 and C_6. The breakdown of these two types of linkages is controlled by two specific enzymes. It was formerly assumed that the conversion of glycogen to glucose took place by simple hydrolysis, but Cori and Cori have shown that there are three distinct steps involved. The initial step has been studied most extensively in regard to the breaking of the 1:4 linkage by the enzyme *glycogen phosphorylase*. This enzyme acts in the presence of inorganic phosphates so that one hydrogen atom of orthophosphoric acid (H_3PO_4) attaches itself to C_4 of one glucose unit and $H_2PO_4^-$ combines with the C_1 of the other unit. The reaction thus results in the formation of glucose-1-phosphate and the process is called *phosphorolysis* because of its similarity to hydrolysis. The 1:6 phosphorylase probably functions in a similar manner.

The next step is a transfer of phosphate from the 1- to the 6-position of glucose phosphate. This is also an enzymic process and the enzyme involved is *phosphoglucomutase*. The third step is hydrolysis by phosphatase whereby glucose is formed. Magnesium is the activating cofactor for phosphoglucomutase. Glucose-1-phosphate can therefore be obtained from glycogen by incubation with tissue extracts from which magnesium salts have been removed.

Each of the steps whereby glycogen is catabolized to glucose is reversible. Thus the formation of glycogen from glucose may be represented by the following equations:

glucose→glucose-6-phosphate→glucose-1-phosphate→glycogen

These reactions will require a source of energy to proceed and this energy is derived from ATP, so that one of the functions of ATP is to transfer the necessary amount of energy from oxidative processes to glycogen from which it can be released when glycogen is converted to glucose.

Hyperglycemia is produced by certain agents such as epinephrin, asphyxia and certain anaesthetics. These agents do not exert their hyperglycemic effect in hepatectomized animals. Houssay and his associates found similarly that the hyperglycemic action of extracts of the anterior pituitary cannot be elicited in liverless animals. Soskin believes that liver glycogen is the only source of blood glucose in the fasting organism and that glycogen in peripheral tissue cannot be made available for this purpose. However, lactic acid can accumulate in muscle tissue to an appreciable extent during anaerobic metabolism, and this lactic acid may be transported to the liver and converted to glycogen. In this way the lactic acid from muscle glycogen may reenter the circulation as glucose. This *lactic acid cycle* has been described by Geiger, Himwich, Cori and others. Its chief significance is during periods of stress.

Glycogenesis is the formation of glycogen, and *glycogenolysis* pertains to its breakdown. Carbohydrates are not the only source of material for glycogenesis; the formation of carbohydrate from protein has been described in Chapter 7. Soskin finds evidence for conversion of fat to carbohydrate, while Stadie has summarized evidence against this process in mammals.

Protein upon hydrolysis produces amino acids which when oxidised and deaminized, form compounds which occur in the intermediary metabolism of carbohydrates. Alanine for instance can be converted to pyruvic acid and this in turn to lactic acid.

It is reasonable to assume that many metabolites have certain intermediary compounds in common and that their conversion from one to another structure takes place through a common 'pool' of such compounds. Many interconversions of substances with large molecules become easier to understand if this viewpoint is kept in mind, and if it is recalled that large molecules, whether protein, fat, or carbohydrate, are constantly reacting in a state of equilibrium with small molecular components in reversible reactions. Hastings and his associates have studied the conversion of lactic acid containing isotopic carbon to glycogen. They found that CO_2 from the carboxyl-group is expired and that the 2-carbon compound remaining may serve as a building stone in the formation of glycogen. Even CO_2 may take part in glycogen synthesis since isotopic carbon can be found in liver glycogen after experimental animals are given sodium bicarbonate containing the isotope.

The fate of the amino acid present at any moment in the liver depends on the amount of carbohydrate available. When they are deaminized they no longer serve as building stones in protein metabolism but as fuel for the organism. The rate of deamination in the liver decreases as the amount of available carbohydrate increases. Carbohydrates are therefore said to have a *protein-sparing* action. The demands on the fat storage of the organism for purposes of energy also depend upon available carbohydrates. It has been shown in Chapter 6 that excessive utilization of fat in carbohydrate deficiency may result in ketogenesis which is promptly diminished on administration of carbohydrate. In other words the carbohydrates have an *antiketogenic* effect.

GLYCOGEN STORAGE DISEASE (VON GIERKE'S DISEASE)

This condition is characterized by abnormally large deposits of glycogen in the liver, kidney, heart, and other tissues. Schoenheimer did not find any abnormal properties of the glycogen isolated from the organs of patients, but the disease apparently is associated with some interference with glycogenolysis. The blood contains an increased amount of glycogen and the patients show a hyperglycemic type of glucose tolerance test. In the fasting state hypoglycemia and ketosis are present and hypersensitivity to insulin is a characteristic feature. The ketosis is aggravated by epinephrin but the usual hyperglycemic effect of this substance is markedly decreased. The underlying etiology of the disease is not understood at present.

INTERMEDIARY METABOLITES

It has already been stated that the breakdown of glycogen involves phosphorylation at C_1 of glucose and a subsequent transfer of the phosphate to C_6. Blood glucose is phosphorylated at C_6 before it either participates in the glycogenic reactions or undergoes further breakdown directly. The intermediary pathways of glucose oxidation are complicated and are not completely understood. Recent years have advanced knowledge in this field so that it is possible to outline various intermediate steps, although glucose may be oxidized according to more than one metabolic scheme.

It is convenient to consider the intermediary metabolism in two stages. The first involves the degradation of glucose to pyruvic acid and the second the breakdown from pyruvic acid to carbon dioxide and water.

Glucose-6-phosphate is first changed to the isomer fructose-6-phosphate and this in turn is further phosphorylated through the action of ATP to form fructose-1:6-diphosphate. This diphosphate compound breaks down and the metabolism continues through a series of phosphorylated trioses until phosphopyruvic acid is formed. All these steps are reversible. Phosphopyruvic acid is dephosphorylated in contact with adenylic acid and Meyerhof considered this reaction as irreversible. Recently it has been shown that pyruvic acid can participate directly in glycogenesis by first being converted into phosphoenolpyruvic acid. It is interesting that practically all these intermediary steps are the same as those involved in the fermentation of sugar by yeast. Pyruvic acid is converted by a carboxylase-cocarboxylase system in yeast to acetaldehyde and CO_2. However, muscle tissue does not contain such an enzyme system.

The intermediary steps between glycogen and pyruvic acid are indicated in the chart.

The first step in the oxidation of the trioses formed from fructose-1:6-diphosphate involves diphosphopyridine nucleotide (DPN) which becomes reduced, the conversion products undergoing molecular rearrangement and dephosphorylation to produce pyruvic acid. The reduced DPN may be reoxi-

Glycogen
⇅
Glucose-1-Phosphate
⇅
Glucose-6-Phosphate
⇅
Fructose-6-Phosphate
⇅
Fructose-1:6-Diphosphate
⇅
Glucose→3-Glyceraldehyde Phosphate+Dihydroxyacetone Phosphate
⇅
1:3-Glyceraldehyde Diphosphate
⇅
1:3-Diphosphoglyceric Acid
⇅
3-Phosphoglyceric Acid
⇅
2-Phosphoglyceric Acid
⇅
2-Phosphopyruvic Acid
⇅
Phosphoenolpyruvic Acid
⇅
Pyruvic Acid

dized in the presence of oxygen through the possible mediation of a flavo-protein. Under anaerobic conditions the pyruvic acid becomes reduced to lactic acid by accepting hydrogen from the reduced DPN. This reaction may be indicated as follows:

$$
\begin{array}{cccccc}
CH_3 & & & CH_3 & & \\
| & & & | & & \\
CO & + & H_2DPN & \rightarrow & CHOH & + & DPN \\
| & & & | & & \\
COOH & & & COOH & & \\
\text{Pyruvic Acid} & \text{Reduced DPN} & & \text{Lactic Acid} & \text{DPN}
\end{array}
$$

Glycolysis thus results in the formation of lactic acid which process permits utilization of some energy from carbohydrate during anoxia. With insufficient oxygenation such as occurs during sudden muscular contraction lactic acid accumulates. During the recovery of the muscle the lactic acid is gradually reconverted to glycogen, but by the use of isotopes it has been demonstrated that only part of the lactic acid is resynthesized to glycogen and that the rest is oxidized to carbon dioxide and water.

The formation of lactic from pyruvic acid is inhibited in the presence of adequate amounts of oxygen so that oxygen suppresses glycolysis. This phenomenon is the *Pasteur effect*. Its explanation depends on many factors involving the rates of oxidation of metabolites, the effect of oxygen on enzyme systems and the rate of synthesis of ATP.

The final breakdown of pyruvic acid to carbon dioxide and water is not only of interest in relation to carbohydrate metabolism, because pyruvic acid is formed in the course of metabolism of proteins and possibly fats. Szent-Györgyi observed that muscle tissue increased its oxygen absorption in the presence of small amounts of fumaric, succinic, and malic acid. Krebs made the same observations in regard to citric and α-ketoglutaric acid. These acids act catalytically and the oxygen consumption is accounted for by the oxidation of pyruvic acid. Krebs suggested a *'tricarboxylic acid cycle'* as the mechanism whereby oxidation of pyruvic acid takes place. Details of his scheme have been modified by Wood, Werkman and Evans. The cycle contemplates an initial condensation of 1 molecule of pyruvic acid with 1 of oxalacetic acid to form a 7-carbon-atom acid which reacts through numerous stages to reform oxalacetic acid, the net result of the cycle being the oxidation of 1 molecule of pyruvic acid. Many of these lower intermediary steps involve phosphorylation but always the transfer of phosphate to form ATP makes available the energy of the lower degradation products of carbohydrate metabolism in the form of high-energy phosphate bonds.

INSULIN

A number of endocrine factors influence the metabolism of carbohydrates; the most important is the antidiabetic hormone, insulin, of the pancreas. Banting and Best obtained the first preparation of this hormone to alleviate diabetic manifestations in depancreatized dogs.

Insulin is a protein with the characteristics of an albumin. It may be obtained in pure crystalline form at a pH of 6.5, slightly above its isoelectric point. The hormone crystallizes only in the presence of certain metallic ions of which zinc is usually employed. The metal combines in stoichiometric proportions, indicating a specific chemical linkage.

The mode of action of insulin is not well understood. Its effect in lowering blood glucose in normal and diabetic organisms is unquestionable. It is not essential for the formation of glycogen, as Cori has shown that glycogen can be synthesized in vitro in absence of insulin. In the normal animal its administration does not increase the storage of glycogen in the liver, but it does increase the rate of deposition of glycogen in muscle tissue. Deposition of both muscle and liver glycogen is rapidly increased under the effect of insulin in the diabetic animal. The rate of deposition depends upon the blood glucose concentration. Therefore, at abnormally high blood sugar levels the formation of glycogen proceeds much more rapidly than it would at normal sugar levels. Apparently insulin acts to accelerate the formation of glycogen at normal blood glucose concentrations to values comparable with those observed at high concentrations of glucose in insulin deficiency.

The rise in the respiratory quotient when insulin is given to normal and diabetic animals has been taken as evidence of increased oxidation of sugar. Critical analyses of available data by Soskin and his coworkers leads to the conclusion that this may not be true. In fact, their experiments tend to prove that "When one compares the rate of utilization of the normal animal at its usual normal blood-sugar level with the rate of utilization of the diabetic animal at the hyperglycemic levels which it ordinarily maintains, it is apparent that the diabetic animal habitually uses as much or more than the normal animal" (see Chapter 14).

The proteolytic and ketogenic reactions which are prominent in the absence of insulin are brought within normal limits upon its administration, presumably as a result of the shift of the total metabolism from protein and fat toward more abundant utilization of carbohydrates. Mirsky and his associates have demonstrated that the same results may be obtained in acutely diabetic animals if a sufficiently high level of blood glucose is maintained.

Administration of insulin decreases the inorganic phosphate of blood. At present it seems likely that this may be associated with an increased rate of phosphorylation, probably of one of the hexoses. Such a reaction could account for the observations on carbohydrate utilization in relation to administered insulin in diabetic animals, i.e. that the individual steps in the metabolism of carbohydrates can proceed in the absence of insulin, but that its presence is necessary for the speed of one or more reactions to attain sufficient velocity for what is termed 'normal carbohydrate metabolism.'

OTHER SUGARS

Fructose is converted to glucose in the liver and possibly in other organs such as the kidneys. The conversion probably proceeds through fructose-6-phosphate. Fructose may accumulate in the blood in hepatic disease and under such circumstances it appears readily in the urine due to low threshold value for this substance. *Essential fructosuria* is a hereditary condition in which ingested fructose fails to be converted to glucose.

Galactose is probably converted to glucose in the liver. *Lactose* is formed in the mammary tissue and, being a disaccharide composed of glucose and galactose, presumably galactose must be made by the breast during lactation. Galactosuria and lactosuria may be mistaken for glucosuria. The lactosuria occasionally suspected in pregnant and lactating women often proves to be glucosuria.

Pentoses are constituents of a number of essential biochemical compounds, such as nucleoproteins, di- and triphosphopyridine nucleotides and riboflavin. They can be synthesized from glucose in the animal organism. *Essential pentosuria* is hereditary and the abnormal metabolism underlying this condition is unknown.

SUPPLEMENTARY READING

CORI, C. F.: Phosphorylation of glycogen and glucose. *Biol. Symp.,* 5:131, 1941.

CORI, G. T., COLOWICK, S. P., and CORI, C. F.: The enzymatic conversion of glu-cose-1-phosphoric ester to 6-ester in tissue extracts. *J. Biol. Chem., 124:*543, 1938.

CORI, G. T., and CORI, C. F.: Crystalline Muscle Phosphorylase IV. Formation of glycogen. *J. Biol. Chem., 151:*57, 943.

ELLIOTT, W. B., and KALNITSKY, G.: The oxidation of acetate. *J. Biol. Chem., 186:*487, 1950.

HASSID, W. Z., and CHAIKOFF, I. L.: The molecular structure of liver glycogen of the dog. *J. Biol. Chem., 123:*755, 1938.

HIMWICH, H. E.: Role of lactic acid in living organism. *Yale J. Biol. & Med., 4:*259, 1932.

JENSEN, H. F.: *Insulin: Its Chemistry and Physiology,* P. 62., Oxford University Press, 1938.

KREBS, H. A.: The intermediary stages in the biological oxidation of carbohydrate. *Adv. in Enzymol., 3:*191, 1943.

KREBS, H. A.: The Tricarboxylic Acid Cycle. *The Harvey Lectures,* P. 165, Charles C Thomas, Publisher, 1948-49.

LAZAROW, A.: Factors controlling the development and progression of diabetes. *Physiol. Rev., 29:*48, 1949.

LIPMANN, F.: Metabolic generation and utilization of phosphate bond energy. *Adv. in Enzymol., 1:*99, 1941.

MEYERHOF, O.: Intermediate carbohydrate metabolism. In: *A Symposium on Respiratory Enzymes.* University of Wisconsin Press, 1942.

NACHMANSOHN, D.: Metabolism and Function. A collection of papers dedicated to Otto Meyerhof. *Biochem. et Biophys. Acta.,* Vol. 4, Nos. 1, 2, 3, January 1950.

OESPER, P.: Sources of the high energy content in energy-rich phosphates. *Arch. Biochem., 27:*255, 1950.

PALMER, L. J.: Insulin in the treatment of diabetes mellitus. *J.A.M.A., 132:*502, 1946.

ROBERTS, J. T., and YATER, W. M.: Comparison of the clinical use of protamine zinc insulin and globin insulin in equal doses. *Ann. Int. Med., 26:*41, 1947.

SOSKIN, S., Role of the endocrines in the regulation of blood sugar. *J. Clin. Endocrin. 1, 4:*75, 1944.

STADIE, W. C.: Relation of insulin to phosphate metabolism. *Yale J. Biol. & Med., 16:*539, 1944.

STERN, J. R., and OCHOA, S.: Enzymatic synthesis of citric acid by condensation of acetate and oxalacetate. *J. Biol. Chem., 179:*491, 1949.

STETTEN, DEWITT, JR.: The endocrine regulation of carbohydrate metabolism. *J.A.M.A., 132:*373, 1946.

SUTHERLAND, E. W., COLOWICK, S. P., and CORI, C. F.: The enzymatic conversion of glucose-6-phosphate to glycogen. *J. Biol. Chem., 140:*309, 1941.

WOLFROM, M. L.: Carbohydrates I. In: Gilman, H., *Organic Chemistry,* P. 1532, John Wiley & Sons, Inc., 1943.

WOOD, H. G.: The fixation of carbon dioxide and the interrelationship of the tricarboxylic acid cycle. *Physiol. Rev., 26:*198, 1946.

Chapter 9

PORPHYRINS

M OST of the respiratory pigments of animals and plants contain a hetero-cyclic nucleus which includes four pyrrol rings united through methene (—CH=) radicals. Pyrrol has the following structure:

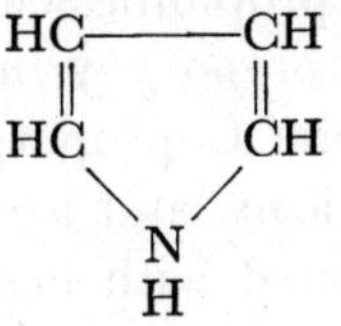

$$
\begin{array}{ccc}
HC & \!\!\!\!\!\!\!\!\!\! & CH \\
\| & & \| \\
HC & & CH \\
& N & \\
& H & \\
\end{array}
$$

PYRROL

The union of the four pyrrol rings may be depicted thus:

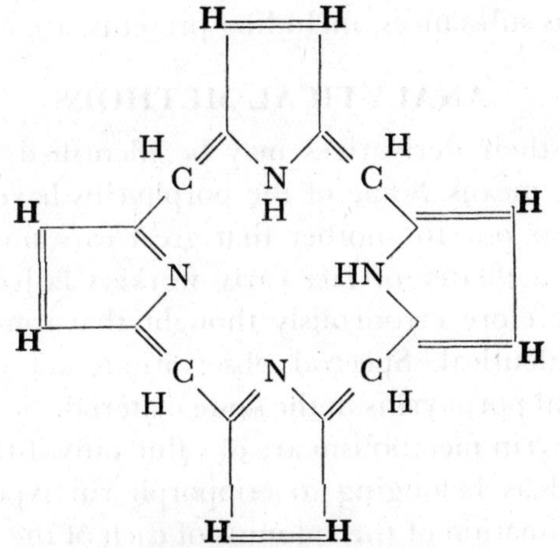

PORPHIN STRUCTURE

This porphin structure should not be assumed to represent the true nature of bonds between the pyrrol rings, as x-ray studies show adjacent nitrogen atoms to be closer together than opposite ones, indicating the possibility of hydrogen bridges between them.

The eight 'peripheral' hydrogen atoms in the porphyrin nucleus are replaceable by certain groups. If all eight hydrogens are exchanged for methyl and ethyl groups in equal numbers four isomeric porphyrins result. These isomers have been synthesized and are designated *etioporphyrins I - IV*. Etioporphyrins serve as reference substances in the study of natural porphyrins, of which types I and III only have been encountered.

Hemoglobin consists of the etioporphyrin III nucleus combined with ferrous iron and the protein globin. The porphyrins from chlorophyll, cyto-chrome, and catalase also have the etioporphyrin III structure. Catalase contains the same porphyrin-iron complex as hemoglobin but it is conjugated with a different protein. Catalase does not possess the property of combining reversibly with oxygen, and hemoglobin exhibits only weakly the ability of catalase to decompose hydrogen peroxide. Therefore it appears that to a large extent the protein part of these naturally occurring porphyrin derivatives determine their physiological properties.

The porphyrin nucleus found in vertebrates has methyl, ethyl, vinyl ($-CH=CH_2$), acetic acid, and propionic acid groups substituted for the eight 'peripheral' hydrogen atoms. *Protoporphyrin* which contains two acid radicals is the porphyrin of hemoglobin. Coproporphyrins occur predominantly in feces; they have four acid radicals; and *uroporphyrins* which are excretion products in the urine are united with eight acid groups. Protoporphyrin combines with ferrous iron to form *heme,* which is widely distributed in nature as a constituent of hemoglobin, cytochrome, catalase, and in plants, including lower plants without chlorophyll. Compounds of heme with various nitrogenous substances, including proteins, are *hemochromogens.*

ANALYTICAL METHODS

Porphyrins and their derivatives may be identified and determined by spectrophotometric means. Some of the porphyrins have absorption spectra which are so similar one to another that great care must be used in their differentiation. As a matter of fact early workers failed to notice spectral differences and therefore erroneously thought that some of the important porphyrins were identical. Spectral observations are complicated by the occurrence of several porphyrins in the same material.

Studies on porphyrin metabolism are of value only if the various members can be determined as belonging to etioporphyrin types I or III. Simple methods for the estimation of the amounts of each of the isomers in mixtures are lacking. At present it is necessary to fractionate a mixture and purify each individual member so that it can be identified by its melting point. The methyl esters are usually employed for the latter purpose.

Porphyrins are normally excreted in feces and urine in small amounts as colorless *porphyrinogens.* These can be converted to the colored porphyrins by oxidation with halogens or permanganate, or slowly by air.

HEMOGLOBIN

It has already been stated that hemoglobin consists of protoporphyrin, ferrous iron, and globin. The protoporphyrin has the etioporphyrin III nucleus and it contains two vinyl and two propionic acid groups.

Certain changes occur in hemoglobin if it is treated with alkali. Formerly it was thought that the alkali disrupted the union between the chromogen and the globin and the name *hemochromogen* was applied to the altered compound. This term should be compared with the more recent definition of hemochromogens as given above to avoid confusion. Anson and Mirsky have shown that the reaction with alkali results in denaturation of the globin but that the postulated splitting of the molecule does not take place. The altered hemoglobin behaves differently toward oxygen; it is still capable of combining with it, but the combination does not give up the oxygen readily. Hemochromogen of hemoglobin contains iron in the ferrous state and differs from hemoglobin only in that it contains denatured rather than native protein.

Heme in hemochromogen may be oxidized by chemical agents, involving a change of ferrous to ferric iron. This is *cathemoglobin* which thus consists of oxidized heme and denatured globin. At times oxidized heme is called *hematin*.

When oxyhemoglobin is heated with acetic acid and sodium chloride a crystalline compound *hemin* is formed. This reaction was discovered by *Teichmann* in the middle of the last century and the procedure is still used for the analytical identification of suspected blood stains. Hoppe-Seyler's work on hemin led to an understanding of its chemical structure and he subsequently prepared the first porphyrin. Fischer and Zeile in 1929 successfully synthesized hemin and established its structure to be

HEMIN

Hemoglobin of blood may be estimated quantitatively in various ways. The oxygen capacity of blood gives a satisfactorily reliable measure of its concentration. The iron content of blood can be determined by use of standard quantitative methods and the hemoglobin may be computed on the basis of its iron content being 0.34 per cent by weight. A simple procedure for the clinical estimation of hemoglobin consists of converting it to hemin and comparing the color obtained with standard hemin solutions or colored glass plates. The light absorption of unaltered oxyhemoglobin may also be used for its determination but variable factors, such as the proportion of hemoglobin to oxyhemoglobin, make this type of analysis less desirable.

Muscle tissue contains the heme compound, *myoglobulin,* which is of smaller molecular weight than hemoglobin, and which is capable of very rapid transfer of oxygen. It serves as an oxygen reservoir during periods of sudden muscular contraction.

OXYHEMOGLOBIN

The importance of hemoglobin as a respiratory pigment is due to its ability to form a loose combination with oxygen (oxygenation). One gram of hemoglobin combines with 1.35 cc. of oxygen at 0° C. and 760 mm. pressure. This relationship corresponds to a combination of one molecule of oxygen with one atom of iron. The combination does not involve a change in the valence of iron which remains divalent. Since one molecule of hemoglobin contains four protoporphyrin groups, it is capable of combining with four molecules of oxygen. The reversible reaction may be expressed as follows:

$$\text{Hemoglobin} + 4O_2 \rightleftarrows \text{Oxyhemoglobin}$$

The equilibrium is determined largely by the partial pressure of oxygen. The globin part of the molecule is responsible for its ability to combine with oxygen. Globin is a slightly basic protein; it has not been possible up to the present to combine heme with any other protein to produce a compound having oxygen carrying ability.

METHEMOGLOBIN

This modified hemoglobin contains oxidized heme. It differs from cathemoglobin in that the globin is in the native rather than in the denatured state. Methemoglobin is a true oxide of iron because it is produced from hemoglobin by oxidation of ferrous to ferric iron. Unlike oxyhemoglobin it will not release oxygen readily at diminished oxygen pressures. Reduction of methemoglobin back to hemoglobin can be accomplished by reagents such as sulfhydryl compounds. Methemoglobin is a brown pigment and is formed very slowly in blood after being shed, while a number of chemicals rapidly will lead to its formation from hemoglobin.

Severe methemoglobinemia is characterized by symptoms common to oxygen deficiency. If the degree of methemoglobinemia is sufficient to produce cyanosis the color of the skin is modified by the brown tint of the pigment. Drugs and poisons are the most common causes of methemoglobinemia. The extensive medical use of coal tar derivatives such as acetanilide, antipyrine, acetphenetidin, and sulfanilamide have resulted in many cases of methemoglobinemia. Industrial or accidental exposure to aniline, nitrobenzene, nitro-phenols, hydroquinone, etc., may produce similar effects. Nitrites are among known etiological agents and cases have been reported where intestinal formation of nitrites from bismuth subnitrate has been the causative factor. Methemoglobinemia is at times associated with hemolytic processes, the pigment being found in the plasma as well as in the cells. A few cases of congenital methemoglobinemia have been described. The cause is unknown.

The degree of methemoglobinemia may be estimated by determination of hemoglobin based on the oxygen capacity of the blood and the total hemoglobin by some other method. The difference represents methemoglobin.

SULFHEMOGLOBIN

This compound is formed from hemoglobin by the action of hydrogen sulfide. It may be distinguished from methemoglobin by its spectral characteristics. *Sulfhemoglobinemia* may be mistaken for methemoglobinemia and the two conditions may well occur simultaneously. Sedative drugs containing a sulfone group, such as sulfonal and trional, may cause sulfhemoglobinemia. The condition may also be caused indirectly by acetanilide and acetphenetidin. The mode of formation is not known and it has been suggested that these coal tar derivatives in some way facilitate the transfer of hydrogen sulfide from sulfhydryl groups to the hemoglobin molecule. Sulfhemoglobin is capable of combining with carbon monoxide in the same manner as hemoglobin indicating that sulfhydryl and carbon monoxide attack hemoglobin at different positions in the molecule.

CARBONYLHEMOGLOBIN

Carbon monoxide has a much greater affinity than oxygen for hemoglobin. Carbonylhemoglobin which is formed has a characteristic cherry red color which becomes evident in the skin and mucous membranes of victims of carbon monoxide poisoning. An experienced observer readily suspects the presence of carbon monoxide by the color of the patient's blood. Carbon monoxide and oxygen combine with hemoglobin in the same proportions and both reactions are reversible. Because of the great affinity of carbon monoxide for hemoglobin small amounts in the inhaled air may displace large amounts of oxygen from oxyhemoglobin, but if the patient is exposed to fresh air or oxygen, the carbon monoxide is removed from the blood in a matter of a few hours.

The presence of carbonylhemoglobin may be confirmed by spectroscopic means but instruments of a better quality than are ordinarily available in clinical laboratories are required for detection of small amounts. Chemical tests are fairly reliable. Carbon monoxide reduces palladium ions to metallic palladium and the reaction may be used for qualitative or quantitative purposes. More exact gasometric determinations of the carbon monoxide content of blood may be performed in the Van Slyke apparatus.

ANEMIA

The various types of anemia and their treatment may affect certain chemical constituents of the body. Regeneration of hemoglobin requires a source of protein, which is obtained from the tissue and the plasma regardless of the amount of protein in the diet. During treatment of anemia it is possible to produce a negative nitrogen balance by rapid regeneration of hemoglobin provided the dietary protein is inadequate. This may explain the occasional occurrence of edema during periods of rapid improvement of anemia and emphasizes the necessity for administration of sufficient protein for hemoglobin synthesis. During recovery from anemia the nitrogen output may be very low even when the caloric requirements are met entirely by carbohydrate and fat in the diet. This suggests a rapid utilization of the organism's stores of protein for production of hemoglobin. Occasionally low concentrations of blood non-protein nitrogen are encountered during regeneration of hemoglobin. This may be explained by utilization of protein metabolites for synthesis rather than for energy, and the non-protein nitrogen may be increased by augmenting the protein component of the diet. A higher-than-normal concentration of non-protein nitrogen in the blood in the presence of anemia points toward renal impairment with the anemia as a secondary manifestation.

PORPHYRIN EXCRETION

Early investigations on excretion of porphyrins in the urine, feces, and bile led to the assumption that they represented break-down products from destruction of hemoglobin whether this destruction was within normal limits or abnormally high, as occasionally observed in certain pathological states. The term *hematoporphyrin* was formerly applied to these excretion products and has been widely used in spite of the fact that such a substance does not occur in nature. Hematoporphyrin is obtained from hemoglobin or hemin when these are subjected to the action of strong mineral acids.

Porphyria is the excretion in urine of abnormal amounts of porphyrins. Correlation of the structures of the excreted porphyrins with those of the etioporphyrins has led to certain conclusions in regard to their metabolism. In a case of idiopathic porphyria Hans Fischer demonstrated that the excreted copro- and uroporphyrins did not belong to the same isomer type as the patient's hemoglobin. This can be explained by assuming either synthesis by a series of reactions through which hemoglobin would not be formed, or that some degradation product from hemoglobin is changed to an isomeric form which is then converted to the excretory product. The latter would involve extensive molecular changes which are highly unlikely to occur. Experiments with patients and dogs with external biliary fistulas have failed to give evidence for conversion of protoporphyrin (which belongs to type III) to porphyrins of type I.

Coproporphyrin I occurs normally in small amounts in urine and feces. Quantitatively determinations of the coproporphyrin excreted during the regenerative phase of pernicious anemia and in animals with induced repeated hemorrhages point to a relationship with the rate of erythropoiesis. Dobriner and Rhoads have shown that coproporphyrin excretion is increased in refractory anemias with hyperplastic marrow while in true aplastic anemias it is generally decreased.

Coproporphyrin III may predominate in the porphyrin excretion products in acute porphyria and in certain cases of poisoning with lead, mercury, arsenic, and sulfanilamide. This phenomenon is likely a result of disturbances in the synthesis of hemoglobin. Rimington believes that the synthesis of porphyrins is under control of an enzyme system and that the synthesis normally follows the pathway leading mainly to type III compounds but with small amounts of corresponding compounds of type I. The increase of type I excretion products during reticulocytosis would thus be explained, as an augmented production of porphyrins from a common pool of pyrrol precursors would occur. Rimington postulates that in congenital porphyria the enzymic system functions abnormally, resulting in a shift of the main line of synthesis from type III to type I.

The excretion of coproporphyrin III in acute porphyria and in the toxic conditions described above may be explained by assuming interference by a toxin with the normal formation of hemoglobin. If this normal synthesis is 'blocked' somewhere, the porphyrins of type III are excreted instead of proceeding to combine with iron and globin to form hemoglobin. It is interesting that the symptoms of lead poisoning are in many respects similar to those of acute porphyria. Other pathological conditions associated with mild anemia result in toxic manifestations and increased excretion of coproporphyrin III. Such observations have been made in patients with rheumatic fever.

Idiopathic porphyria occurs in an acute and a congenital form. The acute form usually is found in females in the third to the fifth decades of life and is characterized by abdominal and nervous manifestations. The congenital form occurs generally in males in infancy or early childhood and shows skin manifestations that may become mutilating. The dermatological symptoms are commonly ascribed to photosensitization due to excessive amounts of porphyrin in the tissues, but cases with skin manifestations have been reported in the absence of porphyrinuria.

BILE PIGMENTS

These are mainly *bilirubin* and *biliverdin*. Biliverdin is present in human bile in very small amounts only. The bile pigments are oxidation products of porphyrins. As a result of the oxidation one of the methene bridges is removed with opening of the porphyrin ring complex. The three remaining unsaturated methene bridges may be hydrogenated in turn, giving rise to different pigments. Bilirubin is produced by saturation of one of the methene bridges. Its structure is

BILIRUBIN

Biliverdin contains the three methene bridges linking the four pyrrol rings unchanged. Enzyme systems can convert it to bilirubin by reduction. All bile pigments readily undergo oxidation. Fuming nitric acid may serve as the oxidizing agent and gradually produces a series of oxidation products of which each has a characteristic color. These color changes are the basis for *Gmelin's test* for bile.

Bilirubin may be determined quantitatively by the *Van den Bergh reaction*. This determination depends upon the conversion of bilirubin to a red-violet azobilirubin by Ehrlich's diazo reagent. The color is compared with that from a known quantity of bilirubin similarly treated, or with an arbitrarily prepared cobalt sulfate solution having practically the same color. Bilirubin in blood, *hemobilirubin,* seems to behave differently toward Ehrlich's reagent than does the bilirubin in bile, *cholebilirubin.* Both are probably complexes of serum protein, but the former is much more stable than the latter and requires additional treatment to split the complex before the bilirubin can react to form azobilirubin. Cholebilirubin, which does not require this additional treatment is said to give a *direct,* whereas hemobilirubin gives an *indirect* Van den Bergh reaction. Hemobilirubin is usually split with ammonium sulfate and alcohol for the color development. Conversion of hemobilirubin to cholebilirubin may take place in the presence of substances such as bile salts and soaps which reduce surface tension.

Urobilin is a brown pigment found in feces. It is produced by reduction of bilirubin and contains one methene bridge, the other two bridges being saturated. Reduction of the remaining methene carbon atoms of urobilin gives rise to *urobilinogen* which is a colorless compound formed in the intestine. It is in part absorbed from the intestinal tract and excreted in the urine, the remainder being excreted in the feces. Obviously urine cannot contain urobilinogen unless bilirubin is present in the gastro-intestinal tract except in an occasional case where bilirubin may be reduced by bacterial action at a site proximal to obstruction to the flow of bile. Urinary urobilinogen can be detected with Ehrlich's aldehyde reagent (p-di-methylamino-benzaldehyde in hydrochloric acid solution.) The compound formed is red and an approximate quantitative test may be obtained by determining the dilution of urine which gives a barely visible reaction *(Wallace and Diamond test).*

Bile pigments are formed by breaking down hemoglobin in the reticuloendothelial system. There is no change in the rate of their formation in animals after removal of the liver and spleen. Human plasma contains normally 0.2 to 0.5 mg. bilirubin per 100 cc.

CYTOCHROME

This term applies to heme compounds consisting of hemochromogens a, b, and c. They are widely distributed in nature and their importance in oxidation-reduction reactions has been discussed in Chapter 5. Recently it has been demonstrated that the three cytochromes may consist of several identifiable individual cytochromes. The cytochromes a and c are not autooxidizable; they require cytochrome oxidase for the transfer of oxygen, or for the electron exchange resulting in the ferrous iron passing to the ferric state. The two forms may be identified by their spectral absorption as the ferrous compound has distinct bands while the ferric compound shows diffuse absorption. Cytochrome b is autooxidizable but the reaction with oxygen is sluggish.

The heme in the cytochromes occurs in two structures of which one is identical with heme in hemoglobin. The conjugated nitrogenous compounds in the cytochromes are unknown.

CHLOROPHYLL

This pigment is the agent in plants which, through the photosynthetic action, transforms the energy of the sun into chemicals which ultimately are the source of all foods and of most of the material used for heat and power (coal, oil, wood, etc). Willstatter and his associates separated chlorophyll into two compounds. Chlorophyll contains metallo-porphyrins in which magnesium is the metal. In the plants the porphyrin complexes of chlorophyll are combined with protein, giving a structure comparable with hemoglobin.

SUPPLEMENTARY READING

CORWIN, A. H.: The chemistry of the porphyrins. In: Gilman, H., *Organic Chemistry.* John Wiley & Sons, Inc., 1943.

DOBRINER, K.: Urinary porphyrins in disease. *J. Biol. Chem., 113:*1, 1936.

DOBRINER, K., and RHOADS, C. P.: The porphyrins in health and disease. *Physiol. Rev., 20:*416, 1940.

KILLICK, E. M.: Carbon monoxide anoxemia. *Physiol. Rev., 20:*313, 1940.

NESBITT, S., and WATKINS, C. H.: Acute porphyria. *Am. J. Med. Sc., 203:*74, 1942.

SOBOTKA, H.: *Physiological Chemistry of the Bile.* The Williams & Wilkins Co., 1937.

WATSON, C. J.: The porphyrins and diseases of the blood. *A Symposium on the Blood and Blood-forming Organs.* University of Wisconsin Press, 1939.

WATSON, C. J.: Some recent studies of porphyrin metabolism and porphyria. *The Lancet, 1:*539, 1951.

WATSON, C. J., and SCHWARTZ, S.: A simple test for urinary porphobilinogen. *Proc. Soc. Exper. Biol. & Med., 47:*393, 1941.

Chapter 10

THE LIVER AND THE BILIARY TRACT

T_{HE} liver, being the principal site of activity of many enzymes, serves a multitude of functions in metabolism, so that impairment of its capacity to carry on these functions, as in disease, may produce many varieties of biochemical manifestations. The activity of these enzyme systems is so great that the normal liver has a capacity of performance far in excess of average requirements for most, if not all, of its tasks. Therefore, this organ must be damaged extensively before failure becomes apparent by application of laboratory procedures.

HEPATIC FUNCTIONS

These are secretory, excretory, metabolic and detoxifying in nature.

Secretory and excretory functions: The polygonal cells of the liver secrete *bile* which is transported through the bile capillaries and the bile ducts to the intestinal tract. A considerable portion of the bile is concentrated in the gall bladder where it remains for a limited time. The secretory action of the liver is able to operate against considerable pressure which amounts to approximately 250 to 300 mm. of water. During periods of fasting the sphincter of Oddi is contracted and bile flows into the gall bladder when the pressure in the duct reaches 40 to 70 mm. of water. The gall bladder, by a process of reabsorption of water and electrolytes, concentrates the liver bile tenfold.

The formation of bile is continuous, the rate of secretion being approximately 50 per cent higher during waking hours than during sleep. The total volume secreted in 24 hours is about 500 cc. The discharge of bile into the duodenum, however, is intermittent, being governed by digestive demands. It is not clearly understood how this mechanism operates, particularly in view of the anatomical features of the gall bladder whose wall is so poorly equipped with muscle fibers that it would seem to be unable to produce enough force for expulsion of its contents. Relaxation of the sphincter of Oddi and contraction of the gall bladder appear to take place simultaneously. There are definite indications that a nervous control operates, possibly involving intrinsic systems in the walls of the ducts. Such systems might well receive stimuli from plexuses of the upper gastro-intestinal tract. Excitation through the vagus and the sympathetic system is known to produce weak motor action in the gall bladder, and section of the right vagus nerve has an inhibitory effect upon its contractility. Adrenalin promotes the motor effect. The movements of the gall bladder also involve a humoral control because after all connections between the nerves of the intestinal and biliary tracts and between these and the central nervous system have been interrupted, contractions can be brought about by fat in the duodenum.

Bile contains a number of metabolic waste products, such as the *pigments,* of which bilirubin is most important (see Chapter 9). The *bile salts* are the sodium salts of glycocholic and taurocholic acids, which are amides of cholic acid with glycine and taurine respectively. Taurine is formed from methionine, as isotopic sulfur introduced as isotopic methionine can be demonstrated subsequently to be present in taurine. The bile acids are largely reabsorbed by the intestinal mucosa so that a cycle of excretion from the liver and reabsorption conserves bile salts to the organism. If reabsorption is prevented by draining the bile through a fistula, precursors, however, are adequate to maintain a normal concentration of bile salts in the bile. *Cholesterol* in free form is a normal constituent of bile, cholesterol esters being absent. *Lecithin* is present in amounts approximately $1/3$ that of cholesterol. Lecithin is synthesized in the body with choline as a participant in the process. The lipotropic action of choline presumably depends on this process because lecithin is necessary for the transport of fatty acids.

Bile is important in the digestion of fats because its ability to lower surface tension aids in their emulsification, permitting more intimate contact between the fat particles and the fat digestion enzymes. Most of the surface tension effect resides in the bile acids. Bile salts enter into complexes with fatty acids in which form these acids are absorbed from the intestine. In the absence of bile, ingested fat may undergo almost complete hydrolytic cleavage in the intestinal tract, but the absorption is impaired greatly. Bile also affects the absorption of fat-soluble accessory food factors such as vitamins A, D, E, K, and carotene. Vitamin A is assimilated in the absence of bile but probably at a very slow rate.

Bile salts have a stimulating effect upon peristalsis and a choleretic action upon the liver. The total daily production of bile depends to some extent upon the diet, being lower during periods of starvation. Many drugs have been employed in the past for their presumed ability to stimulate the formation of bile. Such drugs include aloes, podophyllin, and calomel, but it cannot be demonstrated that their effects are significant. Emptying of the gall bladder is stimulated by the presence of fat in the digestive tract; a similar action results after ingestion of magnesium sulfate.

Metabolic function: The processes by which carbohydrates, proteins, and fats are metabolized take place to a large extent in the hepatic tissues (see Chapters 6, 7, and 8). The liver, therefore, supplies intermediary metabolites which, by their further degradation there, and in other tissues, furnish energy. Many of these substances constitute the common 'pool' of intermediaries which participate in the interchange of molecular components between the major groups of compounds.

Although special studies have been made in recent years to determine the site of formation of the several plasma proteins, their origin is still in doubt. It seems likely that *fibrinogen* is produced exclusively by the liver and that likewise albumin and globulin are at least in part, hepatic in origin. Albumin concentrations in plasma are lowered considerably in the presence of extensive liver damage. Other products seemingly formed in the liver are *prothrombin, heparin, vitamin A,* and the anti-anemic or *hematinic principle* in the adult.

Detoxifying function: The liver is the major organ of detoxication by chemical means. In it, the toxins from bacterial or other sources are destroyed, or are conjugated with other products to decrease their toxicity and are then eliminated.

FUNCTIONAL TESTS

A number of tests have been designed to measure the capacity of the hepatic tissue to carry on its usual metabolic actions, as well as the functioning of the excretory system. It has already been emphasized that demonstrable metabolic disturbances indicate widespread damage to the liver tissue. Impairment of the various functions does not occur to an equal extent in progressive damage, so that, in specific conditions, certain tests may appear more sensitive than others. In general such degrees of sensitivity are not sufficiently constant to be made the basis for differential diagnosis.

Functional tests may be divided into two groups, those pertaining to disturbances of excretion and those designed to detect impairment of normal metabolic processes. In the use of liver function tests for differential diagnostic purposes the entire biliary system must be considered, as excretory dysfunction may be due to damage in the liver tissue or to interference in the duct system. If of sufficiently long duration, the latter may cause secondary damage to the liver, so that tests may indicate a combination of obstructive as well as hepatocellular pathological states.

Bilirubin of the blood may be determined quantitatively by the *Van den Bergh test* as described in Chapter 9, or by a number of modifications of the original procedure. The *indirect* and the *direct* tests are designed to differentiate between bilirubin conjugated with protein before and after elimination of the pigment from the plasma by the liver cells. A simple comparison of the color of serum in proper dilution with that of a standard solution of potassium dichromate may be expressed as the *icteric index.* This gives a rough measure of the degree of retention of bile pigments in the plasma. It may not parallel quantitative Van den Bergh determinations because of the presence of other yellow pigments, and it may be used only as a semi-quantitative test.

The *chloroform-solubility* of the bilirubin is occasionally used to differentiate between the "indirect" and the "direct" pigment. The pigment form which gives the indirect Van den Bergh reaction is soluble while that which gives the direct reaction is insoluble in chloroform. The test is performed by extracting the plasma with chloroform and measuring the color of the chloroform against an arbitrary color standard. The bilirubin concentration then may be calculated in mg. per 100 cc. of plasma. Comparison of this figure with the total concentration of pigment in plasma, estimated by the quantitative Van den Bergh reaction, gives the percentage of chloroform-soluble pigment.

Normal bilirubin levels in plasma range between 0.2 and 0.5 mg. per 100 cc. Some investigators think that higher values may be normal, but it is doubtful if pigment concentrations higher than 0.5 mg. per 100 cc. are ever found in healthy individuals. The range between normal levels of bilirubin concentrations and those resulting from frank jaundice, is termed *latent jaundice.* By simple inspection of the color of skin, sclera, or plasma, jaundice is unquestionable in patients with more than 2 mg. of bilirubin in 100 cc. plasma. If the jaundice is of long standing the change in color of the tissues tends to become apparent at lower bilirubin concentrations than in rapidly developing cases.

Urobilinogen is formed from bilirubin by bacterial reduction in the intestinal tract. It is reabsorbed by the intestinal mucosa and is carried to the liver in the portal blood. Part is subsequently re-excreted by the liver, but details of the fate of urobilinogen in the portal circulation are not well understood. A small fraction of the reabsorbed urobilinogen is eliminated in the urine. Watson estimates that this fraction does not normally exceed 4 mg. per 24 hours, while the total daily excretion in the feces commonly ranges between 100 and 250 mg. The fecal elimination of urobilinogen parallels the rate of excretion of bilirubin, being high in hemolytic conditions. If the liver is intact, increased formation of urobilinogen may not be attended by a greatly augmented elimination in the urine. The liver's ability to reexcrete urobilinogen appears to be altered quite readily and urinary urobilinogen concentrations may increase as a result of diffuse liver damage. On the other hand, complete obstruction to the discharge of bile results in the disappearance of urobilinogen from the feces as well as from the urine. Occasionally small amounts of urobilinogen are present in urine in complete obstruction because bacteria reduce bilirubin in sites proximal to the obstruction. Jaundice due to partial obstruction with diffuse liver damage may result in greatly increased excretion of urobilinogen in the urine. The *Wallace* and *Diamond test* for urobilinogen in urine is discussed in Chapter 9. The recent introduction of *Watson's quantitative urinary urobilinogen test* gives a simplified method for serial tests which are helpful in following the course of acute hepatitis.

Certain liver function tests are based upon the ability of the liver to excrete injected material within a stated time. Bilirubin has been used for this purpose, but is expensive and its estimation requires a high degree of analytical accuracy. The test is performed by intravenous injection of 1 mg. of bilirubin per kg. of body weight, determinations of the bilirubin concentrations in the blood being made just prior to, and five minutes subsequent to the injection. The increase in bilirubin level over this five minute interval represents 100 per cent of injected pigment, and the rate of its elimination is determined by quantitative tests four hours after the injection. Soffer states that six per cent retention represents the upper limit for normal excretion.

The *bromsulfalein test* is used also to determine excretory function of the liver. The test depends on the ability of the liver to remove the dye from the blood as determined by the amount of dye retained after a certain time interval. Recent procedures include the use of photoelectric equipment which permits more accurate determinations of dye concentrations in the blood. Originally 2 mg. of dye per kg. of body weight was recommended as the test dose; now it is more common to use 5 mg. Some investigators believe that a residual amount of dye of more than 4 per cent at the end of 45 minutes is confirmatory in suspected parenchymal damage.

The *rose bengal test* is similar to the bromsulfalein test in principle. It is performed by the intravenous injection of 5 to 10 cc. of a saline solution containing 1 to 2 per cent rose bengal. The amount of color in the plasma, withdrawn two minutes later, serves as a 'standard.' Exactly six minutes later blood is again obtained and the color of the plasma compared with that of the 'standard.' More than 50 per cent retention of dye as determined by this comparison is considered indicative of liver damage.

Increased serum levels of *alkaline phosphatase* may reflect inability of the liver to excrete the enzyme phosphatase normally. It is not known to what extent liver cells may participate in the production of phosphatase of the blood. Jaundice is practically always associated with some increase of the blood phosphatase level, the increase being generally less in hepatocellular jaundice than in the obstructive forms. The majority of cases of pure hepatocellular damage show phosphatase values less than 10 Bodansky units, while in obstructive jaundice these values may become exceedingly high. There is, however, enough overlapping of values in the two types of jaundice to make interpretation difficult. Cirrhosis occasionally exhibits extremely high concentrations of phosphatase in the serum. In interpretations of phosphatase levels other causes of high phosphatase concentrations in serum, such as diseases of bone, and the normally elevated values in growing children, must be considered.

The *cholesterol* content of blood usually increases in obstructive jaundice while in intrahepatic disease normal or slightly reduced values may be found.

Combinations of the two types of pathological states may frequently be confusing. Free cholesterol is about equally distributed between cells and plasma, while plasma normally contains approximately 50-80 per cent of the total cholesterol in the form of esters. In obstructive jaundice with high total cholesterol of the blood, the ratio between the free and esterified fractions remains approximately constant, while in intrahepatic disease a relative lowering of the ester fraction may occur.

Investigators disagree as to what constitutes an abnormally low ester fraction. Values below 50 per cent of the total may not be present in healthy individuals although concentrations below 30 per cent carry a much more positive significance. It is not entirely clear why cholesterol concentrations in blood should increase in obstructive jaundice, unless it be the retarded elimination in the bile. Other factors are probably involved.

Interpretations of changes in the composition of *plasma proteins* in hepatic disease are made difficult by the lack of definite understanding of the mechanism and the site of formation of the various protein components. *Fibrinogen* undoubtedly is produced by the liver. Normally it ranges between 0.2 and 0.6 grams per 100 cc. of plasma, most values falling between 0.2 and 0.4 grams. Reductions to below normal are seen in severe forms of liver damage such as swiftly progressing acute yellow atrophy and in poisoning, resulting in extensive or total destruction of liver tissue. During milder inflammatory conditions in which damaged tissue is regenerated at a rapid rate, the fibrinogen fraction of plasma may become higher than normal.

The *albumin* concentration of plasma is frequently diminished in hepatocellular disease. Several explanations can be offered for this phenomenon. The disease may interfere with formation of albumin, which is based upon the assumption that the liver is the organ of synthesis of albumin. Some of the plasma albumin may be lost to the ascitic fluid and part to the urine if the liver condition is accompanied by albuminuria. Liver disease of long duration is associated with anorexia, and the low intake of food may well be a contributing factor in a low protein concentration of the blood.

Concentrations of serum globulin deviate from normal in several liver conditions. A chronic disease process with slow but extensive destruction of the hepatic tissue may exhibit normal or low globulin concentrations, while relatively active disease, characterized by destruction of cells, but with simultaneous regeneration of new liver substance may tend to increase the level in serum. Patients with cirrhosis in whom compensatory features are evident often have very high serum globulin levels. Fibrinogen, being a globulin, is included in the total plasma globulin fraction.

Albumin and globulin concentrations in serum do not generally undergo appreciable change in early acute hepatitis or in obstructive jaundice unless the latter condition is accompanied by secondary hepatocellular changes.

Prothrombin is formed in the liver. This may be its main source, so that liver disease interfering with its production results in an increased blood coagulation time, which, however, does not become apparent until the prothrombin concentration of the blood falls considerably below normal, perhaps to less than 20 per cent of the normal. Hypoprothrombinemia may be caused by lack of vitamin K, and this condition can be corrected by parenteral administration of the vitamin. Vitamin K is always present in adequate quantities in the intestinal tract partly because of both the dietary content and the synthetic processes in the alimentary tract by bacteria. However, in the absence of bile, vitamin K is not readily absorbed. The lack of vitamin K results in hypoprothrombinemia evidenced by bleeding tendency in obstructive jaundice of long duration. Dicumarol apparently destroys one of the components of the prothrombin complex, and thus has the effect of a deficiency of vitamin K. Acute yellow atrophy and liver dystrophies with extensive destruction usually produce an increased prothrombin time. This does not respond to injection of vitamin K, as the liver's ability to use this vitamin in synthesizing prothrombin is impaired.

Damage to the liver which is extensive enough to affect the normal metabolic processes should be evident through failure to keep metabolic products within their normal limits of concentration in the blood. This is exemplified by the occurrence of low *urea* and *glucose* values, and of concentrations of amino acid nitrogen above normal, which, however, become apparent only with extensive hepatic impairment.

Leucine and *tyrosine* crystals in urine may upon rare occasions be observed in severe liver damage. These two amino acids have been considered as indicating autolysis of liver tissue. Massive tyrosinuria has been found in acute yellow atrophy. Only minor degrees of tyrosinuria are present occasionally during degenerative processes of extrahepatic tissues. It appears that increasing tyrosinuria in general is associated with rapidly progressing destruction of liver parenchyma and a poor outlook, but quantitative measurement of tyrosine in the urine cannot be considered a reliable prognostic barometer. It is possible that the appearance of leucine and tyrosine crystals in the urine is the result of general failure of the liver to deaminize amino acids and, because of their relative solubility, they are observed more readily than other amino acids.

Benzoic acid is detoxified in the liver by combination with glycine. The resulting *hippuric* acid is excreted in the urine. This detoxication process may be used as a liver function test provided renal function is normal. The test is performed by giving the patient 6 grams of sodium benzoate by mouth and determining the amount of hippuric acid excreted in the urine during the following four hours. The healthy adult eliminates approximately 3 grams under the conditions of the standard test. Excretion of less than 1.5 grams is considered to be indicative of severe liver damage.

The *galactose tolerance test* is one of the most commonly employed tests for liver function. Galactose is probably converted in the liver to glucose through certain steps involving phosphorylation. There is some evidence, however, that the glycogen formed from galactose is somewhat different from ordinary glycogen. This conversion of galactose is a rather sluggish process and damage to the liver slows it up, resulting in excretion of part of the galactose by the kidneys. At the beginning of the test the patient is given 40 grams of galactose orally, and the excretion of sugar in the urine is determined over a five hour period. Hepatocellular damage is indicated by elimination of more than 3 grams of galactose during the time stated. Acute hepatitis frequently results in a positive galactose tolerance test but other forms of diffuse liver disease such as cirrhosis may show a negative test even though there may be extensive involvement. The test is usually negative in obstructive jaundice. The influence of the thyroid on the rate of absorption of galactose from the intestinal tract will be discussed in Chapter 13. The rate of excretion of galactose by the kidneys is also a factor influencing the results of the oral galactose tolerance test. Bassett, Althausen and Coltrin, have introduced an *intravenous galactose test*. They inject 1 cc, of a 50 per cent solution of galactose per kg. of body weight and determine the concentration in the blood of unmetabolized galactose 75 minutes later. Parenchymal liver damage is indicated by the presence of more than 20 mg. of galactose per 100 cc. at the end of the test period.

The *fructose tolerance test* is similar in principle to the galactose tolerance test, determinations being made of fructose levels in the blood after administration of fructose by mouth. In the normal adult the maximum blood concentration during the test should be less than 20 mg. per 100 cc. This concentration is reached in approximately one hour, and at the end of two hours it should fall below 8 mg. per 100 cc. Failure on the part of the liver to metabolize fructose (levulose) results in blood values higher than those stated.

The *cephalin flocculation test* is used in an effort to distinguish between hepatocellular and other types of jaundice. A diluted mixture of serum from a patient with liver disease and a cephalin-cholesterol emulsion may show a one to four-plus flocculation reaction in the presence of a process destroying liver tissue. The intensity of the reaction is related to the severity of the pathological process. The chemical changes upon which flocculation depends are not understood; they may be associated with the absence of a protective action of albumin and/or alterations in the gamma globulin.

The *thymol turbidity test* is of similar nature. Turbidity results when a 'positive' serum is added to a buffered supersaturated solution of thymol.

Positive reactions point toward hepatocellular destruction. There is accumulating evidence that cephalin flocculation and thymol turbidity tests are based upon somewhat different underlying chemical changes, but which are not known at present.

Several other tests based upon an increased concentration of globulin in the serum have been employed. The *Takata-Ara test* is of this nature; it has been almost completely discarded. The *formol gel test,* if positive, exhibits changes in viscosity with or without changes in translucency upon addition of formaldehyde to serum. It is performed very easily and may serve as a good screening test in studies upon larger groups of patients.

JAUNDICE

This condition occurs when the biliary system excretes bilirubin at too slow a rate to maintain its concentration in the blood within normal limits. Three conditions may produce jaundice, namely (1) hemolytic processes leading to formation of bilirubin in excess of the maximum excretory capacity of the liver; (2) decrease in the excretory capacity of the liver due to damage to the liver tissue; and (3) intrahepatic and extrahepatic obstruction to the discharge of bile. These three conditions are classified as hemolytic, hepatocellular, and obstructive jaundice. The occurrence of these pathological states as clear-cut entities would permit the proper diagnosis by laboratory procedures without difficulties, but jaundice often results from simultaneous existence of more than one disease entity, although the initial disturbance may well have been purely hemolytic, hepatocellular, or obstructive.

Hemolytic processes resulting in jaundice occur in congenital hemolytic jaundice, icterus neonatorum, pernicious anemia, polycythemia, hemolytic transfusion reactions, erythroblastosis fetalis, etc., and these conditions have no obvious relationship to the excretory function of the liver. However, if the hemolytic state continues, the excretory cells of the liver become affected and eventually some injury may be sustained by the bile capillaries. Thus a pathological process remote from the liver may have an initial stage of purely hemolytic features and subsequently proceed to show characteristics of hepatocellular and obstructive lesions. It is likely that a degree of damage to the liver cells is actually present before jaundice of the hemolytic type becomes apparent, because the liver naturally has a large reserve capacity in respect to removal of excess bilirubin from the plasma. The most damaging factor is probably the anoxemia which is part of the physiological picture in excessive hemolysis. Depletion of plasma proteins may also play a role in the impaired capacity of the liver to excrete large amounts of bilirubin. Occasionally formation of pigment stones may be responsible for obstruction. It should not be inferred that there is a progression from the hemolytic type toward the other types of jaundice, a true hemolytic jaundice will probably appear predominantly so in the various functional tests, but evidence of the presence of the 'direct' pigment becomes more definite as the condition progresses.

Conditions other than those named above may be associated with hemolysis, possibly with a direct toxic effect upon the excretory cells of the liver. Various septicemias, malaria, black water fever, and a number of toxic compounds may be responsible for this instability of the red cell.

The bilirubinemia of hemolytic jaundice usually is mild, and rarely leads to bilirubin values in excess of 7-8 mg. per 100 cc. unless hepatocellular and obstructive features become prominent. The pigment resulting from hemolysis shows less permeability than that from obstruction and, therefore, in contrast to the latter, does not appear in the urine. Thus the finding of bilirubin in the urine is of diagnostic importance.

Hepatocellular jaundice is produced by any etiological agent capable of injuring the polygonal cells. Among infectious agents are the causative organisms of acute viral hepatitis, yellow fever, suppurative cholangitis, and Weil's disease. There are many 'chemically' toxic agents which, in various ways, are capable of injuring liver cells. Direct injury may be caused by chloroform, carbon tetrachloride, carbon disulfide, benzene to a major extent, nitrophenols, nitrotoluenes, arsphenamines, cincophen, arsenic, phosphorus, and many others. Chemicals causing hemolysis may also cause direct damage to liver cells, or the products of hemolysis (pigments and stromata) may be responsible for the injury. The saponins and snake poisons fall in this group. Also included are such substances as sulfonamides, phenylhydrazine, arsine, etc. The question of sensitivity enters into many cases of liver damage from chemicals. At times severe liver destruction occurs upon exposure to amounts which would be far too small to have demonstrable effects in most people. Such observations lend support to theories of sensitivity. The clinician should keep in mind that an agent toxic to the liver often tends to inflict injury to the kidneys. Acute yellow atrophy and eclamptic liver lesions manifest severe toxic reactions.

Laboratory data obtained in patients with hepatocellular jaundice may vary considerably as the disease progresses. The pigment initially retained in the plasma probably is preponderantly of hemolytic origin. At a later stage obstructive features become evident and reabsorbed pigment accentuates the jaundice. The Van den Bergh reaction becomes 'biphasic,' showing the presence of pigments of both types and their relative concentrations can be estimated approximately by difference after determination of the part soluble in chloroform. The alkaline phosphatase activity of the blood increases, but the value seldom exceeds 10-12 Bodansky units unless there is a large obstructive element in the pathological process. The elimination of urobilinogen in the urine is frequently increased several fold. The prothrombin time is prolonged if the liver damage is sufficient to interfere with prothrombin formation. Tests such as cephalin flocculation and thymol turbidity, which are designed to differentiate between hepatocellular and other types of jaundice generally become positive and the ester fraction of the total blood cholesterol tends to become lower than normal. The galactose tolerance test frequently becomes positive.

Obstructive jaundice is characterized by hyperbilirubinemia caused by the 'direct' pigment. If the obstruction is intermittent the degree of jaundice will fluctuate, but if it is complete the jaundice increases progressively at a rate depending upon the retention of the pigments. The values of the quantitative Van den Bergh reaction and the icteric index increase proportionately. Phosphatase levels in the serum are augmented considerably beyond those found in the hepatocellular type of jaundice. Total obstruction prevents bile from reaching the intestinal tract, hence the 'putty' colored stool and the absence of urobilinogen in urine. Because of the greater diffusibility of the 'direct' pigment the bilirubin of obstructive jaundice appears in the urine. The elimination of bilirubin through the kidneys becomes apparent at concentrations in the plasma exceeding approximately 1.6 mg. per 100 cc. Extrahepatic obstruction gradually produces damage to the bile capillaries and to the polygonal cells so that laboratory criteria of hepatocellular disease eventually may be added to those applicable to the obstructive phase.

In cases of recent obstruction the prothrombin time is usually normal but it increases gradually if absence of bile from the intestinal tract prevents absorption of vitamin K. This condition and the manifestations of increased hemorrhagic tendencies can be corrected by parenteral administration of the deficient vitamin. If injected vitamin K fails to bring about a decrease of prothrombin time to normal in 6 hours it is safe to assume that at least moderate hepatic impairment is associated with the obstruction. Uncomplicated obstructive jaundice generally exhibits negative cephalin flocculation and thymol turbidity tests, and the plasma albumin and globulin concentrations remain within normal limits.

CIRRHOSIS (LAENNEC'S CIRRHOSIS)

Jaundice occurs in many patients with cirrhosis; it has often been described as mild and transient and as appearing frequently in the early stages of the disease, but without later recurrence. Present evidence points to a high incidence of jaundice in cirrhosis, and of recurring jaundice on the basis of cell damage as a factor in the progress of the disease. Perhaps the most striking biochemical feature of the disorder is the fact that the liver can undergo such extensive changes without jaundice being an invariable rule. The bromsulfalein test is particularly valuable in determining reduced excretory capacity in Laennec's cirrhosis. Serum phosphatase occasionally reaches exceedingly high levels, values of 40 to 60 Bodansky units are not unusual. Low plasma albumin concentrations generally are present. The globulin values vary greatly; they tend to be high in the patient with a protracted course with compensatory changes in the liver. Cephalin flocculation tests are usually strongly positive in Laennec's cirrhosis.

Ascites may accompany both acute and chronic liver disease. Important factors in the mechanism of its production may include increased pressure in the portal veins, reduction in osmotic pressure of the blood because of lower protein concentrations, and changes in capillary permeability. Recently an anti-diuretic pituitary factor has been reported to be present in the urine of patients with ascites. Possibly the liver, if sufficiently impaired, fails to destroy this substance.

Ascitic fluid usually contains less than 1 gram of protein per 100 cc., and only in rare cases does this value exceed 1.5 grams. The loss of albumin from plasma associated with the formation of ascites may be contributory to the low plasma concentration of protein observed in cirrhotic patients. However, albumin and globulin may often occur in approximately equal concentrations in ascites without any demonstrable tendency to reduce serum globulin values.

Biliary cirrhosis develops as a pathological process extending up through the bile capillaries. The jaundice associated with this condition is much more intense than that in Laennec's cirrhosis. Serum phosphatase levels tend to equal those occurring in extrahepatic obstructive jaundice. Cephalin flocculation and thymol turbidity tests are usually negative. In most cases there are no alterations in the plasma proteins except that disturbances may appear in the late stage of the disease.

SUPPLEMENTARY READING

AGGELER, P. M., HOWARD, J., LUCIA, S. P., CLARK, W., and ASTAFF, A.: Standardization of the Quick prothrombin test. *Blood, 1:*220, 1946.

HANGER, F. M.: The flocculation of cephalin-cholesterol emulsions by pathological sera. *Tr. A. Am. Physicians, 53:*148, 1938.

HOAGLAND, C. L.: The therapy of liver diseases. *Bull. New York Acad. Med., 21:*537, 1945.

KIMBALL, S., CHAPPLE, W. H. C., and SANES, S.: Jaundice in relation to cirrhosis of the liver. *J.A.M.A., 134:*662, 1947.

MACLAGAN, N. F.: The thymol turbidity test as an indicator of liver dysfunction. *Brit. J. Exper. Path., 25:*234, 1944.

MATEER, J. G., BALTZ, J. I., COMANDURAS, P. D., STEELE, H. H., and BROUWER, S. W.: Further advances in liver function tests and the value of a therapeutic test in facilitating the earlier diagnosis and treatment of liver impairment. *Gastroenterology, 8:*52, 1947.

MATEER, J. G., BALTZ, J. I., STEELE, H. H., BROUWER, S. W., and COLVERT, J. R.: Chronic subclinical impairment of the liver. Early diagnosis and treatment. Further improvement and evaluation of certain liver function tests. *J.A.M.A., 133*:909, 1947.

METCOFF, J., and STARE, F. J.: The physiologic and clinical significance of plasma proteins and protein metabolites. *New England J. Med., 236*:26, 1947.

MURPHY, T. L., CHALMERS, T. C., ECKHARDT, R. D., and DAVIDSON, C. S.: Hepatic coma. Clinical and laboratory observations on forty patients. *New England J. Med., 239*:605, 1948.

NEEFE, J. R.: Results of hepatic tests in chronic hepatitis without jaundice. *Gastroenterology, 7*:1, 1946.

POST, J., and PATEK, A. J.: Serum proteins in cirrhosis of the liver. *Arch. Int. Med., 69*:67, 1942.

SNELL, A. M.: The management of jaundiced patients. *J.A.M.A., 133*:1175, 1947.

TUMEN, H., and BOCKUS, H. L.: The clinical significance of serum proteins in hepatic disease. *Am. J. Med. Sc., 193*:788, 1937.

WATSON, C. J., and RAPPAPORT, E. M.: A comparison of the results obtained with the Hanger cephalin-cholesterol flocculation test and the Maclagan thymol turbidity test in patients with liver disease. *J. Lab & Clin. Med., 30*:983, 1945.

WATSON, C. J., SCHWARTZ, S., SBOROV, V., and BERTIE, E.: Studies of urobilinogen: V., A simple method for the quantitative recording of the Ehrlich reaction as carried out with urine and feces. *Am. J. Clin. Path., 14*:605, 1944.

WHITE, F. W., DEUTSCH, E., and MADDOCK, S.: The comparative value of serial hippuric acid excretion, total cholesterol, cholesterol ester, and phospholipid tests in diseases of the liver. *Am. J. Digest. Dis., 6*:603, 1939.

WITTS, L. J.: A review of the dietetic factors in liver disease. *Brit. Med. J., 1*:1, 1947.

Chapter 11

THE KIDNEYS AND THE URINARY TRACT

THE kidneys are primarily organs for elimination of the waste products of metabolism. In the performance of this function they exhibit an amazing ability, within the limits required for normal physiological activities, to regulate the concentration of various constituents of the blood. Most of the products eliminated in the urine are stable during this process. The kidneys may also synthesize ammonia, which permits the excretion of acid ions with a conservation of an equivalent amount of sodium or other fixed base.

Experimental evidence indicates that the kidneys also elaborate enzymes, which aid in (1) conserving base, e.g., carbonic anhydrase, glutaminase, and renal amino acid oxidase; (2) carbohydrate and fat metabolism; and (3) a blood pressure regulating enzyme, renin, which in conjunction with aminopolypeptidase, gives rise to a pressor substance, hypertensin, a polypeptide. Evidence that this renal pressor substance participates in the regulation of blood pressure in the normal individual is inconclusive at present.

Failure of the kidneys obviously must result in accumulation in the blood of those substances which are not eliminated, and these are decreased correspondingly in the urine. Examination of the patient's blood indicates abnormal retention of such waste products as urea, creatinine, and other nonprotein nitrogen containing substances. The term *azotemia* is used to indicate elevated values of non-protein nitrogen in the blood.

Laboratory procedures applicable in renal disease may reveal the retention of normal waste products in the blood by their deficiency in the urine. However, such determinations are not too practical because of the difficulties in subjecting patients to controlled metabolic balance studies. It is much easier to determine the relative rate of elimination of certain substances by the clearance technique which will be described subsequently. Certain laboratory procedures performed under standard conditions may give valuable information as to the functional status of the kidneys. For instance, their ability to excrete concentrated or dilute urine may be judged after determining the specific gravity under specified conditions. Other simple tests of chemical and microscopic nature are used routinely to detect blood cells, casts, abnormal amounts of protein, or other abnormal urinary constituents.

It is regrettable that a discussion of diseases of the kidneys cannot be based upon a universally accepted system of classification. At present, classification cannot be made according to etiological factors because so many of them are

152

still unknown. Undoubtedly certain kidney diseases are the result of specific infections of known etiology, but it cannot be stated that the pathological changes are produced directly by the infecting organism or by products elaborated by it, nor can it be stated that the characteristic morphological and functional changes in individual cases must, of necessity, result from the action of a specific organism. Frequently pathological changes are progressive, and important and distinct phases of a disease may not become apparent until long after the initiating infection has subsided. Furthermore, the same etiological agent does not always produce identical pathological manifestations in the kidneys. For these reasons it is important that diagnosis of abnormal function of the kidneys according to the common clinical classifications should be correlated with accurate pathological description of the lesions. It has been postulated that the development of renal disease may be dependent upon an original sensitizing factor and that subsequent events are in the nature of a 'sensitization reaction.'

It is to be expected that damage to the nephron may be of selective nature because of the functional characteristics of each of its anatomical divisions. A few specific agents, notably chemical poisons such as mercury, induce pathological changes in rather sharply demarcated portions of the nephron. Most other kidney diseases variably involve the glomeruli and tubules, although adequate studies have not yet been made to determine in disease the segmental damage of the tubules, as has been done in connection with chemical poisons.

FORMATION OF URINE

The glomerular tuft serves as a filter permitting the excretion of a fluid which Bordley, Richards, Walker, Reisinger, Westfall, and Finley, showed in experiments on frogs to be identical in composition with the protein- and lipid-free plasma. Walker reports confirmatory analyses of fluid from the glomerular capsule of the mammalian kidney. Such experiments indicate that a potential urine is formed by filtration in the glomeruli and, after complicated processes of reabsorption have occurred as this fluid passes through the tubules it eventually becomes the true bladder urine. It is important to remember that the filtrate extractable from the glomerular capsule is not urine. Urine formation begins and ends in the tubule regardless of whether urinary constituents are immediately derived from intracapsular or from peritubular fluid. The processes involved in urine formation are commonly designated as filtration (glomerular), secretion, and reabsorption (tubular). Formation of the filtrate is unrelated to its subsequent modification.

Modern physiologists accept the theory that urine is formed by a process of filtration and selective reabsorption but are divided concerning the contribution to urine formation by secretion, i.e., the passage of substances directly from the peritubular capillaries across the epithelium of the tubule into the lumen. Direct evidence is available which indicates that certain foreign substances are excreted by the tubules. Following an injection of phenol red, the dye is found in the plasma in both a filterable and a non-filterable form, the latter being a combination between the dye and protein. If the volume of blood flowing through the kidneys during a known interval be calculated, it can be shown that the urine content of phenol red exceeds the total amount of filterable dye in the volume of blood estimated to have passed through the glomeruli. This has been interpreted as an indication of additional excretion by the tubules. Diodrast and para-amino hippuric acid are two substances eliminated by tubular excretion. Their use in measuring the renal blood flow will be discussed later. Evidence for tubular excretion in man has been presented by comparing creatinine and inulin clearance. Those who have considered inulin clearance as a standard of reference for glomerular filtration exclusively (see below) have shown that clearance of ingested creatinine exceeds that of inulin, the conclusion being that the tubules participate in the elimination of creatinine. Richards points out that uncertainties in regard to the origin of urinary creatinine do not permit acceptance of clearance determinations as absolute proof of tubular creatinine excretion in man. Furthermore, it is conceded by many workers that endogenous creatinine clearance may measure glomerular filtration rate with greater accuracy than inulin.

Comparisons of concentrations of plasma and urine constituents reveal the selective nature of tubular reabsorption. Certain substances are reabsorbed to such an extent that they normally are present in minute concentrations only in the urine. Renal threshold to a particular substance generally is visualized as a distinct plasma concentration above which the substance in question appears in the urine. It is a common expression that such and such a plasma component begins to 'spill over' at a more or less defined level. While threshold may be a convenient expression from the standpoint of definition it is a senseless term from the standpoint of physiology. As an example, glucose is present in the glomerular filtrate in concentrations approximately equal to that in plasma. The relatively high threshold of glucose is produced by its complete reabsorption in the tubules. As the concentration of glucose in the plasma and glomerular filtrate increases, the amount of glucose which must be reabsorbed by the tubules in order to keep the urine free of glucose increases. Eventually a point is reached beyond which the tubules cannot absorb all of the glucose in the glomerular filtrate and glucosuria results. From a practical standpoint it means that the renal threshold for glucose is not a property inherent in glucose as such, but is a value established by and subjected to variations of a number of factors. Considerable variations are to be expected and are actually found even in the same individual at different times. It should not be overlooked that the glucose concentration in the glomerular filtrate is dependent upon the plasma concentration of glucose in the arterial blood at the particular moment, while the practical establishment of the threshold in a patient is generally judged by the glucose concentration in the venous blood. In the postprandial phase the difference in glucose concentration in the arterial and venous blood may be quite considerable and correlations attempted on the basis of glucose concentration from venous blood are therefore erroneous. Also it must be remembered that blood and urine specimens in ordinary clinical practice are not simultaneous specimens. Obviously various pathological processes involving the kidney may very materially alter threshold values from the average. It is common to observe elevated threshold values in patients with advanced arteriosclerosis and with nephritis. High values frequently observed in elderly diabetics may be associated with nephrosclerotic changes. While the correlation of threshold may be useful from the clinical standpoint it might be better abolished as applying to substances which appear in the bladder urine regardless of their glomerular concentration.

As already mentioned 'clearance' is a measurement of great usefulness. A 'clearance' is the volume of blood or plasma which seems to be completely cleared of a particular substance in unit time by the kidneys. It is the volume of blood or plasma which, at the existing plasma concentration, would contain the amount of a certain substance eliminated in the urine in unit time. The value is expressed as cc. of blood, or of plasma, cleared per minute. The clearance of substances to which the cell membrane acts as a barrier should be expressed in cc. of plasma, rather than of blood, to avoid corrections for variations in cell volume.

Within certain limitations which will be discussed later the clearance of a substance may be computed as equal to UV/P. U and P are its concentrations in urine and plasma respectively, and V is cc. of urine formed per minute. If the equation is applied to the clearance of inulin or mannitol which are not reabsorbed by the tubules, this measurement becomes an expression of the *rate of glomerular filtration* and it has been determined for a normal man to be equal to approximately 125 cc. of plasma per minute.

It is obvious that clearance of a substance which is excreted by the glomeruli only cannot exceed the volume of plasma filtered. Therefore, any substance with a clearance higher than 125 cc. per minute must be excreted by the tubules as well as by the glomeruli. If a substance such as glucose is normally completely absorbed by the tubules so that it does not appear in the urine, its clearance is zero. A value of 175 for the clearance of ingested creatinine is considered by Shannon and Homer Smith to be proof of the tubular excretion of creatinine. As creatinine presumably is not reabsorbed, its glomerular clearance must be equal to the glomerular filtration rate which

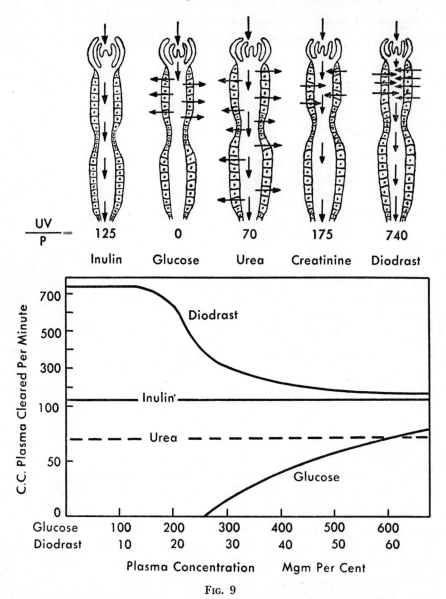

$$\frac{UV}{P} =$$

125	0	70	175	740
Inulin	Glucose	Urea	Creatinine	Diodrast

FIG. 9

is 125 and the difference (175 minus 125) must be due to tubular excretion. Creatinine clearances without ingested creatinine are practically the same as the values for inulin clearance, which indicates that creatinine normally is eliminated by the glomeruli only. Urea clearance which is approximately 70, is lower than the glomerular clearance rate, and is due to partial reabsorption of urea, a process which is assumed to be simple diffusion.

The clearance of diodrast and of para-amino hippuric acid are particularly interesting because these substances appear to be removed from the renal arterial blood during one passage through the kidney tissues. Diodrast (or para-amino hippuric acid) clearance therefore, measures the rate of the flow of blood through the kidneys. *The effective renal blood flow* as measured by the diodrast clearance is approximately 740 cc. per minute. On the assumption that diodrast is completely removed from the plasma during its passage through the kidneys, its clearance, when compared with that of inulin, shows that glomerular filtration of the plasma entering the kidneys only comprises about 1/6 of the total.

Clearance values can be expected to remain independent of plasma concentrations only as long as the concentration of the substance involved remains within the functional capacity of the kidney for excreting the substance. Figure 9 (from Homer Smith and J. L. Gamble) illustrates the characteristic mode of excretion of inulin, glucose, urea, creatinine, and diodrast and also the limitations of excretion for these substances. It shows that the maximal and constant clearance of diodrast is obtained only when the plasma concentration is low. Above concentrations of approximately 12 mg. per 100 cc. of plasma, the capacity for tubular excretion is surpassed, and the clearance consequently falls below its maximum. Measurements of effective renal blood flow are therefore made at plasma concentrations of diodrast not exceeding about 10 mg. per 100 cc. Inulin and urea clearances are constant at all plasma concentrations. The clearance of glucose at values below its threshold become zero; above the threshold the clearance increases as indicated in Figure 9. As mentioned previously the tubular excretion of diodrast reaches a maximum at a plasma concentration of about 12 mg. per 100 cc. This *maximal tubular excretory capacity* is assumed to represent the amount of actively functioning tubular tissue mass.

The *maximal tubular reabsorptive capacity* may be determined after elevating the plasma concentration of glucose because the tubules cannot increase the rate of reabsorption of this substance beyond a certain limit. The total amount of glucose passing through the tubules per minute is equal to the glomerular filtration per minute multiplied by the plasma concentration. This amount of glucose, minus the amount of glucose in the urine over the corresponding period, represents the maximal tubular reabsorptive capacity.

The composition of urine has been discussed previously (Chapter 4).

FUNCTIONAL TESTS

The amazing reserve capacity of various organs to carry on their functions is nowhere more evident than in the performance of the kidneys. Only a small fraction of this capacity is used for normal functioning, and damage must be so excessive as to encroach upon this minimum of functioning tissue before renal failure can be demonstrated by commonly accepted standards.

Failure to excrete metabolic waste products at a normal rate by the kidneys results in an increase in concentration of these products in the blood. Advanced impairment shows retention of such substances as *urea, creatinine, uric acid,* and *phosphate* and *sulfate* ions.

The composition of urine as compared with that of plasma indicates that tubular reabsorption is selective and that the ultimate concentrations of many components of urine are determined by 'active' cellular processes which must involve expenditure of energy. In contradistinction, reabsorption of part of the urea excreted in the glomerular filtrate is considered to be a 'passive' diffusion process. Such a process should result in stationary clearance values for the particular substance regardless of changes in plasma concentration, whereas with plasma components characterized by 'active' reabsorption in the tubules stationary values will be found only at plasma concentrations which require less than the maximum amount of work the tubules are able to perform in the 'active' reabsorption process.

The statement that a large proportion of the functional renal tissue must be destroyed before failure of excretion becomes manifest holds true for urea as well as for other waste products. However, it should be understood clearly that accepted 'normal' concentrations cover a wide range of values, and that variations from mean values may be significant even when they are within so-called 'normal' limits.

It can be shown that there is a progressive increase in the urea clearance as the urine flow increases, but that this effect is unimportant when the flow of urine is between 1.5 and 12 cc. per minute. According to Smith, Goldring, and Chasis, the mean normal value for urea clearance is 70.0 ± 7.4 cc. per minute. When the urine flow falls below 1.5 cc. per minute, the urea clearance does not represent a measure of the ability of the kidney to 'clear' urea because other factors, such as dehydration and reduced filtration rate, influence elimination.

Austin, Stillman, and Van Slyke found that direct proportionality between urea excretion and blood urea concentration does not hold true below a urine volume of 2 cc. per minute in adults. They call this the 'augmentation limit.' In confirmatory experiments, Möller, McIntosh, and Van Slyke found the augmentation limit to vary from 1.7 to 2.5 cc. of urine per minute.

Urea clearance is frequently employed for clinical purposes. It has been shown above that the necessary data for the calculation include the concentrations of urea in blood and urine and the volume of urine excreted in a known time interval. UV/P represents the urea clearance provided the urine output is at any volume above the augmentation limit, because the rate of excretion of urea then is at maximum. Van Slyke and his associates call urea clearance in the normal adult above the augmentation limit, the *maximum blood urea clearance* or the *maximum clearance.* It represents, of course, the volume of blood which one minute's excretion suffices to clear of urea when the urine volume is large enough to permit a maximum urea output.

Austin, Stillman, and Van Slyke demonstrated that below the 'augmentation limit' the urea excretion rate falls, and that the reduction in excretion on the average is more nearly in proportion to the square root of the volume rather than to the volume itself. Therefore, urea clearance values below the 'augmentation limit' (2 cc. urine per minute) are calculated from $U\sqrt{V}/P$. Because this formula refers the urea clearance to a standard volume of urine output, Van Slyke and his associates called clearance below the augmentation limit, the *standard blood urea clearance*.

Clinicians should have a clear understanding of the term 'normal' as applied to blood concentrations of substances eliminated by the kidneys. It has already been mentioned that significant changes may take place within limits of 'normal' because these limits of necessity must be wide enough to allow for several variables. Goldring and Chasis have presented evidence to show that in hypertensive disease and in diffuse glomerulo-nephritis an inverse relationship between concentrations of blood urea and urea clearance occurs. If the organism is in nitrogen- and water-balance the relationship can be expressed thus:

$$\text{blood urea} \times \text{urea clearance} = \text{constant}.$$

According to this equation, and to the data obtained by Goldring and Chasis, the blood urea concentration increases simultaneously with the decrease in clearance values when kidney function becomes impaired.

Usually the upper limit of normal urea concentration in the blood is considered to be approximately 40 mg. per 100 cc., corresponding to 19 mg. of urea nitrogen per 100 cc., while the average normal value in adults is approximately ½ of this figure. Imbalance between nitrogen and water metabolism may readily produce concentrations of urea in blood greater than average, but less than upper normal in absence of renal disease. On the other hand, such values may be the result of impaired kidney function. These remarks about the relation of urea clearance to the function of diseased kidneys may seem to be contradictory to statements made previously, namely that considerable destruction of kidney tissue must take place before obvious retention of the waste products in the blood occurs. The latter statement is true, in so far as it applies to the ability of the kidneys to maintain the organism functionally normal in the presence of reduced excretory capacity. It does not mean that such changes in excretory rates are undetectable.

The low urea clearance values of cardiac decompensation result from a diminished flow of blood through the kidneys even in the absence of pathological changes.

The rate of excretion of urea is dependent on the size of the individual, varying directly as the surface area. Mean values for renal functional measurements are usually corrected to a surface area of 1.73 sq. m. This correction becomes of significance in children and small adults; it may be applied in the formula for maximum and standard clearances by multiplying V by the factor 1.73/A in which A represents the body area in square meters as computed from the subject's height and weight.

Phenolsulfonphthalein (PSP) *excretion* was first studied by Rowntree and Geraghty. In principle the determination consists of an intramuscular or intravenous injection of a known amount of dye and measurement of the percentage of the dye excreted in the urine after definite time intervals. Many modifications of the test have been employed, most of which prescribe the collection of urine after one and two hour intervals. The test dose is 6 mg. of dye, 10 minutes being allowed for absorption when the dye is injected intramuscularly. Normally 40 to 60 per cent of the injected dye is excreted during the 1st hour and an additional 20 to 25 per cent is recoverable during the 2nd hour, making a total of 60 to 85 per cent excreted. The one and two hour test is very insensitive and is of little use in detection of early renal impairment. The elimination of PSP is mainly by tubular excretion; however, the amount of dye used is usually insufficient to give a plasma concentration high enough to bring about maximal tubular excretion. Damaged tubular tissue may retain sufficient activity to 'clear' the dye unless the time for the first collection is short. A fractionation technique in which the 1st specimen is collected at the end of 15 minutes generally shows an excretion of more than 25 per cent of the injected dye by normal individuals. A high percentage of individuals with renal disease excrete less than this amount over the 15 minute period, whereas if the one and two hour test is used the slow rate of excretion would not be observed. Goldring and Chasis found the average rate of excretion in 25 normal individuals to be 30 per cent in the 1st 20 minutes and 55.4 per cent in the 1st hour.

One of the most fundamental characteristics of the normal kidney is its ability to vary the concentration of urine to meet excretory requirements within the wide limits of available water. Structural damage gradually depresses this variability so that the specific gravity of the urine tends to converge to a constant figure. The specific gravity of urine from kidneys which have lost practically all concentrating and diluting power is approximately 1.010. Concentrating is generally impaired before diluting power, although the reverse is occasionally true (pre-renal azotemia, acute nephritis).

Volhard introduced tests to determine *concentrating* and *diluting power* for clinical purposes. Many modifications (Lundsgaard, Fishberg) have been introduced. The reader is referred to texts on clinical pathology for details of these tests. Mosenthal proposed a test based upon variations in volume and specific gravity during the day and night. The subject receives regular meals during the test, but no fluid outside of that taken at meals. Urine is collected every two hours from 8 a.m. to 8 p.m. and a single specimen is collected the following morning, the sample comprising all urine formed between 8 p.m. and 8 a.m. Normally a specific gravity of 1.018 or greater should characterize one or more of the two hour specimens, and there should be a difference of not less than 0.009 between the maximum and minimum specific gravities observed. The volume of the night urine should be less than 750 cc.

UREMIA

This condition is characterized by abnormal retention of urinary constituents which then accumulate in the blood. A multitude of symptoms have been associated with uremia, but the essential feature necessary for the diagnosis is the increased level of non-protein nitrogen.

Some of the symptoms of uremia may be easily explained as resulting from the abnormally high concentrations of certain substances in the organism. It can be demonstrated that the concentration of phenols in plasma and cerebrospinal fluid is elevated in uremic patients with subjective symptoms. The depressive symptoms of uremia have been explained as a result of this phenomenon. Another explanation is found in reduced cerebral blood flow in acidosis. Nitrogen retention in itself apparently does not produce uremic symptoms. The essentially non-toxic nature of urea, uric acid, and creatinine has been demonstrated in experiments on animals, in which exceedingly high blood concentrations of these substances have been obtained by injection without eliciting signs of intoxication. Furthermore, acute nephritis may result in fairly high degrees of nitrogen retention without increases in the blood phenols and without uremic symptoms. The *xanthoproteic reaction* is a simple laboratory procedure which gives a rough estimation of the amount of phenols present.

Guanidine poisoning also produces many symptoms in common with those of uremia. Since uremic patients show retention of guanidine which is normally present in traces only, this substance has been investigated as a possible cause of the neuromuscular hyperexcitability in such patients. At present it can be stated that there is not proof that guanidine is responsible either wholly, or in part, for these symptoms.

Phosphate retention is a prominent feature as the failure of the kidneys progresses. As the phosphate concentration increases, a reduction in the concentration of ionized (and total) calcium is to be expected. These changes in phosphate and calcium levels occur almost invariably as kidney failure progresses toward the terminal stage, and the low calcium level undoubtedly is the major reason for the increased neuromuscular excitability in patients in an advanced uremic state. It is interesting that rather high phosphate concentrations may be present in plasma without a corresponding decrease in the calcium. This phenomenon may possibly be ascribable to secondary hypertrophic changes in the parathyroid glands, which changes can be demonstrated occasionally.

Clinicians frequently have the opportunity to observe that tetany is not always present in uremic patients with low plasma calcium concentrations which in other individuals would result in convulsions. It is possible that retained substances such as free phenols and magnesium ions, may have a sufficiently depressive effect on nervous excitability to counteract to some degree the usual effect of low levels of ionized calcium. Another factor is the state of acidosis which increases the degree of ionization of available calcium.

The disturbances in electrolyte balance which result from renal failure usually produce severe acidosis. In the advanced stage of uremia, coma may result partly from the depressant action of retained organic substances as described, but acidosis is responsible primarily. Comatose patients may be aroused temporarily by the intravenous injections of base forming substances, such as sodium lactate, which will increase the carbon dioxide combining power of the blood.

Uremic patients often suffer from persistent vomiting. The loss of chloride in excess of sodium in the vomitus is a factor in the low serum chloride concentration of these patients. The formation of ammonia in the kidneys, which is an important base-saving mechanism in the normal organism, gradually fails in the diseased kidney, resulting in relatively larger losses of sodium and other fixed bases by way of the urine. This contributes to the depletion of the alkali reserve.

It is common to find elevated blood urea concentrations in patients in the last few days of life, even if they have not previously suffered from kidney disease. Some of these patients exhibit hydropic degeneration of tubular tissue which may be a contributing factor to the azotemia. Low blood pressures in extremely ill patients cause decreased renal blood flow which results in a lowered glomerular filtration rate until tubular reabsorption is practically equal to glomerular filtration. The decreased flow of blood may also cause anoxia, which in turn brings about pathological changes in the renal tissue.

Azotemia is observed frequently after sudden hemorrhage in the gastrointestinal tract. The increase in non-protein nitrogen may be partly derived from digestion of the blood, but other factors such as shock, dehydration, and low blood pressures probably enter into the picture.

EDEMA

Edema may be produced in several ways, namely (1) reduction in osmotic pressure of plasma; (2) changes in blood pressure in the capillaries; (3) increased capillary permeability, and (4) obstruction in the lymph channels.

Clinicians are concerned mainly with edema of cardiac or renal origin, the differential diagnosis often being a major factor in the treatment of the patient. From a physiological standpoint such sharp differentiation cannot be made.

From the middle of the last century until approximately 30 years ago the theory of 'backward' failure in cardiac insufficiency was accepted generally. Since then the concept of 'forward' failure has arisen, newer experimental data being elicited in favor of the latter theory and against the older school. In spite of extensive investigation the conflicting viewpoints have not been brought into harmony. The 'backward' failure theory has been supported by observations on isolated heart-lung preparations which demonstrated the accumulation of blood on the venous side of the system in analogy with obvious events in the patient with heart failure. The "backward failure' theory does not explain the harmful effect of salt in the edematous patient.

The 'forward failure' concept postulates a decrease in cardiac output to a point below that demanded by the activities of the organism. This may result in reduction in renal blood flow and glomerular filtration. In 1944 Warren and Stead found that fluid retention preceded the elevation of venous pressure. They postulated that cardiac edema appears as the result of a deficit in sodium excretion leading to retention of water with resultant increase in volume of extracellular fluid and increased venous pressure. Measurements have confirmed the inability of patients in cardiac failure to excrete excessive or even normal amounts of ingested salt. According to these viewpoints cardiac edema becomes fundamentally the result of inability of the kidneys to excrete sodium in amounts sufficient to balance the intake. Factors pertaining to simple mechanical failure of the heart must be added to the above viewpoints in order to explain the predisposition to pulmonary edema. The concept of forward failure visualizes the following order of events in congestive heart failure: (1) decreased cardiac output; (2) decreased excretion of salt by the kidneys; (3) increased blood volume; (4) formation of edema; (5) elevation of venous pressure. It seems established that sodium retention is a primary factor in the mechanism of formation of edema but many observations remain unexplained by the simple theory of insufficient cardiac output. Decreased renal blood flow and glomerular filtration are observed in patients with chronic glomerulonephritis, essential hypertension, and in shock without the appearance of edema. Primary sodium retention should be reflected in an elevated, or high normal, concentration in the serum during development of failure. Such is not the case. These patients frequently have low or low normal, sodium levels. Cardiac edema may develop and disappear without any significant alteration in renal blood flow and glomerular filtration. However, whatever the mechanism, sodium retention is unquestionable. Absolute proof of decreased glomerular filtration of sodium in edematous patients is lacking. Many workers believe that the phenomenon is ascribable to alterations in tubular reabsorption.

The 'forward failure' theory implies that cardiac decompensation is a manifestation of the inability of the heart to satisfy metabolic requirements. Increased metabolic demands may produce a picture similar to that of myocardial failure, thyrotoxicosis illustrating such a situation. Under such demands cardiac output may be normal or above normal and still be below requirements. Anemia is another condition in which demands may outstrip cardiac ability with resulting failure.

Reduction of osmotic pressure resulting from hypoproteinemia is the important mechanism in the nephrotic syndrome. The edema usually appears when there is a large loss of protein in the urine, indicating that this is the major cause of the deficiency in the plasma. Defective synthesis of proteins may also be a factor. Nephrotic edema is most apparent in dependent tissues but all tissues exhibit increased amounts of extracellular fluid. Nephrosis is a syndrome appearing commonly in an intermediate stage during the development of chronic glomerulonephritis, being frequently the first clinical indication of previous acute damage to the kidneys. In a majority of cases some of the characteristics of the nephrotic state are retained in the further development of kidney disease toward a diffuse, chronic glomerulonephritis. Obviously the antiquated notion of using low protein diets in nephrosis further tends to aggravate the condition. Anorexia is frequently responsible for a patient's failure to compensate for the loss of protein in the urine, a vicious circle being established by the edema of the stomach and small intestine reducing the appetite. In many patients with nephrotic edema the daily urinary loss of protein is not large and the daily intake of protein in the diet appears to be adequate to compensate for losses. Even so the hypoproteinemia may persist and often remains at a relatively constant level. This is particularly true in patients who have progressed into chronic glomerulonephritis. Details of the reaction of edema to protein concentration in the plasma have been discussed in Chapter 4.

It has already been mentioned that a toxic reaction involving the capillary walls may produce edema. Such a mechanism may well be contributory to the edema of acute nephritis.

GLOMERULO-NEPHRITIS

This condition is characterized by an inflammatory process in which the glomeruli primarily are affected. Clinicians recognize acute and chronic forms of the disease, and they also recognize a transition or latent period between the acute and chronic stages.

Attacks of acute glomerulo-nephritis may vary considerably in their severity. During the acute stage, evidence of an inflammatory reaction in the kidney is evidenced by variable degrees of albuminuria and hematuria. Edema is a common symptom. The urea clearance reveals impairment of renal function. Patients in whom acute kidney disease subsides with apparent eventual recovery usually exhibit nitrogen retention to a lesser degree than do those with chronic nephritis. In most cases the urea nitrogen concentrations do not exceed 40 mg. per 100 cc. at any time. Other substances may be retained; the creatinine level of the blood seldom increases to more than 2 mg. per 100 cc.

Glomerulo-nephritis may be limited to a single acute attack with complete, or almost complete recovery of kidney function. However, many patients develop a chronic form of the disease as a result of repeated acute attacks or of progressive pathological changes initiated by the acute attacks. The state between the acute and chronic phases of the disease may occupy a long time. During the latent stage, the urine frequently shows evidence of inflammatory activity by mild hematuria and the presence of casts. During this period the loss of albumin is usually too slight to result in a plasma protein deficit. Many of the plasma constituents remain at approximately normal concentrations, although concentration tests and urea clearances may continue to reveal some impairment of renal function.

The chronic stage of glomerulo-nephritis is characterized by progressive impairment of kidney functions, eventually resulting in uremia. The loss of plasma protein in urine may vary considerably; large losses are common in the early stages of chronic glomerulonephritis, while the disease still shows many of the characteristics of acute nephritis. Edema is a prominent feature. As a matter of fact, patients with acute nephritis, who have very low concentrations of plasma albumin during the acute attack are more apt to progress into a chronic type of the disease than those patients in whom albuminuria and plasma protein deficit are less severe. As chronic glomerulo-nephritis proceeds toward its terminal stage, the albuminuria becomes less pronounced and may even disappear entirely. The decreasing loss of protein in the urine results in an elevation of plasma albumin toward normal levels, resulting in disappearance of the edema. As the disease progresses, the failure of the kidneys becomes more and more apparent because of the increased retention of the various substances. The biochemical chain of events resulting from the progressive failure of the kidneys has been discussed under uremia.

As the kidneys lose more and more the ability to function, increases of non-protein nitrogen to above 200 mg. per 100 cc. are common. The urea nitrogen constitutes by far the major portion of the retained NPN. Creatinine usually is not retained in quite the same proportion as the NPN although its level in advanced chronic nephritis may well exceed 15 mg. per 100 cc. Patch and Rabinowitch have pointed out that retention of nitrogen because of obstructive lesions in the urinary tract may be associated with relatively smaller increases in blood creatinine concentrations than are seen in intrinsic renal disease with comparable nitrogen retention. This feature is usually not regular enough to be of aid in the differential diagnosis of obstructive versus intrinsic renal disease.

NEPHROSIS

This class of renal disease includes a number of conditions in which the characteristic pathological changes consist of degeneration of the tubular epithelium as the dominant feature. The lesions may vary widely in severity and duration; the nephrotic syndrome may be the sole or preponderant manifestation of the patient's illness or it may be part of a more generalized disease, such as the acute and chronic forms of glomerulo-nephritis, amyloidosis, obstructive jaundice, vascular degeneration in diabetes, poisoning by chemicals (mercury, lead, arsenic, or organic solvents), fevers, toxemias of pregnancy, and other causes which cannot always be defined.

The rapidity of the degenerative process may determine the biochemical characteristics of the disorder. Proteinuria is always part of the symptom complex, in most cases being severe and resulting in depletion of the plasma proteins and in marked edema. The nephrotic syndrome is not characterized by azotemia unless the nephrosis is part of some other disorder such as glomerulo-nephritis which is responsible for the nitrogen retention. If degeneration of the tubular tissues proceeds rapidly, as in severe mercurial poisoning, kidney function may be impaired to the point of anuria, which, if not relieved promptly, develops into uremia and results in death. In such cases the proteinuria may be mild and is not the cause of edema. The plasma of nephrotic patients generally shows a high content of lipids especially of total cholesterol.

Lipoid nephrosis is characterized by proteinuria, hypoproteinemia, edema, hyperlipemia, hypercholesterolemia and excretion of abnormal amounts of cholesterol (cholesterol esters) in the urine. Hematuria, azotemia, and hypertension are absent, distinguishing the disorder from the nephrotic phase of an active nephritic process. Lipoid nephrosis is a disease of young individuals. A fatal outcome is usually attributable to intercurrent infections, particularly pneumococcal peritonitis. The cause of the malady has been ascribed to metabolic disturbances or to tubular degeneration as a specific reaction to some unknown toxin. The etiology is still obscure. Epstein, Mirsky, and others have shown abnormalities in the chemical nature of the protein in both urine and plasma, but it cannot be determined at present if these abnormalities are related to etiological factors, or are relatively inconsequential sequelae of a primary cause.

The reason for the concentration of plasma lipids is not understood; it is probably not based on any primary interference with normal utilization. Possibly there is some interference with fat transportation; a large proportion of patients show a higher-than-average content of plasma cholesterol esters.

HYPERTENSIVE KIDNEY DISEASE

People approaching death as the result of hypertensive disease practically always have pathological changes in the arterioles of the kidneys. The gradually developing sclerotic changes in the renal arterioles in essential hypertension are seldom the cause of death because some acute episode in the brain or heart usually terminates life before renal failure becomes marked. In a certain number of cases, however, rapidly progressing changes characterized by a superimposed necrotizing process in the arterioles occur. This stage is referred to as malignant hypertension (malignant nephrosclerosis), and is responsible for most of the deaths from kidney failure in hypertensive disease. Approximately 7 to 8 per cent of all deaths due to hypertensive disease are caused by renal failure.

In the benign type of nephrosclerosis, the urine usually contains small amounts of protein. Increasing degrees of albuminuria and of edema, if present, are more often attributable to cardiac failure, and tend to regress upon appropriate treatment of the heart. Proteinuria is seldom of such severity that a deficit of plasma protein develops. The urine frequently contains casts and a relatively small number of red cells. Phenolsulfonphthalein excretion may show some decrease in clearance, this probably being caused by a reduction in the renal blood flow rather than by tubular damage. Changes in the volumes of the day and night urine are likely to occur, there being a relative increase in the volume excreted during the night. If this is attributable to cardiac failure the night urine may be comparatively concentrated while if renal failure is predominating it will be dilute. For all practical purposes essential hypertension may be long standing and may result in advanced damage to the brain or heart before changes in the kidneys occur to the point of failure.

The malignant phase of essential hypertension shows a very different set of phenomena. As a result of the rapidly progressing necrotizing process in the arterioles, the proteinuria and hematuria may be severe. Elimination of waste products in the kidneys slows down and the patient dies in uremia or from hemorrhage in the brain prior to the uremic stage.

OTHER KIDNEY DISORDERS

Failure of renal function may result from a number of diseases not previously discussed.

Pyelonephritis is frequently difficult to differentiate from glomerulonephritis. The condition may exist over a long period of time with progressive destruction of renal parenchymal tissue. Ultimately the patients may die in uremia. Often these patients exhibit a remarkable ability to carry on their daily routine long after failure of kidney function is evident by azotemia and lack of concentrating ability.

Polycystic disease is a congenital disorder but the patients as a rule live many years before renal impairment becomes obvious. Because of the slow development of functional failure, hypertension and cardiac enlargement become prominent before death occurs. The patients commonly suffer from proteinuria and hematuria and eventually develop azotemia and uremia. In well developed cases renal arteriosclerosis is frequently present, so that the clinical picture may be one of arteriolar nephrosclerosis in addition to the changes of function to be expected from the cystic destruction of renal parenchyma.

Urinary calculi in the renal pelvis may occasionally be large enough to destroy the function of a kidney. Space is too limited in this book to go into details of the various theories as to the formation of calculi and of the therapeutic measures based upon the composition of the stones. Urinary calculi are rarely 'pure' stones, but usually contain several of the common components of calculi. As a rule, one component is present in predominant amount, permitting classification of the stone as a guide to possible therapeutic measures. Uric acid and urates, calcium oxalate, phosphates, and calcium carbonate are common stone constituents. Calculi may also contain cystine and xanthine, but stones containing these subtances are not often found.

SUPPLEMENTARY READING

Austin, J. H., Stillman, E., and Van Slyke, D.D.: Factors governing the excretion rate of urea. *J. Biol. Chem., 46:*91, 1921.

Beyer, K. H.: Functional characteristics of renal transport mechanisms. *Pharmacol. Rev., 99:*227, 1950.

Bloom, W. L., and Seegal, D.: The nephrotic phase; its frequency of occurrence and its differential diagnostic value in determining the nature of the renal lesion.in 120 patients who died of renal failure. *Ann. Int. Med., 25:*15, 1946.

Chapmen, E. M.: Further experience with the fractional 'phthalein test. *N. England J. Med., 214:*16, 1936.

Fishberg, A. M.: *Hypertension and Nephritis.* Lea & Febiger, 1939.

Gamble, J. L.: *Chemical Anatomy, Physiology and Pathology of Extracellular Fluid.* Harvard University Press, 1950.

Goldblatt, H.: Studies on experimental hypertension: V. The pathogenesis of experimental hypertension due to renal ischemia. *Ann. Int. Med., 11:*69, 1937.

Goldring, W., and Chasis, H.: *Hypertension and Hypertensive Disease.* The Commonwealth Fund, 1944.

Miller, G. E.: The role of water and salt in the development of heart failure. *New York State J. Med., 51:*1725, 1951.

Möller, E., McIntosh, J. F., and Van Slyke, D. D.: Studies of urea excretion. II. Relationship between urine volume and the rate of urea excretion by normal adults. *J. Clin. Invest., 6:*427, 1928.

Page, I. H.: A method for producing persistent hypertension by cellophane. *Science, 89:*273, 1939.

PATCH, F. S., and RABINOWITCH, I. M.: Urea and creatinine contents of the blood in renal disease. A statistical analysis of five thousand observations. *J.A.M.A., 90:*1092, 1928.

RICHARDS, A. N.: Processes of urine formation. *Proc. Roy. Soc., London, S.B., 126:*398, 1938.

ROWNTREE, L. G., and GERAGHTY, J. T.: An experimental and clinical study of the functional activity of the kidneys by means of phenolsulfonphthalein. *J. Pharmacol. & Exper. Therap., 1:*579, 1910.

SHANNON, J. A.: Renal tubular excretion. *Physiol. Rev., 19:*63, 1939.

Seminar on Renal Physiology. *Am. J. Med.,* The American Journal of Medicine, Inc., 1950.

SMITH, H. W.: *The Physiology of the Kidney.* Oxford University Press, 1937.

SMITH, H. W.: The application of saturation methods to the study of glomerular and tubular function in the human kidney. *J. Mt. Sinai Hosp., 10:*59, 1943.

SMITH, H. W., GOLDRING, W., and CHASIS, H.: The measurement of the tubular excretory mass, effective blood flow and filtration rate in the normal human kidney. *J. Clin. Investigation, 17:*263, 1938.

THORN, G. W., Physiologic considerations in the treatment of nephritis. *New England J. Med., 229:*33, 1943.

VAN SLYKE, D. D.: The effect of urine volume on urea excretion. *J. Clin. Investigation, 26:*1159, 1947.

WARREN, J. V., and STEAD, E. A., JR.: Fluid dynamics in chronic congestive heart failure. *Arch. Int. Med., 73:*138, 1944.

WELLEN, I., WELSH, C. A., TAYLOR, H. C., JR., and ROSENTHAL, A., The filtration rate, effective renal blood flow, tubular excretory mass and phenol red clearance in specific toxemia of pregnancy. *J. Clin. Investigation, 21:*63, 1942.

Chapter 12

THE HYPOPHYSIS

T HE various functions of the 'master gland' have been studied by performing total hypophysectomies on animals, and subsequently observing effects of replacement therapy with various fractions of extracts of the gland. The recognition of the specific effects of the several hormones has not been determined by use of hormones in chemically pure form, but rather by use of partially purified preparations. If a preparation can be shown to correct one special defect of those produced by hypophysectomy without significant improvement of others, it can be assumed that the preparation contains a single hormone. Because of sharp physiological distinctions between hormones of the anterior and posterior lobes of the gland and also in their anatomical origins, it is most convenient to consider the hormones involved in these two parts separately.

ANTERIOR PITUITARY HORMONES

Some of the anterior pituitary hormones have been isolated in forms which satisfy criteria for pure proteins; they are adrenotropic, lactogenic, growth, luteinizing, and follicle-stimulating hormones. The thyrotropic hormone has been obtained in a highly purified form but has not been isolated as a pure protein. Extracts of the anterior lobe possess properties indicating other specific hormonal effects which, however, cannot be linked at present to isolated substances.

The pituitary hormones all are assayed by the specific therapeutic response in hypophysectomized animals. The *adrenotropic hormone* may be determined by its ability to re-establish the normal anatomical appearance of the fasciculata, the reticularis, and the normal distribution of lipid deposits in the adrenal cortex. Maintenance of the weight of the adrenal glands of hypophysectomized rats by injection of pituitary extract over a period of time has been used in quantitative assays. The adrenotropic hormone has a specific action on the adrenal cortex, although hypertrophy of both the cortex and medulla has been observed in acromegaly and pituitary basophilism. Pituitary cachexia is associated with adrenal atrophy. The injection of the adrenotropic hormone in large doses into hypophysectomized animals leads to hypertrophy of the adrenal cortex.

The secondary effect of the adrenotropic hormone on the thymus is interesting because, although administration of the hormone tends to produce atrophy of the thymus, this effect is not observed in hypophysectomized and adrenalectomized animals. The changes in the thymus apparently do not result from the action of steroid sex hormone-like substances, which are normally secreted by the adrenal cortex, because administration of the adrenotropic hormone in large quantities to animals from which the gonads have been removed will produce hypertrophy of the adrenal cortex with simultaneous atrophy of the seminal vesicles and the prostate.

Upon administration of single doses of adrenotropic hormone, the content of cholesterol and ascorbic acid in the adrenal cortex diminishes. Continued administration results in larger deposits of lipids. Possibly these lipid particles represent cortical steroid hormones or their precursors which may be cholesterol. Adrenotropic hormone appears to stimulate production of the hormones having an oxygen at the C_{11} position, the other cortical steroid hormones not being affected.

Adrenotropic hormone influences growth in young animals. The results of administration of the pure growth hormone to hypophysectomized animals are reduced if the adrenotropic hormone is administered simultaneously. This retarding action is strikingly demonstrated by atrophic changes in epiphyseal discs.

The demonstration of a *lactogenic hormone* in the anterior lobe of the pituitary gland was accomplished by Riddle, who named this hormone *prolactin*. The biological activity of a given preparation of the lactogenic hormone is measured by injecting it into immature pigeons. This method is based on Riddle's observation that the lactogenic hormone is capable of stimulating the development of the crop glands. Formerly it was assumed that milk secretion was under functional control of sex hormones and that the development of the mammary glands during and after pregnancy was determined by a disturbance in the balance between the two groups of ovarian hormones. However, it has been shown subsequently that normal lactation does not take place in the absence of the hypophysis, unless extracts of the anterior lobe are injected. The lactogenic hormone appears to stimulate milk secretion in glands which are already developed for this purpose, but the pure hormone does not bring about complete development of the glands in hypophysectomized animals.

The lactogenic hormone has a specific tropic action on the function of the corpus luteum because the injection of the hormone into normal female animals will prolong the lutein phase of the vaginal cycle.

The *growth hormone* of the anterior pituitary gland has been isolated as a pure protein. Abundant evidence has been available for many years that the anterior lobe of the pituitary gland influences skeletal growth. Many clinical and post-mortem examinations on man have demonstrated anatomical changes in the gland in such conditions as giantism, dwarfism, and acromegaly. Also, many experiments on animals have demonstrated the growth pro-

moting properties of anterior pituitary extracts when these have been injected into normal or hypophysectomized animals. Growth retardation associated with hypofunction of the so-called target organs for the pituitary
gland (thyroid and adrenal glands, and the gonads) is a well known phenomenon, and it might be surmised that lack of growth in a hypophysectomized
animal may be caused by secondary atrophic changes in these target glands.
That this is not the case can be demonstrated easily, because injection of the
corresponding hormones from these glands will not stimulate growth except
possibly to a small degree, and certainly not to a degree comparable to that
instituted by administration of the pure growth hormone.

The growth hormone can be measured by observing its effect on the width
of the epiphyseal cartilage of hypophysectomized rats injected with this hormone. The hormone also stimulates the formation of protein in the organism
as evidenced by retention of nitrogen. This hormone is not the only anterior
pituitary hormone which influences growth; when immature pigeons are
used to standardize preparations of the lactogenic hormone it is observed
that it has also a stimulating effect on growth. However, the mechanism of its
action seems to be of a different nature because the growth stimulating properties of the lactogenic hormone are not observed in hypophysectomized
mammals.

The growth hormone is assumed to be elaborated by the acidophilic cells;
giantism and acromegaly are frequently observed in patients with acidophilic cell tumors. The content of the growth hormone in the pituitary gland
does not diminish after full growth has been attained but the function of the
hormone in the adult organism is not understood.

The *gonadotropins* of the anterior pituitary gland have been shown to
consist of *luteinizing hormone,* or *interstitial-cell-stimulating hormone*
(ICSH) and the *follicle-stimulating hormone* (FSH). Selye discovered that
certain cells of the follicles in hypophysectomized animals undergo characteristic changes and he called these 'deficiency' or 'wheel' cells. Hypophysectomized male animals show similar changes in the Leydig cells. The wheel
cells are restored to their normal appearance by the injection of extracts of
the anterior pituitary lobe. The injection of FSH into a hypophysectomized
male rat will maintain the seminiferous epithelium. This action is also obtained by the use of ICSH, although this hormone can be shown in the hypophysectomized female to be distinctly specific for maintenance of interstitial
tissue. The ability of ICSH to maintain the seminiferous epithelium is
thought to be a secondary result of the increased secretion of testosterone,
which is brought about by the stimulation of the Leydig cells by the pituitary hormone. Certain methods for the quantitative estimation of ICSH are
based on observations ascribable to the increased secretion of testosterone
through the above mechanism. Other methods of assay depend upon the
stimulating action upon the female sex glands to produce estrus. In order to

bring about the uterine response, the animal must be given FSH simultaneously with ICSH, but containing an amount of FSH insufficient to initiate estrus by itself.

The urine of pregnant subjects possesses gonadotropic properties which are responsible for the biological phenomena on which the *Aschheim-Zondek* and *Freidman tests* depend. Originally it was thought that the gonadotropic properties were exerted by anterior pituitary hormones in the urine, but Collip and his associates have shown that the urinary gonadotropic substance is identical with the gonadotropic substance of the placenta. It is referred to as *chorionic gonadotropin* or *anterior-pituitary-like* (A.P.L.) *substance.*

The anterior pituitary lobe elaborates a *thyrotropic hormone.* Following hypophysectomy, animals show atrophic changes in the epithelium of the thyroid vesicles and collections of colloid in the manner characteristic of the hypothyroid state. Upon injection of the thyrotropic hormone, the flattened epithelium changes to low cuboidal cells which tend to become columnar upon prolonged treatment. At the same time reabsorption of the colloid occurs. The administration of a thyrotropic hormone in excessive amounts produces signs of hyperthyroidism, decreasing the iodine content simultaneously. Anderson and Evans demonstrated in experiments on rats injected with thyrotropic hormone, that a sufficient intake of iodine could prevent increases in metabolic rate in spite of the hyperplasia produced by the pituitary hormone. The symptoms of hyperthyroidism following injection of the thyrotropic hormone cannot be elicited in the absence of the thyroid gland.

Various observations suggest that the anterior pituitary lobe secretes a substance with a specific influence on the parathyroid glands. This hypothetical substance is referred to as the parathyrotropic hormone. The most serious objection to the assumption of the existence of this hormone may be found in the fact that hypophysectomy, even in growing animals, does not change calcium metabolism, although it has been reported that diminution of epithelial cells of the parathyroids occur in association with hypopituitarism. The calcium level of the serum remains unchanged after hypophysectomy but hypercalcemia and parathyroid hyperplasia may result from the injection of anterior pituitary extracts. Simultaneous removal of the hypophysis and the pancreas has been observed to result in atrophy of the parathyroids and hypocalcemia.

Cushing's syndrome as seen in pituitary basophilism includes the development of osteoporosis. An association between the pathological changes in the hypophysis and the bone manifestations is not obvious because Cushing found degenerative changes rather than hyperplasia in the parathyroid glands, which might have explained the decalcification of the bones.

THE HYPOPHYSIS AND CARBOHYDRATE METABOLISM

The pituitary gland has been long recognized as playing a primary role in carbohydrate metabolism. Diabetes in patients with acromegaly was found as early as 1908 and later investigations have corroborated the importance of this gland in producing abnormal blood glucose levels.

Overactivity of the anterior pituitary lobe of the hypophysis results in hyperglycemia, glycosuria, and lower glucose tolerance. Underactivity of this gland caused by disease and by total surgical removal show opposite effects. A lowered blood sugar level is present in an adequately fed hypophysectomized animal and fasting produces a rapid hypoglycemia which may result in death.

There are two possible explanations of the extreme hypoglycemia in the fasting hypophysectomized animal: (1) that utilization of glucose is increased beyond the capacity of the liver for gluconeogenesis; or (2) that sugar formation from non-carbohydrate precursors is decreased until sugar is inadequate even for normal use. A choice between these two explanations involves clarification of the role of the peripheral tissues in sugar utilization. Soskin and his associates, by injecting known amounts of glucose in eviscerated hypophysectomized and non-hypophysectomized dogs, obtained data on the rate of glucose consumption by the extra-hepatic tissues, which utilized sugar at less than normal rates. Injection of pituitary extracts, which will restore glucose utilization to normal in hypophysectomized animals, had no effect on the utilization rate by the extra-hepatic tissues in the non-hypophysectomized dogs. They concluded that the lowered blood glucose levels shown by fasting dogs after hypophysectomy is "due to a decreased rate of hepatic gluconeogenesis, insufficient to meet even the reduced sugar utilization of the extrahepatic tissues" (Soskin and Levine: *Carbohydrate Metabolism*, p. 227, Univ. of Chicago Press).

Houssay and his co-workers reported studies on dogs with both pancreas and hypophysis removed. Diabetes in these animals was less severe than in depancreatized dogs. The same hypoglycemic effect of fasting is present in the Houssay dog as in the hypophysectomized animal and it is concluded that impairment in gluconeogenesis which causes the lowering of the blood sugar level in the latter, improves the diabetes in the Houssay dog.

The action of the anterior pituitary gland on the conversion of protein to carbohydrate is elucidated by protein feeding experiments upon hypophysectomized animals. Such animals can maintain or restore their blood glucose level if fed large amounts of protein, because these proteins enter the blood stream in the form of amino acids. The large stores of protein in the body, however, cannot undergo catabolism to the amino acid stage in the absence of the hypophysis. The breakdown of tissue protein is at least partly mediated through the thyroid gland, because blood sugar levels in fasting hypophysectomized dogs can be maintained at normal levels by continuous administration of thyroxin. The Houssay animal shows increases in blood sugar levels if protein is fed.

Hypophysectomized animals fed on a fat diet are unable to maintain their blood sugar levels as the fat enters the blood stream as neutral fat which does not differ from that which exists in the body tissue. Pituitary hormones are necessary for gluconeogenesis from fats. In depancreatized animals body fat is lost as fasting progresses because in such animals sugar is produced from both protein and fat. The Houssay animal is unable to utilize directly fat present in the tissues.

Hypophysectomized animals show an increased sensitivity to insulin, small amounts of insulin, which would show little effect in a normal animal, causing a prolonged or even fatal hypoglycemia. This may be due to: (1) failure of the liver to counter-regulate the insulin; (2) failure of tissues to inactivate insulin fast enough; and (3) lack of anti-insulin factor.

A number of experiments involving injections of anterior lobe extract free from thyrotropic hormone, have pointed toward the existence of a *pancreatropic hormone*. The effect consists of stimulation of islet and acinar tissue eventually followed by hydropic degeneration of the beta cells. The changes may result from additional demands for insulin, and the observations have not as yet proved the existence of the hormone. The presence of a true tropic hormone as described should cause atrophic processes in the islets of Langerhans following hypophysectomy. Such changes have not been observed.

POSTERIOR PITUITARY HORMONES

Extracts of the posterior lobe of the hypophysis (*pituitrin*) possess several functional properties.

Injections of such extracts cause stimulation of smooth muscle fibers in such organs as the gall bladder, urinary tract, intestine, and uterus (oxytocic effect). The action upon uterine fibers from virgin guinea pigs is used as a means of testing the potency of posterior pituitary extract. The excitation of smooth muscle is a direct hormonal effect which is exerted regardless of the sympathetic or parasympathetic innervation of the organ.

Posterior lobe extracts have a circulatory pressor effect, causing a rise in blood pressure by constriction of systemic arterioles and capillaries. Coronary constriction also takes place together with dilatation of the heart if large doses are given. The resulting weakening of the heart may account for the reduction in blood pressure which is observed occasionally upon repeated injection of the extract.

Pituitrin exerts a number of metabolic effects. Upon injection it produces hyperglycemia associated with reduction of stored liver glycogen. Pituitrin resembles epinephrin in its hyperglycemic action. Both will raise the blood glucose in depancreatized dogs treated with insulin. Withdrawal of insulin eventually abolishes the hyperglycemic effect, presumably because of exhaustion of the glycogen deposits. Pituitrin is antagonistic to the action of insulin, and in adequate doses is capable of preventing insulin shock. Pituitrin also increases the amount of fat in the liver, an effect which is rapid but of short duration. Protein metabolism is probably not influenced by hormones from the posterior lobe. A temporary drop in urea and creatinine clearance follow the injection of pituitrin; probably the pressor effect, rather than metabolic changes, is responsible. A general decrease in basal metabolic rates is observed during continued administration of pituitrin.

The color of the skin of a frog darkens considerably after injection of pituitrin. This is accomplished by a redistribution of pigments in the chromophore cells, a process which is under control of nerve impulses from the retina and mediated at least partly through a posterior pituitary hormone.

Pituitrin has a marked antidiuretic action which operates through increased tubular reabsorption of water. Tubular reabsorption of chloride is diminished resulting in increased elimination of chloride in the urine.

Pituitrin has been fractionated to yield two different substances of high potency. *Pitocin* is the fraction which exerts the oxytocic effect of the uterus, while *pitressin* appears to be responsible for the vascular, intestinal, and antidiuretic effects. Destruction of pressor and antidiuretic action does not progress at the same rate when pitressin is exposed to heat, a fact which indicates two separate structures in this fraction. The hyperglycemia produced by injection of pituitrin may be produced with either pitocin or pitressin; there is disagreement as to which one has the more pronounced effect. The hyperglycemia is accompanied by an increase in lactic acid in the blood.

Because of the antidiuretic effect of pituitrin, the proposal has been made that this substance be injected into patients with renal disease in order to determine the maximum concentrating ability of the kidneys. However, such tests do not uniformly produce high specific gravities, as do others such as the Addis concentration test. The disadvantage of the latter test is that the patient must be deprived of fluids for 24 hours.

DIABETES INSIPIDUS

Because of the similarity of symptoms of diabetes insipidus to those resulting from removal of the posterior lobe of the pituitary, it is commonly assumed that the manifestations of the former condition are ascribable to a hormonal deficiency. Total hypophysectomy does not produce diabetes insipidus; this points to the existence of a diuretic principle in the anterior lobe so that renal elimination of water is controlled by a balance between the two pituitary principles. The relief obtained in many cases by the injection of pituitrin or pitressin strongly supports the view that diabetes insipidus is a result of a posterior lobe deficiency and that these substances contain an antidiuretic principle or hormone (ADH).

Secretion of ADH appears to be constant. In this respect it differs from other endocrine secretions under nervous control. Quantitative variations in secretion are determined by the osmotic pressure (changes in sodium chloride concentration, etc.) of the arterial plasma. Verney used the term osmoreceptor for the cells which are selectively sensitive to these changes. These cells are connected with or located in the supraoptic and paraventricular nuclei from whence nerve fibers conduct impulses to the secretory cells of the neurohypophysis. Diabetes insipidus may result from injury to any part of the system, namely the nuclei, the nerve tract, or the neurohypophysis. Experimental injury to any of these parts produces clinical diabetes insipidus.

Various states increasing the osmotic pressure of the arterial plasma, such as dehydration or infusion of hypertonic salt solutions, are associated with the presence of demonstrable amounts of ADH in the normal urine. This finding is absent in diabetes insipidus.

ADH exerts its regulating effect on the kidney tubules, more particularly the distal part. More than 85 per cent of the water in the glomerular filtrate is absorbed in the proximal tubules and the loop of Henle. This is a passive process associated with reabsorption of sodium, bicarbonate, and chloride ions, the term 'obligatory reabsorption' being applied to this phase of water conservation. The additional reabsorption of water which takes place before the glomerular filtrate becomes bladder urine is called 'facultative reabsorption.' This is the function which is controlled by ADH. In contradistinction to the obligatory reabsorption, the facultative reabsorption is largely independent of movement of ions.

Experimental evidence implicates the thyrotropic hormone as the diuretic principle of the anterior lobe. Thyroidectomy tends to counteract the changes in renal excretion caused by experimental removal of the posterior lobe. Improvement from this type of surgery in human diabetes insipidus has not been demonstrated convincingly.

The amount of urine eliminated in diabetes insipidus may amount to as many as 20 liters in 24 hours. Such large quantities, of course, exhibit low specific gravities. The inability of the kidneys to concentrate salt in diabetes insipidus is paralleled by inability to concentrate urea. The blood urea tends to be lower than normal. The polyuria causes some increase in urea clearance because less than the normal fraction of urea of the glomerular filtrate is reabsorbed. This may be looked upon as a simple result of the handling of large volumes of fluid by the kidneys.

PITUITARY CACHEXIA (SIMMOND'S DISEASE)

This is a rare disease associated with degeneration of the anterior lobe of the hypophysis. The patients appear to be in a state of advanced senility.

Pituitary cachexia exhibits a number of metabolic changes. The basal metabolic rate drops considerably, and it is common to find BMR's below minus 40 per cent. The thyroid gland atrophies because of lack of thyrotropic hormone, but in contradistinction to thyroidectomized animals the hypopituitary subject shows extreme degrees of tissue wasting, explained by failure to take in adequate amounts of food. The hypothyroid state occasioned by primary pituitary deficiency has been called 'pituitary myxedema.' Carbohydrate tolerance is increased as well as sensitivity to insulin. The glucose tolerance curve has a flattened appearance quite similar to that seen in Addison's disease. The hypoglycemic tendency is undoubtedly brought about by several factors such as deficient absorption of carbohydrates from the intestinal tract, and failure of glycogenolysis and gluconeogenesis. The glycemic response to epinephrine is subnormal. The anorexia and malnutrition may reduce protein metabolism greatly. Because of the atrophic changes in both the gonads and the adrenals as a result of lack of the tropic hormones, the urine of patients with Simmond's disease is practically free from 17-ketosteroids.

The lack of gonadotropic stimulation causes decreased estrogen values in the blood and urine of the female, resulting in hypo- or amenorrhea and sterility. If a patient suspected of hypopituitarism exhibits normal or even increased amounts of gonadotropins the diagnosis falls in the group of primary hypogonadism.

The differentiation of *anorexia nervosa* from Simmond's disease may be difficult, the beneficial response to psychotherapy in the former being the best criteria upon which to base the diagnosis. The urinary excretion of pituitary gonadotropin and 17-ketosteroids generally is lower in pituitary cachexia but these values tend to be low enough in anorexia nervosa to be inconclusive. Patients suffering from anorexia nervosa often have low blood glucose concentrations and marked hypoglycemic responses to the insulin tolerance test. The hypoglycemia resulting from insulin tolerance tests is more severe in most cases of Simmond's disease but occasionally overlapping values are observed in anorexia nervosa.

DWARFISM

This condition is ascribed to lack of growth hormone as a result of destruction or congenital non-development of the acidophilic cells. The patients are usually fairly well proportioned with some tendency toward dimensional characteristics of childhood; they are generally undeveloped sexually. Abnormal metabolic phenomena are not as consistent as in Simmond's disease. The basal metabolic rate often is less than normal, but not invariably so. Carbohydrate tolerance varies, some patients showing tendency toward the flat glucose tolerance curve as seen in Addison's and Simmond's disease.

GIANTISM AND ACROMEGALY

These two conditions are ascribed to excessive formation of the growth hormone in acidophilic cell tumors. Giantism results if the condition occurs before ossification is complete while acromegaly is the response in the adult. Secondary hypertrophic or adenomatous changes in the adrenal, thyroid and parathyroid glands are common, and increased sexual function may occur early in the disease, subsequently developing into atrophy of the gonads.

The basal metabolic rate is usually elevated. The acromegalic patient often exhibits signs of diabetes which at times are difficult to control by treatment with insulin. The diabetes as judged by the blood sugar level is generally mild and occasionally clears up spontaneously. If the symptoms of diabetes become severe, the nitrogen excretion may increase considerably. Creatinuria has been reported in anterior lobe diseases, but it is not known if this is referable to a specific hormonal effect.

PITUITARY BASOPHILISM (CUSHING'S DISEASE)

In this syndrome obesity, involving the trunk but not the extremities, is a prominent feature. The skin shows pigmentation, and cyanosis of the face, hands, and feet is common. Other symptoms include purple striae over the abdomen, hirsutism, genital atrophy with sexual dysfunctions, osteoporosis, hypertension, and diabetes. The diabetes may be extremely resistant to treatment with insulin.

It is difficult to evaluate the role played by the other endocrine glands in Cushing's disease. The osteoporosis suggests overactivity of the parathyroids but post-mortem observations tend to disclose atrophic changes. It is also difficult to understand the genital atrophy. The relationship to the adrenal gland is of particular interest because hypertrophic changes in the cortex can produce the syndrome of basophilism. Cushing originally ascribed the various symptoms to adenomatous changes involving the basophilic cells, but small basophilic adenomas may be found without symptoms of basophilism. However, hyaline degeneration of the basophilic cells seems to be associated with the symptoms of Cushing's disease, although recent evidence disputes the necessity of these hyaline changes (Crooke's changes) as part of the development of the syndrome. All the symptoms of basophilism may well be explained by assuming these to be elicited by hypertrophic changes in the adrenal cortex resulting from primary pituitary disease. It cannot be assumed that 'functional hypertrophy' must be demonstrable by anatomical changes. Little doubt exists at present that physiological overactivity of endocrine glands may be present in cases where microscopic technique is inadequate to demonstrate changes.

The excretion of 17-ketosteroids and determination of the 3 (β)-alcoholic fraction in urine has been used in attempts to differentiate adrenal hyperplasia from adreno-cortical tumors. Excretion of more than 50 mg. of total 17-ketosteroids per day with a relatively large percentage (more than 50 per cent) of the 3 (β)-fraction is an indication of the presence of a cortical tumor. Occasionally tumors produce increases in the elimination of 17-ketosteroids which are only two to three times the average normal excretion, and without significant elevation of the 3 (β)-alcoholic fraction. Such assays, therefore, cannot always differentiate between tumor and hyperplasia.

Plasma protein changes are part of Cushing's syndrome. Low plasma albumin and γ-globulin levels have been reported, while corresponding changes in the plasma of patients with acromegaly did not occur. Also of interest are a few recorded cases of Cushing's syndrome in which adrenocortical hyperplasia could not be demonstrated, nor were any tumors present. These cases had low serum potassium levels and alkalosis. Improvement following administration of potassium salts, resulting in increases in the serum potassium level, were accompanied by changes in electrocardiographic patterns.

OTHER PITUITARY DISORDERS

Adiposogenital dystrophy (Fröhlich's disease), is characterized by obesity and failure of growth and of sexual development. The disease may occur either during childhood or adult life. The lesions responsible for this syndrome may involve both the anterior and posterior lobes of the pituitary gland. The syndrome is frequently accompanied by disturbances of carbohydrate metabolism, low basal metabolic rates, and diabetes insipidus. The *Laurence-Moon-Biedl syndrome* is a similar condition but is differentiated from Fröhlich's disease by polydactylism and retinitis pigmentosa.

SUPPLEMENTARY READING

Bodo, R. C. de, Bloch, H. I. and Gross, I. H.: The role of the anterior pituitary in adrenaline hyperglycemia and liver glycogenolysis. *Am. J. Physiol., 137*:124, 1942.

Cluxton, H. E., Jr., Bennett, W. A., Power, M. H., and Kepler, E. J.: Cushing's syndrome without adenomatous or hyperplastic changes in the pituitary body or adrenal cortices and complicated by alkalosis: Report of case with necropsy. *J. Clin. Endocrinol., 5*:61, 1945.

Collip, J. B.: Corticotropic (adrenotropic), thyrotropic, and parathyrotropic factors. *J.A.M.A., 115*:2073, 1940.

Evans, H. M.: Recent advances in our knowledge of the anterior pituitary hormones. *Am. Sc.,* Oct. 1947.

GAUNT, R., and BIRNIE, J. H.: *Hormones and Body Water.* American Lecture Series, Charles C Thomas, Publisher, 1950.

HOUSSAY, B. A., and BIASOTTI, A.: The hypophysis, carbohydrate metabolism and diabetes. *Endocrinology, 15:*511, 1931.

HOUSSAY, B. A.: The hypophysis and metabolism. *New England J. Med., 214:*961, 1936.

LONG, C. N. H., and LUKENS, F. D. W.: The effects of adrenalectomy and hypophysectomy upon experimental diabetes in the cat. *J. Exper. Med., 63:*465, 1936.

MIRSKY, I. A.: The influence of the anterior pituitary gland on protein metabolism. *Endocrinology, 25:*52, 1939.

NEUFELD, A. H., SCOGGAN, S. M., and STEWART, G. S.: The effect of pituitary preparations on the total body glycogen, water, nitrogen and fat of mice. *Endocrinology, 27:*132, 1940.

Pituitary-Adrenal Function. A symposium. *Am. A. Adv. Sc.,* 1950.

RIDDLE, O.: Lactogenic and mammogenic hormones. *J.A.M.A., 115:*2276, 1940.

RUSSELL, J. A.: The relationship of the anterior pituitary to the thyroid and the adrenal cortex in the control of carbohydrate metabolism. *Essays in Biology.* University of California Press, 1944.

SMITH, P. E.: Relationship of the anterior lobe of the hypophysis to other endocrine glands. Glandular Physiology and Therapy. *J.A.M.A.,* 1942.

SOSKIN, S., LEVINE, R., and HELLER, R. E.: Role of the thyroid in the carbohydrate disturbance which follows hypophysectomy. *Am. J. Physiol., 125:*220, 1939.

SOSKIN, S., MIRSKY, I. A., ZIMMERMAN, L. M., and CROHN, N.: Influence of hypophysectomy on gluconeogenesis in the normal and depancreatized dog. *Am. J. Physiol., 114:*110, 1935.

SOSKIN, S., LEVINE, R., and HELLER, R. E.: Carbohydrate utilization in the hypophysectomized dog. *Proc. Soc. Exper. Biol. & Med., 38:*6, 1938.

TAYLOR, R. D., PEIRCE, J. D., and PAGE, I. H.: Use of posterior pituitary extract in tests of urinary concentration. *Am. J. Med. Sc., 209:*235, 1945.

Chapter 13

THE THYROID

THE internal secretion of the thyroid gland is essential for normal growth and development of the young. Removal of the gland in young animals results in a striking decrease in metabolic rate, retardation of growth with delay in ossification of the epiphyses, and failure of sexual development. The hypothyroid state is characterized not only by apathy and mental deterioration at all ages, but also by many changes in metabolic processes.

THE THYROID HORMONE

An extract of the thyroid gland, if administered in proper amounts, can counteract the deficiencies produced by thyroidectomy. The active hormone is an iodine containing globulin, *thyroglobulin*. An active crystalline substance, *thyroxine*, was isolated from thyroid tissue by Kendall in 1916, who demonstrated that the substance had physiological properties similar to those of thyroid extracts. Thyroxine has subsequently been synthesized by Harington and Barger. Approximately 30 per cent of the iodine in the thyroid gland is present in thyroxine, the remainder being *diiodotyrosine*. The latter is inert physiologically but acquires the properties of the hormone when combined with protein. In the protein-conjugated forms thyroxine and diiodotyrosine appear to be of about equal physiological potency so that extracts of thyroid glands can be assayed by determination of their iodine content. The physiological activity of thyroglobulin is greater than the activity of its thyroxine content in the free form. Thyroxine is a 3, 5, 3', 5'-tetraiodo-p-hydroxyphenyl ether of tyrosine. The structural relationships between tyrosine, diiodotyrosine, and thyroxine are as follows:

TYROSINE   DIIODOTYROSINE   THYROXINE

Diiodotyrosine is probably the precursor for thyroxine. Radioactive iodine is rapidly incorporated into thyroglobulin, appearing first in diiodotyrosine, later in thyroxine, and diiodotyrosine is gradually converted to thyroxine in contact with slices of thyroid tissue. It is thought that thyroxine and diiodotyrosine are joined in peptide linkage with other amino acids in the thyroglobulin molecule. Many proteins can be iodinated and thereby produce compounds which resemble thyroglobulin in their physiological action. The thyroid is, therefore, not indispensable for normal metabolism, and it appears likely that lower animals without a thyroid gland may utilize dietary iodinated proteins as metabolic regulators.

METABOLIC EFFECTS OF THE THYROID HORMONE

The thyroid hormone catalyzes oxidative processes of the tissues. This action is exerted directly on the cells and is not mediated through the nervous system. Rate of oxidation in excised tissues is proportional to the metabolic rate of the animal at the time of excision; if the BMR has been increased in an animal by the administration of thyroid hormone, excised tissue will show an increased oxygen consumption.

Carbohydrate metabolism is influenced by the secretion of the thyroid gland. Patients suffering from abnormal thyroid states are apt to show abnormal blood sugar levels, such abnormalities being easily made apparent in glucose tolerance tests.

The rate of transfer of hexoses across epithelial tissues is dependent upon the action of the thyroid hormone, this effect presumably being exerted through regulation of the rate of phosphorylation, because the effect is noted mainly with substances which are readily phosphorylated. The dependence of hexose transfer upon thyroid activity is apparent in absorption from the intestinal tract and in tubular reabsorption of glucose in the kidneys.

Althausen and his associates have investigated absorption of hexoses in hypo- and hyperthyroid states, using the rate of assimilation of galactose from the intestinal tract as a diagnostic test to differentiate thyroid disease from other disorders producing increases in metabolic rates. The test consists of the oral administration of 40 grams of galactose and determination of the blood galactose levels 30, 60, and 120 minutes later.

In the normal individual the peak of the galactose concentration in the blood occurs in the 30 or 60 minute specimen and rarely exceeds 30 mg. per 100 cc., whereas in hyperthyroidism maximum concentrations frequently are two or three times as high. Althausen also found in cases of hypothyroidism, that the galactose concentration in blood is less than the average normal. Hepatic insufficiency may interfere with the metabolism of galactose and thus invalidate the galactose test. With normal liver function, the blood level of galactose returns to near zero at the end of two hours. In Paget's disease there is found an increase in the intestinal absorption rate of galactose which makes the test impossible to interpret in relation to thyroid activity. The abnormal blood galactose levels in hypo- and hyperthyroidism are not observed upon intravenous administration of galactose, indicating that the thyroid effect is exerted upon the absorptive process.

Because of increased cellular activity in the hyperthyroid state an increased rate of utilization of carbohydrates is to be expected. Hepatectomized dogs treated with thyroxine have an abnormally rapid rate of utilization of carbohydrate by the peripheral tissues, resulting in a decrease in blood glucose level which is much more rapid than in the untreated hepatectomized dog.

Abnormal thyroid states effect the glycogen stores in the body. Mild hyperthyroidism may have an insignificant effect, but severe hyperthyroidism depletes the glycogen stores both in the liver and in the skeletal and cardiac muscles. Epinephrine promotes liver glycogenolysis with resulting increase in the blood glucose level, this phenomenon being exaggerated in the hyperthyroid state except in those individuals with glycogen stores depleted as in a severely toxic process.

The postabsorptive blood glucose concentration in the hyperthyroid patient is usually normal or elevated slightly. A glucose tolerance test performed on such individuals tends to give a curve of the diabetic type, but the peak of the curve is lower than in the severely diabetic, nor is the period for the return to normal levels as prolonged, seldom persisting through the third hour. The hyperglycemia is associated with glycosuria which, however, is practically always mild. The glycosuria observed in uncomplicated hyperthyroidism is often distinguishable from that of diabetes mellitus by being intermittent and most prevalent following the morning meal.

Hypothyroidism has a less striking effect on carbohydrate metabolism. Delayed absorption of glucose from the gastro-intestinal tract seems to result in low blood glucose levels, and slow utilization may tend to delay the return of the blood glucose concentration to normal after carbohydrate ingestion.

Hyperthyroidism introduces a serious complication in the diabetic patient. Resistance to the action of insulin results (see Chapter 14) and may account for the ease with which such patients pass into ketosis. The exact relationship between the action of the thyroid hormone and of insulin is not understood, one explanation being that the thyroid hormone increases the tissue demands for carbohydrates which in the diabetic can only be satisfied by increased administration of insulin. According to Houssay and his associates it is possible to remove up to 95 per cent of the pancreas in thyroidectomized rats without producing diabetic symptoms or degeneration of the remaining islet tissue. Administration of thyroid extract in such animals promptly results in the development of diabetes.

Protein metabolism is accelerated by increased thyroid activity, this presumably being the result of increased demand for energy, because normal nitrogen balance can be maintained if the organism is fed adequate amounts of carbohydrates and fats to satisfy caloric requirements. In myxedematous patients the excretion of nitrogen and electrolytes following administration of the thyroid hormone is increased. The initial increase in electrolyte excretion comprises sodium salts preponderantly, followed subsequently by larger amounts of potassium. These findings indicate an early elimination of extracellular material, followed by cellular destruction. Such findings harmonize with the concept that protein concentrations in myxedematous extracellular fluid are much higher than in the normal.

The thyroid hormone stimulates gluconeogenesis. Soskin and his associates demonstrated that hypophysectomized dogs were able to maintain normal blood glucose levels upon administration of adequate amounts of thyroxine and that such treatment increased elimination of nitrogen. It has already been related in Chapter 12 that the thyroid hormone causes the breakdown of blood proteins to amino acids, since production of glucose from ingested amino acids proceeds normally in the absence of the thyroid hormone.

Components of the vitamin B complex participate in metabolic processes involving carbohydrate. Large doses of vitamin B complex may modify or counteract the effect of the thyroid hormone on the glycogen stores. Difficulties in the interpretation of results of administration of thyroid hormone to depancreatized animals may be explained if attention is given to the amount of vitamin B complex available to such animals.

Creatine usually occurs in amounts larger than normal in the urine of hyperthyroid patients. This has been interpreted as a result of muscular degeneration. In the normal subject, creatinuria can be induced either by the administration of thyroxine or the thyrotropic hormone of the hypophysis. Treatment with substances such as dinitrophenol may also cause creatinuria, but this condition is not found always accompanied by increased metabolic rates. Myxedematous patients as a rule do not eliminate creatine in the urine, but may do so after treatment with thyroid hormone.   •

Attempts have been made to interpret the excretion of ingested creatine as a diagnostic test in hyperthyroidism. A given amount of creatine (1 or 2 grams or the equivalent amount of creatine hydrate) is administered, and subsequently the concentration of creatine in the serum and the amount eliminated in the urine are determined. The hyperthyroid patient generally shows high serum concentration of creatine and increased elimination in the urine, but such tests are not sufficiently uniform in results to justify being used as routine laboratory procedures.

The concentration of the *lipids* in the plasma is affected by the activity of the thyroid. This applies particularly to *cholesterol* and *phospholipids*. Variations in the concentration of neutral fats have also been reported, but the findings are not consistent.

Cholesterol determinations are commonly employed as a diagnostic procedure in suspected thyroid disorders. Generally the hyperthyroid state is characterized by low blood cholesterol concentrations while the opposite is found in hypothyroidism, the latter being more consistently observed. These tests only corroborate other findings and are by no means diagnostic in themselves. Difficulty in the interpretation arises from the fact that the limits for normal blood cholesterol concentrations are not established with certainty (see under cholesterol in Chapter 6). Diagnoses either of hyperthyroidism in the presence of a high or high normal cholesterol, or of hypothyroidism in the presence of low cholesterol levels, should be made with great caution.

IODINE METABOLISM

The affinity of thyroid tissue for iodine is strikingly demonstrated by the administration of the radioactive element, the gland in a short time exhibiting radioactivity to a marked degree in comparison with other tissues. Hyperplasia of the gland increases the affinity for iodine. The thyroid gland normally contains approximately $\frac{1}{5}$ of the iodine in the body.

Iodine in the blood is largely in combination with protein which is the principal form in which iodine is excreted in the urine. The concentration of the protein bound iodine in the plasma shows a remarkable correlation with the activity of the thyroid and determinations of the iodine in the plasma proteins are of great aid in diagnoses related to thyroid disease. The content of this iodine normally is between 4 and 8 micrograms per 100 cc. Some patients showing distinctive signs of myxedema have plasma iodine levels of 3 to 4 micrograms, but generally the value is below 3 micrograms and occasionally drops to a fraction of a microgram. Hyperthyroid patients exhibit plasma iodine values from 8 to 35 micrograms, the level being roughly parallel to the severity of the disease. Facilities for plasma iodine determinations are available in relatively few clinical laboratories because of the technical difficulties in the analytical procedure.

The average content of iodine in the thyroid gland is approximately 2 mg. per gram of dried tissue, the total iodine in the gland being about 10 to 15 mg. The glands from hyperthyroid patients are comparatively deficient in iodine; in severe parenchymal disease the content may be as low as 0.25

mg. or less per gram of tissue. Upon administration of iodine to hyperthyroid patients, the content of this element in the thyroid gland increases and may become higher than normal. The low content in the thyroid in thyrotoxicosis is considered resulting from the gland releasing its hormone at an excessive rate. The primary reason for this is not known. Iodine administration, as stated above, increases the iodine content of the thyroid in hyperthyroidism, and a remission of the toxic symptoms occurs, resulting in a decrease in the metabolic rate. Clinical experiences have given the impression that the patient eventually becomes refractory to treatment with iodine and that thyroidectomy, therefore, must be done when the BMR reaches its minimum. Increase in toxic symptoms during iodine treatment, however, does not represent a truly refractory state to iodine because withdrawal of the medication is regularly followed by a further rapid increase in metabolic rate.

The affinity of hyperplastic thyroid tissue for iodine may be measured by an *iodine tolerance test*. Elmer originally used an intravenous test dose of 1300 micrograms of inorganic iodine and determined the amount of iodine excreted in the urine during a six hour period following the injection. Excretion in the normal subject ranges from 12 to 20 per cent of the injected iodine. In the hypothyroid state the amount of iodine eliminated is higher than these figures. Perkin and his associates have modified the test. They determine the iodine content of blood before the administration of 37 mg. of iodine (as Lugol's solution) by mouth, and subsequently determine the blood iodine levels every half hour for $2\frac{1}{2}$ hours. Normal subjects as well as those with non-toxic adenomatous goiter show higher iodine concentrations (up to 180 micrograms per 100 cc.) than do patients with hyperthyroidism. The latter have maxima around 40 micrograms per 100 cc.

Iodine is recognized as an essential dietary mineral. Colloid enlargement of the thyroid is endemic in areas where geological conditions have permitted iodides to be washed out of the soil. Normally the daily iodine intake should be approximately 50 micrograms. Iodine is present in drinking water, fruits, vegetables, meats, and many sea foods. Drinking water generally contains less than 2 micrograms of iodine per liter; in goiter districts this value may be as low as 0.2 micrograms or less. Iodized table salt is commonly employed prophylactically in the goiter belts in the United States.

The normal thyroid gland produces on the average 0.3 mg. of thyroxine daily. About $\frac{2}{3}$ of thyroxine is iodine so that the daily metabolic turnover of thyroid hormone iodine is about 0.2 mg. The greater portion of this iodine is used repeatedly in the synthesis of new hormone, the balance (approximately $\frac{1}{4}$) being excreted in the urine with traces present in the feces. Urinary and fecal excretion of iodine is increased in hyperthyroidism.

In recent years, *thiourea, thiouracil, propylthiouracil,* and many other derivatives of thiouracil have been known to effect a reduction or remission of the toxic manifestations of hyperthyroidism. They appear to inhibit the formation of thyroxine and of diiodotyrosine; an action which ceases upon discontinuation of the drugs. Thiouracil derivatives do not alter the action of injected thyroxine. The hypothyroid state produced by these drugs is associated with hyperplasia of the thyroid indicating that the drugs stimulate the secretion of the thyrotropic hormone in addition to blocking the production of the thyroid hormone. Administration of thiourea causes a considerable increase in the glycogen content of the liver of rats; this effect is not abolished by administration of thyroid extract in animals on controlled diets.

THYROID DISEASES

The general biochemical changes resulting from abnormal thyroid activity have been discussed in the preceding pages; the following pertains to the various clinical entities of thyroid disorders.

The term *goiter* implies an enlargement of the thyroid gland in the absence of acute inflammatory or neoplastic changes. Enlargement may be diffuse or nodular, and may occur in hypo- as well as hyperthyroidism.

Simple goiters exhibit enlargement without general constitutional manifestations. They may be characterized by parenchymal changes with epithelial cells of the high columnar type and very little colloid in the alveoli. Such glands may eventually undergo exhaustion atrophy with replacement of secretory with fibrous tissue. If the patient with parenchymatous goiter is treated with iodine the gland may change to the colloid type with large accumulations of colloid in alveoli lined with low cuboidal or flattened epithelial cells. The diffuse parenchymatous goiter has a very low iodine content while the colloid type has approximately a normal iodine content but decreased concentration because of the larger mass of glandular tissue.

Determinations of the relative distribution of individual amino acids in thyroglobulin have been made in the various types of goiters. The iodine content of thyroglobulin from colloid goiters is low. While approximately ½ of the iodine in the normal gland is in the form of thyroxine, the proportion of iodine in this form is much less in thyroglobulin from the colloid goiter. It has been found that in thyroglobulin there is usually an inverse relationship between the tyrosine and thyroxine and diiodotyrosine contents, while the proportion of other amino acids appears to be independent of the thyroid condition. Thyroglobulin from colloid glands contains 0.02 per cent thyroxine as compared to 0.32 per cent in the hormone from normal glands. Such findings corroborate the viewpoint that the essential biochemical defect in goiter is failure of tyrosine to be converted to diiodotyrosine and to thyroxine because of lack of iodine.

Cretinism is a condition brought about by deficiency of the thyroid hormone. It may be caused by atrophic changes in the thyroid gland in iodine-poor areas, or by other factors such as inflammatory destruction or congenital absence of the gland.

Severe thyroid deficiency in older children or adults results in *myxedema*. In such patients the basal metabolic rate is usually from minus 20 to minus 45 per cent, but a number of cases have been reported showing clinical symptoms of myxedema with basal metabolic rates between minus 5 and minus 20 per cent. However, this range includes also many subjects apparently far from metabolic disorders. The thickening of the skin in myxedema is not caused by a true edema. As related above administration of thyroid to myxedematous patients induces excretion of nitrogen and electrolytes, pointing to increased metabolism of extracellular material. These patients have low plasma volumes and high concentrations of protein in the plasma and spinal fluid. It has been suggested that the extracellular protein in myxedema has a greater osmotic effect than the body fluid proteins in general. Whatever the true explanation may be, the picture is that of a change in the normal hydrodynamic equilibrium between the fluids of the various body components. These changes are reversed upon administration of thyroid hormone.

It is recognized that there are degrees of hypothyroidism with constitutional symptoms of the hypothyroid state but without myxedema. Such patients frequently have basal metabolic rates around minus 20 per cent.

Clinical observations as well as animal experiments indicate that other dietary factors besides deficiency in iodine may have a bearing on the development of goiters. Cabbage and cauliflower have a goitrogenic effect on rabbits, which has been ascribed to the cyanogen content of these vegetables. Marine and his associates have produced experimental goiters in rabbits by administration of various cyanides. Cyanates and thiocyanates have a similar action. The once popular method of treating hypertension with thiocyanate has given many opportunities to study its action on the thyroid. Enlargement of the gland unaccompanied by toxic symptoms is a common complication of such treatment, and the gland recedes rapidly in size if thyroid hormone is administered while thiocyanate therapy is being continued. Thiocyanate given to a normal subject causes a decrease in metabolic rate. However, if thiocyanate is given to a hypothyroid patient maintained near normal with thyroid hormone, this effect cannot be obtained. Suggestions have been advanced that the goitrogenic action of the cyanides and cyanates is caused by these substances interfering with enzymic oxidation-reduction systems in the tissues and that enlargement of the thyroid gland is due to a compensatory effort to maintain normal rates of oxidation. The observations cited above, however, point to a primary mechanism operating through the thyroid gland or possibly through the secretion of the thyrotropic hormone.

The response in basal metabolic rates to administration of thyroid hormone is not quantitatively uniform under all conditions. The myxedematous patient responds to comparatively small doses of thyroid; therefore, the clinician who encounters patients with low basal metabolic rates which can be increased only with large doses of thyroid extract should question a diagnosis of hypothyroidism. In true myxedema the goal for thyroid therapy should be remission of clinical symptoms and not a normal basal metabolic rate.

The *hyperthyroid state* is characterized by complex symptoms including increased nervous irritability, accelerated heart action which may become complicated by auricular fibrillation and myocardial failure, changes in metabolic processes involving fats, proteins, and carbohydrates, general tissue wasting, and high rates of basal metabolism. Such patients also exhibit increased excretion of calcium and phosphorus, often resulting in osteoporosis. The increased elimination of phosphorus is beyond that which might be expected from the augmented catabolism of proteins. Somewhat elevated values of the alkaline phosphatase in serum of hyperthyroid patients have been observed. The picture resembles that of a concomitant stimulation of the parathyroids, but proof is lacking that such a mechanism is involved.

Hyperthyroidism may be associated with a diffuse enlargement of the gland or with a toxic adenoma. Approximately 20 per cent of adenomatous goiters undergo changes resulting in toxic symptoms. The exact etiological background for hyperthyroidism is still in doubt, especially for the factors which influence the development of exophthalmos. Plummer held the view that hyperthyroidism without exophthalmos is due to abnormal hormones deficient in iodine. Marine considers that exophthalmic goiters are produced by endocrine disturbances outside the thyroid gland. Hyperthyroidism can be induced easily in animals but this condition only rarely leads to exophthalmos. Another feature which tends to dissociate exophthalmos from the general symptom complex is the fact that the ocular manifestations do not regress upon treatment as do the other symptoms. Exophthalmos can be produced by injection of anterior pituitary extracts in thyroidectomized guinea pigs. Patients with exophthalmic goiters who have been treated successfully for their hyperthyroid symptoms may show excessive amount of thyrotropic hormone in the urine; this also points toward pituitary involvement either as a primary or secondary result of the thyroid disorder.

The effect of the thyroid hormone upon the heart muscle is direct and specific; it is not mediated through nerve connections. Other substances such as dinitrophenol, which will increase basal metabolic rates, do not have a comparable stimulating effect on the pulse rate, so that the increased demand for oxygen cannot be the only explanation for the tachycardia. Cardiac output and pulse rates fall more rapidly than the basal metabolic rate following thyroidectomy.

Thyroiditis is a rare condition. Only the chronic form in which fibrous replacement of glandular tissue takes place has any constitutional effects. When enough glandular tissue has been destroyed the patient develops the characteristic symptoms of hypothyroidism.

SUPPLEMENTARY READING

ALTHAUSEN, T. L., LOCKHART, J. C., and SOLEY, M. H.: A new diagnostic test (galactose) for thyroid disease. *Am. J. Med. Sc., 199*:342, 1940.

ALTHAUSEN, T. L.: The influence of the endocrine organs on intestinal absorption. *Essays in Biology*, p. 11, University of California Press, 1943.

ASTWOOD, E. B.: The chemical nature of compounds which inhibit the function of the thyroid gland. *J. Pharmacol. & Exper. Therap., 78*:79, 1943.

BYROM, F. B.: The nature of myxoedema. *Clin. Sc., 1*:273, 1934.

CAVETT, J. W., RICE, C. O., and McCLENDON, J. F.: Thyroglobulin studies. I. The thyroxine and iodine content of normal and goitrous human thyroglobulin. *J. Biol. Chem., 110*:673, 1935.

CURTIS, G. M., and FERTMAN, M. B.: Iodine in nutrition. *J.A.M.A., 139*:28, 1949.

DRILL, V. A., OVERMAN, R., and SHAFFER, C. B.: Carbohydrate metabolism. I. Effect of B vitamins on liver glycogen of thyroid-fed rats. *Endocrinology, 31*:245, 1942.

KENDALL, E. C.: The active constituent of the thyroid; its isolation, chemical nature, and physiologic action. *Collected Papers of the Mayo Clinic, 8*:513, 1916.

KIMBALL, O. P.: Iodized salt for the prophylaxis of endemic goiter. *J.A.M.A., 130*:80, 1946.

LeBLOND, C. P., and GROSS, J.: The mechanism of the secretion of thyroid hormone. *J. Clin. Endocrinol., 9*:149, 1949.

MARINE, D., BAUMANN, E. J., SPENCE, A. W., and CIPRA, A.: Further studies on etiology of goiter with particular reference to the action of cyanides. *Proc. Soc. Exper. Biol. & Med., 29*:772, 1932.

MEANS, J. H.: *The Thyroid and its Diseases*. J. B. Lippincott Co., 1948.

MEANS, J. H., GOLDSMITH, E. D., DeROBERTIS, E., DEMPSEY, E. W., SALTER, W. T., CHAIKOFF, I. L., TAUROG, A., McGINTY, D. A., ASTWOOD, E. B., LeBLOND, C. P., REINEKE, E. P., ALBERT, A., and RAWSON, R. W. Thyroid function as disclosed by newer methods of study. *Ann. New York Acad. Sc., 50*:279, 1949.

MIRSKY, I. A., and BROH-KAHN, R. H.: The effect of experimental hyperthyroidism on carbohydrate metabolism. *Am. J. Physiol., 117*:6, 1936.

RAWSON, R. W., and McARTHUR, J. W.: Radioiodine: Its use as a tool in the study of thyroid physiology. *J. Clin. Endocrinol., 7*:235, 1947.

SALTER, W. T.: *The Endocrine Function of Iodine*. Harvard University Press, 1940.

Soskin, S., Levine, R., and Heller, R. E.: Role of the thyroid in the carbohydrate disturbances which follow hypophysectomy. *Am. J. Physiol., 125*:220, 1939.

Soskin, S., and Levine, R.: Recent advances in physiology of the thyroid and their clinical application. *Arch. Int. Med., 74*:375, 1944.

Thorn, G. W.: Creatinine studies in thyroid disorders. *Endocrinology, 20*:628, 1936.

Tierney, N. A., and Peters, J. P.: The mode of excretion of creatine and creatinine metabolism in thyroid disease. *J. Clin. Investigation, 22*:595, 1943.

Chapter 14

THE PANCREAS

THE pancreas elaborates an external secretion, rich in enzymes which promote digestion of fats, proteins, and carbohydrates in the small intestine. The glandular alveoli resemble those of the salivary glands, the lining cells containing zymogen granules which become reduced in number after secretory activity. The Islands of Langerhans, which elaborate the internal secretion of the pancreas are groups of cells interspersed among the glandular alveoli.

THE EXTERNAL SECRETION

Pancreatic juice is alkaline, its pH ranging usually between 7 and 8. For details of the chemical processes whereby fats, proteins, and carbohydrates are digested and absorbed, Chapters 6, 7, and 8 should be reviewed. The following discussion will be limited to features of the digestive processes which are of most immediate concern to the medical practitioner.

Fats are brought into intimate surface contact with the fat-splitting enzymes, *pancreatic lipase,* or *steapsin,* through the emulsifying action of bile, dietary phospholipids, proteins and small amounts of soaps from the food. The term lipase should imply a number of enzymes, each of which exerts a catalytic effect upon specific configurations of the lipids. For example, the isolation of β-glyceryl-phosphoryl-choline from incubated beef pancreas has been reported. This is thought to be an intermediary product in the metabolism of lecithin produced by the action of a lecitho-lipase different from the lipase responsible for digestion of simple fats.

The rate of digestion of fats depends on their melting point. Emulsification proceeds slowly in the intestine unless the fat is liquid at body temperature. Fats containing saturated long chain fatty acids, therefore, are poorly digested.

Digestion of protein by pancreatic juice is mediated largely by the proteases, *trypsin* and *chymotrypsin* which are secreted as the inactive trypsinogen and chymotrypsinogen. The activation of both proenzymes in the intestinal tract is accomplished by the enzyme *enterokinase* of the intestinal juice. Trypsinogen may also be activated by ammonium or magnesium salts, by a slightly acid medium, or by digestion with trypsin. Trypsinogen is gradually converted to trypsin even upon standing in a neutral solution. Chymotrypsinogen differs from trypsin, and may be identical with pancreatic rennin.

Proteins appear to be digested completely to amino acids before being absorbed. Minute amounts of unaltered protein, however, are capable of penetrating the absorptive membranes. Demonstration of such unaltered absorbed proteins has been accomplished through serological procedures. Generalized allergic reactions to ingested proteins would be difficult to understand except on the basis of the unaltered sensitizing substance.

The physiological importance of gastric digestion is somewhat difficult to evaluate because protein digestion proceeds seemingly to completion in patients who secrete gastric juice devoid of pepsin and hydrochloric acid, provided pancreatic secretion is normal. Some intestinal digestion of proteins takes place even in the absence of pancreatic enzymes. Although ingested protein undoubtedly is absorbed in the form of amino acids, one cannot take for granted that complete break-down to the individual amino acids is prerequisite to absorption. Consideration of the action of the thyroid hormone when taken by mouth illustrates this point. Thyroxine is ineffective by oral administration, a fact which may be ascribed to its low solubility. Diiodotyrosine is also inert physiologically. However, administration of thyroglobulin by mouth to hypothyroid subjects reveals calorigenic effects which can be accounted for only if both the thyroxine and diiodotyrosine of thyroglobulin are active, indicating absorption of polypeptides which have not undergone complete digestion. It is unlikely that thyroglobulin itself can penetrate the mucosal lining.

As already mentioned trypsin can hydrolyze native protein. Normally its action is to split the proteoses and peptones formed by gastric digestion. The hydrolytic processes go through stages of polypeptides with eventual formation of tetra-, tri-, and dipeptides. These in turn are digested by peptidases.

Ingested carbohydrates undergo a partial break-down through the action of ptyalin of the saliva. Further hydrolysis may take place in the acid medium of the stomach. However, *amylase (amylopsin* or *diastase)* of the pancreatic juice is the most active agent in the intestinal hydrolysis of carbohydrate food. This enzyme hydrolyzes starch, dextrin, and glycogen to maltose, which subsequently is broken down to glucose by *maltase,* contained in the pancreatic and intestinal juices. Lactose and sucrose are hydrolyzed to monosaccharides by the action of *lactase* and *invertase* respectively, found in the succus entericus.

REGULATION OF EXTERNAL PANCREATIC SECRETION

The release of enzymes from the zymogen granules is controlled mainly by the vagus nerve. Excitation is initiated by the presence of proteins and fats in the intestinal tract. Acids in the intestine also have a secretagogue effect. Regulation of the volume of the pancreatic juice is under control of the hormone *secretin,* present in the intestinal mucosa in the form of *pro-*

secretin. Acid promotes the change of prosecretin to the active hormone. A purified preparation of secretin has been used intravenously to stimulate the pancreas to secrete in suspected pancreatic insufficiency, the response to the injection being determined by measurement of the activity of the duodenal contents withdrawn through a tube.

QUANTITATIVE DETERMINATION OF PANCREATIC ENZYMES

For clinical purposes digestive powers of pancreatic enzymes liberated into the small intestine are measured on fluid withdrawn from the duodenum. Trypsin may be determined by digestion under specified conditions of casein with 1 cc. of a diluted (1:50) solution of the duodenal contents. In McClure, Wetmore, and Reynold's method the normal values for nonprotein nitrogen, liberated from the casein, range from 7.5 to 15 grams per 100 cc. of fluid used. The same investigators measure amylolytic activity in duodenal contents by digesting starch with a 1 to 25 dilution of the fluid, determining the reducing carbohydrate formed as grams of glucose liberated per 100 cc. of original duodenal contents. Under the conditions of the test, normal values range between 2.5 and 5.0 grams. McClure and associates also developed a method similar in principle for the determination of lipolytic enzymes. At present this test is rarely employed. Many modifications of tests for pancreatic enzymes have been developed, all based on measuring the products of digestion of each of the enzymes on suitable substrates. For many practical purposes the clinician is interested in ascertaining only the presence or absence rather than the amounts of pancreatic enzymes in duodenal fluid.

Concentrations of serum amylase and lipase may increase in certain acute pancreatic disorders and estimations of their activities are of considerable diagnostic importance. Cherry and Crandall demonstrated that an olive oil splitting enzyme in the serum of dogs increased in concentration following obstruction of the pancreatic ducts. Comfort and Osterberg, as a clinical laboratory test, measured the fatty acid liberated by the action of 1 cc. of serum upon an olive oil emulsion under standard conditions. Normal values were equivalent to 0.2 to 1.5 cc. of 0.05 normal sodium hydroxide. In the Somogyi test for the amylolytic activity of plasma, normal values range between 60 and 180 units, 80 per cent of normal subjects falling between 80 and 150 units. These figures represent the amount of copper-reducing products, expressed as mg. of glucose, formed by the digestion of a standard starch solution per 100 cc. of plasma.

High plasma amylase concentration is responsible for large amounts of this enzyme appearing in the urine. Impairment of renal function may inhibit this excretion so that somewhat elevated values of plasma amylase may be observed in certain kidney disorders.

PANCREATITIS

This disorder may occur clinically as acute or chronic non-hemorrhagic pancreatitis, and acute hemorrhagic pancreatitis (acute pancreatic necrosis).

Acute non-hemorrhagic pancreatitis in its milder form has been recognized frequently in recent years. The disease does not require surgical treatment; early diagnosis is important because practically all other conditions from which acute pancreatitis must be differentiated, are surgical emergencies. Improved differential diagnostic procedures depend mostly upon determinations of pancreatic enzymes in the blood.

Serum amylase levels usually are markedly elevated shortly after the onset of acute pancreatitis. Values between 1,000 and 3,000 units as determined by the Somogyi method are common and they are practically diagnostic. The maximum values should not be accepted as an indication of the severity of the pathological process; the concentrations of serum amylase may fluctuate considerably during the course of the disease. Therefore, it is important that blood amylase determinations be made several times daily in suspected cases as a normal serum amylase does not rule out a diagnosis of pancreatitis. It has been stated already that Somogyi considers plasma amylase values between 60 and 180 as normal. Values slightly above 180 are probably of no particular significance. However, there is a range between the high normal limit and those in unquestionable cases of pancreatitis in which interpretation is difficult. Occasionally minor elevations occur in diseases of the salivary glands, or in disorders of the bile system. In the latter conditions elevations of the blood amylase concentration may be caused by mild secondary involvement of the pancreas. Uncomplicated biliary disease tends to produce blood amylase levels below the normal range. In many cases of acute pancreatitis, the blood amylase values may eventually become considerably less than normal; this may possibly be explained as an effect of pancreatic impairment associated with the pathological process. Elevations of blood amylase concentrations from renal impairment may be differentiated from those from pancreatic sources by determinations being made upon simultaneous specimens of blood and urine.

In pancreatic disease serum lipase concentrations are affected in a manner similar to those of the amylolytic enzyme. The normal lipase activity is low, the upper limit being expressed as 1.5 cc. of 0.05 normal sodium hydroxide, by the method described previously. In acute pancreatitis values as high as 10 cc. or more may be obtained. Fluctuations in blood levels of the lipolytic enzyme are not as marked as are those of amylase, and the return to normal values during recovery from the disease is slow.

The exact mechanism whereby pancreatic enzymes enter the blood stream in increased quantities during pancreatic disease is not known, possible explanations being that the enzymes pass into the lymph and blood by a retrograde process caused by rupture of parenchymal cells or by mechanical obstruction of the pancreatic ducts.

Acute non-hemorrhagic pancreatitis is usually of too mild and transient a character to produce significant changes in intestinal digestion through failure of secretion. Changes in carbohydrate metabolism which might be ascribable to suppression of the production of insulin are rarely observed, although mild hyperglycemia and glycosuria of short duration are occasionally reported.

Chronic pancreatitis may develop following attacks of either acute non-hemorrhagic or hemorrhagic pancreatitis. The condition is characterized by fibrotic changes which may be confined to interlobular tissue or it may involve interacinar tissue as well. Digestive disturbances are common, as evidenced by steatorrhea and the presence of incompletely digested protein in the stool. Symptoms of diabetes occur if the fibrotic process is far advanced and involves interacinar tissue. Such pathological changes form the etiological background for the development of diabetes mellitus as the result of arteriosclerotic changes in the pancreas. Chronic pancreatitis is not accompanied by changes in levels of pancreatic enzymes in the blood.

Acute hemorrhagic pancreatitis usually is a fatal disease. Necrotic change is a prominent feature. The trypsinogen is released and is activated by pancreatic tissue so that it causes autodigestion of the gland and of the surrounding tissues. Lipolytic enzymes digest fat and the resulting fatty acids form insoluble calcium soaps. Changes in blood amylase and lipase concentrations are similar to those in acute non-hemorrhagic pancreatitis except that the necrotic process may be so rapid that high values are not reached before glandular destruction abolishes the source of the enzymes. Lipase levels are apt to be lower than those of amylase, or lipase may be entirely absent in fulminating cases. The course of the disease is usually too rapid to produce essential changes in digestive functions. The stool often contains blood. Diabetic manifestations occur, persisting hyperglycemia being an indication of a poor prognosis.

STEATORRHEA

Inadequacy of external secretion of the pancreas may lead to pancreatic steatorrhea. Other conditions also may lead to a high content of fat in the feces, and these various disorders will be considered together because of similarity in the diagnostic problems.

Non-pancreatogenous steatorrhea is seen in obstructive jaundice (associated with absence of bile in the stool), tropical and non-tropical sprue, and celiac disease. Occasionally fatty stools appear in regional ileitis and in tuberculous infections of the gastro-intestinal tract.

Pancreatogenous steatorrhea is characterized by bulky stools containing large amounts of neutral fat which often separates on standing. Occasionally undigested muscle fibers from ingested meat are found. The lipid content of normal stools expressed in per cent by weight of dry material ranges up to approximately 10, the dry weight being up to 40 per cent of the weight of the stool. These lipids are not necessarily derived from the diet, as the average composition of fecal lipids resembles that of the blood lipids. Therefore, at least a portion of fecal lipids are believed to originate in secretions from the intestinal mucous membrane. It is to be expected that the lipid of the fatty stools in pancreatogenous steatorrhea consists largely of undigested fat, while a high content of fatty acids points toward faulty absorption. Fowweather considers a neutral fat content in fatty stools greater than 55 per cent of the total lipids a sign of deficient enzymic digestion, while 75 per cent or more in the form of digested fat indicates deficiency of absorption. Fat analyses on single stool specimens should not be considered reliable for diagnostic purposes; great fluctuations in lipid excretion may be found in both normal and abnormal conditions. The fatty acids of fecal fat also vary greatly. As already mentioned, more than approximately half the lipids in the form of undigested fat suggests pancreatic disorder but less than that does not rule out deficiency of pancreatic secretion. Metabolic balance studies of fat metabolism are of much more importance than analysis of single specimens of feces, but they are generally too cumbersome to be practical. Stools which on repeated examinations show a high lipid content, even if it is within accepted upper normal limits, should definitely arouse suspicion as to the existence of an abnormal condition.

While the disorders of fat digestion ordinarily are most obvious, it is possible in many cases to arrive at more positive diagnostic conclusions by studying the nitrogen of the feces. The average daily normal excretion of fecal nitrogen is between 1 and 2 grams, of which a portion is derived from non-absorbed food components and the balance from excretory products of the gastro-intestinal system. There is no quantitative relationship between ingested and fecal nitrogen, although, in general, a high protein diet increases, and starvation decreases the fecal nitrogen. In pancreatic steatorrhea fairly large amounts of ingested protein are eliminated in the feces and it has been mentioned that undigested muscle fibers may be recognized microscopically in the stools.

Idiopathic steatorrhea is identical with non-tropical sprue. It is not entirely clear if the etiological background for tropical and non-tropical sprue, and celiac disease, is the same; from a biochemical standpoint it is better to consider these diagnostic entities as non-pancreatogenous steatorrhea. The general characteristics of the stools are the high fatty acid content, and a near normal content of nitrogen. Pancreatic enzymes should be present in the duodenal contents in normal amounts although deficiency in lipase has been reported in several cases of idiopathic steatorrhea. Non-pancreatogenous steatorrhea exhibits various degrees of inflammatory and degenerative lesions in the intestinal tract. Celiac disease is to be distinguished from the steatorrhea of infancy in which pathological changes (such as congenital cystic fibrosis) in the pancreas are responsible.

Steatorrheas obviously interfere with digestion and absorption of food. The amount of fat absorbed varies greatly; at times the fecal loss is relatively unimportant, while at other times it causes a serious reduction in the total caloric intake. In a given case of sprue the percentage absorption of fat remains relatively constant and independent of the amount of fat ingested. This points toward an interference with an enzyme system, possibly in phosphorylation. Ingestion of liver extract and of yeast improves fat absorption, probably through the action of folic acid. Whereas the anemia of sprue responds rapidly to administration of folic acid, the improvement in the fat absorption is slow. Severe and protracted diarrhea may be associated with symptoms of sprue, the steatorrhea of such cases subsiding rapidly upon administration of folic acid. Alterations in intestinal biosynthesis of biotin may be responsible for the sprue-like syndrome in such cases. The general disorder of absorption whether primary, or secondary to changes caused by deficiency of pancreatic enzymes, also influences absorption of other essential food components such as vitamins, calcium, iron, and possibly carbohydrates. The abnormal biochemical changes arising in this manner are both numerous and important, and should be accorded further discussion.

Persistent steatorrhea results in changes in the bones manifested by osteoporosis which may be associated with deformities. Patients exhibiting this condition usually have low concentrations of calcium in the serum, the phosphorus tending also to be low, although it may occasionally be normal or even elevated. Calcium levels within the tetany range are not unusual. The calcium deficiency is caused by failure of intestinal absorption, as is evidenced by the excessive excretion of fecal calcium soaps. However, the large content of insoluble calcium soaps in the feces may be the result, rather than the cause of failure to absorb calcium. It is likely that deficiencies in fat digestion and absorption interfere with assimilation of vitamin D and this in turn inhibits utilization of calcium. Possibly the pathological changes in the intestinal wall in idiopathic steatorrhea may have an influence upon the absorption of calcium as well as of other substances. The effect of excessive amounts of non-absorbed fat in the intestinal tract on the absorption of oil-soluble vitamins is illustrated by the appearance of symptoms of vitamin A deficiency in patients with congenital cystic fibrosis of the pancreas.

The faulty absorption of fat in steatorrhea is associated with a low fasting level of total lipids in the blood, and the rise in lipid concentration following a test meal is less than in the normal subject. It is to be expected that the organism would develop a nitrogen deficit in pancreatogenous steatorrhea, however, patients with idiopathic steatorrhea also present difficulties in maintaining nitrogen equilibrium unless the diet contains large amounts of protein and carbohydrates. Apparently the loss of calories tends to produce a negative nitrogen balance similar to that of starvation. The unfavorable nitrogen balance is reflected in reduced concentrations of serum proteins.

Persons suffering from non-pancreatogenous steatorrhea often exhibit rather flat glucose tolerance curves. This phenomenon has been explained as a result of faulty absorption although Thaysen claims that similar observations may be made following intravenous administration of glucose. His findings have been contradicted. Metabolism of hexoses in the liver and in the peripheral tissues appears not to be affected by the steatorrhea as glycogen storage and the respiratory quotient remain normal.

DIABETES MELLITUS

This disease affords the student of biochemistry opportunity to study several phases of metabolism because the altered chemical processes involve not only carbohydrates, but proteins and fats and disorders of utilization of vitamins as well. While insulin is used for therapeutic purposes, it should be recalled that hormones from other glands affect carbohydrate metabolism. A study of metabolic disturbances in diabetes mellitus should include a review of the metabolism of carbohydrate, protein, and fat, and the effects exerted by the hormones of the pituitary, thyroid, and adrenal glands. It is undesirable to limit the subject to a consideration of diabetes mellitus as a disease of the pancreas only.

GLUCOSE TOLERANCE

The primary manifestation of diabetes is the hyperglycemia and glycosuria which result from failure to metabolize glucose. In untreated diabetes a glucose determination on a single blood specimen, obtained either in the fasting state or following a meal, will usually suffice to confirm the hyperglycemia. Borderline cases often have normal fasting blood glucose levels and, after meals, may show concentrations of glucose ranging on either side of the upper normal limit. In such cases it becomes necessary to study the ability of the patient to metabolize ingested carbohydrate under standardized conditions; the various glucose tolerance tests are designed to serve this purpose.

Before discussing criteria for normal and abnormal glucose tolerances, it is of importance to make clear certain points with respect to the analytical procedures by which they are determined. Various methods are used routinely in clinical laboratories. However, blood contains other reducing substances in varying amounts, the reducing power of which is included in the final result. Therefore, blood glucose concentrations determined by one of the common clinical laboratory procedures (see Chapter 8) represent the reducing power of glucose plus that of a certain amount of non-carbohydrate material. The latter value, if small and constant, would only change the accepted criteria for normal limits of glucose while, if large and variable, would seriously affect judgment based upon figures which are close to the normal limits. Recently Mosenthal and Barry have emphasized that these fluctuations of non-specific reducing substances are sufficient to cause non-diabetics to be diagnosed as mild diabetics, and these investigators recommend that questionable glucose levels be established by methods which will determine true glucose concentrations.

The so-called 'oral glucose tolerance tests' are employed in various modifications. The test dose may be 50 to 100 grams of glucose or may be calculated on the basis of the weight of the subject. In the normal person the blood glucose level is not significantly altered by the amount of glucose taken, while in the diabetic the tolerance curve departs farther and farther from the normal as larger amounts of glucose are ingested. Normal carbohydrate tolerance, as measured by common methods such as the Folin-Wu procedure, is indicated by fasting blood glucose concentrations of 120 mg. or less, and a maximum of 180 mg. per 100 cc., with a return to 120 mg. per 100 cc. or lower 2 hours after the administration of the test dose. Diabetes mellitus is characterized by a 'high and prolonged' blood glucose curve, but it is evident from consideration of the effects of the various endocrine glands on carbohydrate metabolism, that the 'high and prolonged' glucose tolerance curve does not necessarily imply a primary pathological state of the Islands of Langerhans with resulting deficiency of insulin.

In a normal subject the blood glucose in a tolerance test falls below the initial fasting level after approximately two hours. This phenomenon has been explained as caused by stimulation to insulin secretion resulting as it were in the release of more insulin than is necessary for the needs of the organism to metabolize the additional glucose (Allen's paradoxical law). Soskin and his associates have performed experiments on depancreatized dogs in which they provided a constant supply of insulin; these workers have demonstrated that the regulatory function depends on the liver through a delicate endocrine balance rather than through the mechanism postulated by Allen and others. Regardless of the proper explanation, the phenomenon of regulation of glucose utilization has found a useful application in the Exton-Rose glucose tolerance test which employs the administration of glucose in two doses with $\frac{1}{2}$ hour interval between them. With normal carbohydrate tolerance the first dose produces a rise in the blood glucose which remains within normal limits, and the second dose $\frac{1}{2}$ hour later results in glucose concentrations which may be even less than when the second dose was administered, and never causes an increase of more than 5 mg. per 100 cc. All urine specimens should be negative for glucose during the test.

Criteria for normal limits of blood glucose concentrations generally apply to venous blood. In fasting the difference in glucose levels in the arterial and venous blood is small, the former usually being not more than 10 mg. per 100 cc. higher than the latter. During the digestive phase this difference commonly increases to approximately 30 to 40 mg. per 100 cc. and may become occasionally considerably greater. The glucose concentration in capillary blood is closely similar to that of arterial blood, so that the difference in levels in arterial and venous blood becomes important when micromethods are used with blood from small puncture wounds. Because of the difference in arterio-venous glucose levels, it is incorrect to attempt to correlate renal thresholds for glucose with venous blood sugar concentrations. Such correlations should be made with arterial blood glucose levels, and determinations performed on capillary blood are much more suitable for this purpose.

In adults glycosuria occurs occasionally as a result of a low renal threshold to glucose. However, this condition is observed often in infants and young children. For the reasons stated previously such thresholds should not be judged by venous blood glucose determinations, although these may properly be employed for purposes of diagnosis.

THE REGULATION OF BLOOD GLUCOSE

The earliest indication of the role of the pancreas in regulating the concentration of glucose in the blood came through the observations of von Mering and Minkowski on depancreatized dogs. The discovery of insulin by Banting and Best demonstrated the mechanism of regulation of the blood sugar level in so far as the pancreas is involved. The properties of insulin are discussed in Chapter 8, in which it is pointed out that the exact locus in the chain of events of carbohydrate metabolism in which insulin exerts its effect has not been determined.

Best and his associates found that administration of insulin to eviscerated cats results in increased utilization of glucose and that the amount utilized corresponds to the amount of glycogen simultaneously deposited in the muscles and to the equivalent of glucose in terms of extra oxygen consumed. They interpreted these findings as indicating increased oxidation of carbohydrate in the liverless animals under the conditions of the experiment. Soskin and his associates have questioned these conclusions, and have performed experiments to show that insulin does not increase the utilization of carbohydrates in the organism as a whole but permits utilization of glucose in an intact animal at a rate which is attained in the depancreatized animal only at much higher blood glucose levels. In other words, insulin does not affect the amount of glucose which the tissues are able to metabolize, but catalyzes the reactions involved.

In the previous discussion of glucose tolerance it has been stated that the return of a normal glucose tolerance curve to below the fasting level at the beginning of the test has been interpreted as the effect of 'excess' stimulation of insulin secretion, but that Soskin's experiments show that no additional secretion of insulin is necessary for adequate regulation if sufficient insulin is present to maintain a constant blood glucose concentration. Other experiments on hepatectomized dogs in which normal blood glucose levels were maintained by constant injection of glucose proved that with such animals glucose tolerance curves of the diabetic type are obtained. Apparently the regulation of the blood sugar depends upon having a normal liver, rather than on regulation of peripheral utilization by insulin. The liver appears to respond to the supply of glucose in the blood so that an augmented demand for glucose by the organism is met by increased glycogenolysis while excessive amounts of glucose in the blood immediately inhibit this process and stimulate glycogenesis. The low level of blood glucose reached toward the end of a glucose tolerance test in the normal subject may be explained as the result of this function to re-establish the normal glucose level. In addition to the regulatory mechanism described, the pituitary, adrenal, and thyroid glands contribute in establishing the concentration of glucose in the blood. Failure of gluconeogenesis in the adrenalectomized animal may make it impossible to maintain glucose levels as high as those in the intact organism. Among non-pancreatic endocrine disturbances associated with hypoglycemia may be mentioned pituitary cachexia, hypothyroidism, and Addison's disease, while hyperglycemia is common in Cushing's syndrome (pituitary basophilism and hyperadrenocorticalism), hyperthyroidism, and pheochromocytoma.

THE METABOLIC DISORDERS IN DIABETES MELLITUS

Two theories have been advanced to explain the metabolic phenomena in diabetes mellitus. In spite of the tremendous amount of work which has been devoted to the study of the subject since pancreatic diabetes was discovered by von Mering and Minkowski, it has not been possible to present totally convincing evidence in favor of one or the other theory.

The *under-utilization* hypothesis states that the diabetic organism is able to utilize carbohydrate only slowly or not at all. Von Mering and Minkowski found support for this viewpoint in the quantitative recovery of glucose in the urine of depancreatized animals following a carbohydrate meal. Minkowski also found a definite relationship between the amounts of glucose and nitrogen excreted in the urine of his animals when these were fasting or were fed lean meat. His explanation was that glucose derived from the metabolism of protein could not be utilized by the pancreatectomized animal and, therefore, it appeared in the urine in definite ratio to nitrogen. Phenomena pertaining to the utilization of fat also were interpreted to support the under-utilization theory. The respiratory quotient of the fasting animal is approximately 0.7 which is considered an indication of the utilization of fat as the chief source of energy. The early investigators found that feeding carbohydrate increased the R.Q. toward unity in the non-diabetic animal, while the depancreatized animal continued to show an R.Q. around 0.7. This was taken as further confirmation of the inability of the diabetic animal to utilize carbohydrate. The appearance of ketone bodies found a simple explanation in the assumption that 'fats burn in the flame of carbohydrates' and that faulty carbohydrate metabolism, therefore, would make complete oxidation of fat degradation products impossible.

A serious objection to the non-utilization hypothesis is the fact that hepatectomized animals die in hypoglycemia within a short time whether the pancreas has been removed or not. It is rather difficult to explain how a pancreatectomized and hepatectomized animal can develop hypoglycemia without the glucose being excreted unless the peripheral tissues are able to utilize glucose.

The *over-production* hypothesis explains glycosuria as a phenomenon which occurs when the liver pours out glucose in excess of the rate of utilization in the peripheral tissues. Obviously such a mechanism can account, just as well as the under-utilization hypothesis, for Minkowski's observations in regard to quantitative urinary elimination of glucose. The oxidation of fat is described in Chapter 6 in which it is pointed out that ketone bodies are readily utilized by peripheral tissues, independent of carbohydrate metabolism. However, a relationship between carbohydrate and fat metabolism may be indicated through the utilization of the available oxidation-reduction systems. The occurrence of diabetic ketosis is hardly compatible with the under-utilization hypothesis. The over-production theory may imply excessive formation of ketones as well as of glucose, and the increased disposal of ketone bodies by oxidation in the peripheral tissues may diminish the utilization of glucose, resulting in its accumulation in the blood.

DIABETIC ACIDOSIS

If the diabetic state is independent of the ability of the peripheral tissues to metabolize ketone bodies, it must be assumed that ketosis is the result of a rate of production of these substances in the liver in excess of the utilization capacity of the tissues. Diabetic acidosis develops when demands for caloric energy exceed the capacity of the peripheral tissues to oxidize ketone bodies.

At rest, or whenever the caloric demands are low, ketonuria may be absent even in the presence of markedly depressed carbohydrate metabolism. Mirsky and his associates have demonstrated that ketosis can be abolished or prevented in the uncontrolled diabetic by the administration of large excesses of carbohydrates.

Diabetic acidosis is characterized by hyperglycemia, glycosuria, polyuria, hypochloremia, and a reduced carbon dioxide combining power of the plasma. As the patient proceeds into more severe acidosis, emesis occurs frequently which markedly contributes to the chloride deficiency. The cations lost include potassium as well as sodium and the loss of potassium may be considerable, at times reaching the same order of magnitude as that of sodium. The potassium deficit is not reflected in plasma levels until after treatment has been instituted. Several factors may be responsible for the low potassium levels observed during treatment, the most obvious being simple dilution as a result of hydration therapy with large volumes of fluid not containing potassium. Another factor may be the glycogenic effect of insulin as it has been demonstrated that increased storage of glycogen in the liver is accompanied by increased deposition of potassium. The hypopotassemia may be avoided by addition of potassium salts to the intravenous fluid. Caution should be exercised in the adjustment of dosage in order to avoid potassium intoxication. The severe muscular weakness occasionally observed in patients otherwise recovered from diabetic acidosis may illustrate a relationship between potassium deficiency and familial periodic paralysis.

TREATMENT OF DIABETIC ACIDOSIS

Mild acidosis in the diabetic is often unnoticed. Proof is lacking that ketone bodies have any specific toxic effect, and the problem of harmful effects of ketosis in patients who have no subjective complaints is linked to the question of whether degenerative processes are accelerated more in mild uncontrolled diabetics than in well controlled more severe diabetics, using blood glucose and the absence of ketonuria as criteria.

The comatose patient requires immediate therapy. Adequate amounts of insulin must be administered and fluid as well as electrolyte balance should be restored. Standardized schemes for treatment of diabetic coma are to be avoided, therapy being guided by the need for insulin, water, and electrolytes as determined in each individual instance. As an emergency procedure the intravenous administration of sodium lactate may help in providing an immediate supply of alkali to increase the alkali reserve.

The practice of injecting glucose intravenously in diabetic coma has aroused some controversy. Actually the amount of glucose available even with high blood glucose levels is comparatively small. In view of the higher rate of utilization of glucose which may be associated with high blood glucose concentrations it would seem that reduction of glucose back to normal levels need not take place immediately. However, this increased utilization of glucose may be of minor significance compared to the effect of adequate doses of insulin. Sufficient amounts of glucose must be available at all times during treatment to insure a maximum conversion of blood glucose to glycogen in the liver. Administration of a temporary excess of glucose has a practical advantage in that adequate amounts of insulin can be given with small risk of producing hypoglycemia. A harmful action of hyperglycemia upon the pancreas has not been proved in human subjects.

EXPERIMENTAL NON-SURGICAL DIABETES

Phlorhizin is a glucoside which upon injection into animals produces a syndrome resembling diabetes, except that the glucose level in the blood is low. Excessive loss of carbohydrate in the urine is characteristic of both pancreatic and phlorhizin diabetes. The latter is produced by the drug interfering with phosphorylation in the tubules thus preventing the normal reabsorption of glucose. Interference with phosphorylation is not confined to the kidneys but this organ is the site of the most conspicuous effect because phlorhizin attains its highest concentration there, and the kidneys as compared to muscle have a limited ability to destroy the drug.

Alloxan is a substance resembling in structure the nitrogenous components thymine, uracil, and cytosine of nucleic acid. Injections of alloxan into animals produce hypoglycemia; if the dose is insufficient to cause death such animals may develop permanent diabetes. The drug appears to act specifically on the β-cells to cause their destruction and leaves the α-cells intact.

Diabetes can be produced by the injection of *anterior pituitary* extract over a period of time. Initially the extract causes stimulation of the secretion of insulin and, if continued long enough, eventually results in its suppression.

HYPOGLYCEMIA

Low levels of glucose in the blood may be caused by many factors. Prolonged and excessive demands for energy by the organism may result in temporary lowering of blood glucose concentrations. Most cases of clinical significance are produced by failure of the liver to supply adequate amounts of glucose to the blood. This may be brought about by extensive destruction of liver cells, or by disturbances in hormonal control of gluconeogenesis such as occurs in diminished activity of the anterior pituitary, the thyroid, and the adrenal glands, or in hyperinsulinism. The last named should be assumed to be the causative factor in hypoglycemia only if a tumor involving islet cells can be demonstrated.

SUPPLEMENTARY READING

BANTING, F. G., and BEST, C. H.: The internal secretion of the pancreas. *J. Lab. & Clin. Med., 7:*251, 1922.

BELL, E. T.: Experimental Diabetes Mellitus. American Lecture Series, Charles C Thomas, Publisher, 1948.

BEST, C. H., DALE, H. H., HOET, J. P., and MARLES, H. P.: Oxidation and storage of glucose under the action of insulin. *Proc. Roy. Soc., London, B, 100:*55, 1926.

BRIDGE, E. M.: The action of insulin on glycogen reserves. *Bull. Johns Hopkins Hosp. 62:*408, 1938.

CHERRY, I. S., and CRANDALL, L. A.: The specificity of pancreatic lipase: its appearance in the blood after pancreatic injury. *Am. J. Physiol., 100:*266, 1932.

COMFORT, M. W.: Serum lipase: its diagnostic value. *Am. J. Digest Dis. and Nutrition, 3:*817, 1937.

EXTON, W. G., and ROSE, A. R.: The one-hour, two-dose dextrose tolerance test. *Am. J. Clin. Path., 4:*381, 1934.

FOWWEATHER, F. S.: The determination of the amount and the composition of the fat of faeces. I. Investigation of a "wet" method and comparison with the "dry" method. *Brit. J. Exper. Path., 7:*7, 1926.

LUKENS, F. D. W.: Alloxan diabetes. *Physiol. Rev., 28:*304, 1948.

McCLURE, C. W., WETMORE, A. S., and REYNOLDS, L.: New methods for estimating enzymatic activities of duodenal contents of normal man. *Arch. Int. Med., 27:*706, 1921.

MIRSKY, I. A., FRANZBLAU, A. N., NELSON, N., and NELSON, W. E.: Diabetes mellitus. The role of excessive carbohydrate intake in the etiology of diabetic coma. *J. Clin. Endocrinol., 1:*307, 1941.

MOSENTHAL, H. O., and BARRY, E.: Advantages of true venous blood sugar values for glucose tolerance tests. *New York State J. Med., 46:*2513, 1946.

NICHOLSON, W. M., and BRANNING, W. S.: Potassium deficiency in diabetic acidosis. *J.A.M.A., 123:*1292, 1947.

SMELO, L. S.: Insulin resistance. *Proc. Am. Diabetes A., 8:*75, 1948.

SMITH, G., HERSHMAN, B., and THANNHAUSER, S. J.: The isolation of α-glycerylphosphorylcholine from incubated beef pancreas: its significance for the intermediary metabolism of lecithin. *J. Biol. Chem., 161:*523, 1945.

SOMOGYI, M.: Micromethods for the estimation of diastase. *J. Biol. Chem., 125:*399, 1938.

SOSKIN, S., ALLWEISS, M.D., and COHN, D. J.: Influence of the pancreas and the liver upon the dextrose tolerance curve. *Am. J. Physiol., 109:*155, 1934.

SOSKIN, S., and LEVINE, R.: On the mode of action of insulin. *Am. J. Physiol., 129:*782, 1940.

SOSKIN, S., and LEVINE, R.: *Carbohydrate Metabolism.* University of Chicago Press, 1946.

STETTEN, DeW., JR.: Altered rates of certain metabolic processes in hypo- and hyper-insulinism. *Proc. Am. Diabetes A., 7:*67, 1947.

THAYSEN, T. E. H.: Ten cases of idiopathic steatorrhoea. *Quart. J. Med., 4:*359, 1935.

YOUNG, F. G.: The endocrine approach to the problem of diabetes. *Proc. Am. Diabetes A., 10:*11, 1950.

Chapter 15

THE ADRENALS

Aᴌᴛʜᴏᴜɢʜ work prior to 1855 had demonstrated that the adrenal glands are essential to life, detailed study of the functions of these glands dates from the clinical observations of Addison. The medulla and cortex are functionally separate structures and in some lower animal forms they are not fused into one organ as is true in most higher forms. The medulla is derived from the ectoderm and therefore has a common origin with the sympathetic nervous system. The cortex is mesodermal in orgin, consisting of three layers, the zona glomerulosa, the zona fasciculata, and the zona reticularis. Adrenals of the fetus are very large relative to those of the adult, mainly because of the X-zone which degenerates and disappears almost entirely in the first few months after birth.

THE ADRENAL MEDULLA

Epinephrine was the first hormone to be isolated. Determination of its chemical structure was followed by its synthesis in 1904. For years it was thought that epinephrine was the only hormone with mediating effect on the organs which are innervated by the sympathetic nervous system. It was well established that its release occurs in response to a variety of stimuli such as fear and rage, sudden demands on the temperature regulating mechanism, accelerating physical effort, and hypoglycemia. In the last few years the discovery of nor-epinephrine in adrenergic nerve fibers has also led to demonstrations of the presence of this substance in the adrenal medulla.

Nor-epinephrine (arterenol) is a primary amine. It differs from epinephrine by the absence of the terminal methyl-group attached to the nitrogen.

EPINEPHRINE   NOREPINEPHRINE

The presence of nor-epinephrine in vivo was discovered by the physiological effect of extracts of postganglionic nerves of cattle. Separation of racemic epinephrine made it possible to show that, as in the case of epinephrine, its greatest physiological effect is in the levo form.

Phenylalanine has been shown to be a precursor of tyrosine and thus may be regarded as a possible precursor of both epinephrine and nor-epinephrine. It is possible that the biosynthesis from phenylalanine involves transformation to 3,4-dihydroxyphenylalanine followed by decarboxylation to hydroxytyramine. Mammalian tissues contain enzyme systems capable of catalyzing these reactions. The mechanism whereby the hydroxyl groups are introduced into the side chains is entirely unknown. Recently it has been found that dihydroxyphenylserine can be decarboxylated by mammalian tissue suggesting another possible biosynthetic pathway. Methylation of nor-epinephrine to epinephrine may take place in vivo with choline as the methyl donor. Pigmentation in Addison's disease has been linked to medullary destruction and interference with the normal synthesis of epinephrine. The process through dihydroxyphenylalanine may proceed in the direction of melanin-like structures. Proof of such a mechanism is lacking, and the absence of excessive pigmentation in adrenalectomized animals make such theories questionable.

The method of inactivation of epinephrine in the body is not well understood. Both epinephrine and nor-epinephrine are oxidized by air at pH 7, adrenochrome and nor-adrenochrome being formed. It has been suggested that such an oxidation mechanism may be catalyzed by cytochrome-indophenoloxidase. Adrenochrome has been found in chromaffin tumor tissue.

Amine-oxidase appears to be too slow in action to explain the rapid inactivation of epinephrine. Esterified epinephrine and nor-epinephrine in urine appears to have other sources than the adrenal medulla since they are eliminated in equal or even increased amounts in cases of Addison's disease resulting from tubercular destruction of both adrenals. After intravenous infusion of nor-epinephrine only a small fraction of the total can be recovered in the urine indicating that elimination through the kidneys as a means of inactivation is questionable.

Epinephrine and nor-epinephrine produce increases in systolic and mean arterial pressure. The mechanism whereby this is accomplished differs. The hypertension from epinephrine is caused by increase of cardiac output in spite of decrease of total peripheral resistance. Nor-epinephrine does not evoke an increase in cardiac output; the hypertension being due to an increase in total peripheral resistance. Epinephrine causes increase of oxygen consumption, a property which is much less pronounced in nor-epinephrine and probably lacking in the amounts normally present in the body. Similarly epinephrine has a much more pronounced hyperglycemic effect than that of nor-epinephrine.

The secretion of the adrenal cortex is increased by epinephrine. The primary site of action of epinephrine appears to be the anterior lobe of the pituitary or the hypothalamus resulting in the release of ACTH as an intermediary. Nor-epinephrine may not exert this effect in the normal physiological range. In a higher range the quantitative relationship of epinephrine to nor-epinephrine for the same physiological response appears to be approximately identical in the release of ACTH and production of hyperglycemia. Nor-epinephrine does not have the typical central nervous system response of epinephrine.

The adrenal medulla is not essential to life: adrenalectomized animals may carry on physiological functions by treatment with cortical hormones only. Production of epinephrine by extramedullary chromaffin tissue under such circumstances is small at best and completely lacking in some animals. Resting secretion of the adrenal medulla is far below the amount necessary to obtain the hypertensive and hyperglycemic effect of epinephrine. The question arises if secretion of the 2 hormones in the adrenal medulla is in constant proportion or if their secretion is controlled by separate mechanisms. The former appears to be the case. In animals such as man with a relatively small percentage of nor-epinephrine the secretion of a mixture does not require modification of our older viewpoints because the small amount of nor-epinephrine does not significantly alter the effect of epinephrine. Under emergency conditions the increased release of medullary hormone mixture conforms essentially to experimental observations made by injection of epinephrine.

Abnormalities such as might result from insufficiency of secretion of the adrenal medulla are not known. On the other hand chromaffin tissue tumors, pheochromocytomas, are characterized by the effect of excessive epinephrine formation including severe hypertension which may be paroxysmal or sustained. Removal of the tumor usually results in striking improvement. The paroxysms of certain pheochromocytomas are presumably due to physiological stimulation (acetylcholine and histamine). However, the effect of such tumors at rest may result in changes in basal metabolic rate or persistent hyperglycemia only indicating that the hypertension requires larger doses of epinephrine than those necessary for the metabolic changes. Many patients with severe pheochromocytomas have persistent hypertension, such patients generally show large urinary output of epinephrine and nor-epinephrine. Clinical manifestations in patients with pheochromocytomas may vary according to whether the excessive secretion is predominantly epinephrine or nor-epinephrine. Those with large quantities of epinephrine may at times present a clinical picture of essential hypertensive vascular disease, metabolic disturbances being minimal or absent in such cases. In patients with pheochromocytomas of long standing a secondary hypertension may be observed which apparently does not depend upon epinephrine or nor-epinephrine for its maintenance. Such patients will remain hypertensive for varying lengths of time after the surgical removal of the tumors.

Certain pharmacological methods may aid in differentiating chromaffin tissue tumors from essential hypertension. Benzodioxane and a number of compounds containing a benzodioxane group have been characterized as adrenolytic drugs, their antagonistic effect on epinephrine being ascribed to their similarity in chemical structure, making them possible competitors for the epinephrine acceptors. These drugs also have a sympathomimetic effect probably elicited through their action on the central nervous system. Thus benzodioxane compounds may produce sympathetic responses such as tachycardia, flushing, sweating, and hyperpnea while, at the same time, blocking the pressor effect of injected epinephrine.

The benzodioxane test is only applicable in patients with pheochromocytoma with sustained high blood pressure. In such cases the injection of benzodioxane tends to produce a sizable fall in blood pressure in contradistinction to the response in cases of essential hypertension. It is obvious that in the 'non-humoral' phase of pheochromocytoma described above the response to benzodioxane cannot be expected. Therefore a negative test does not rule out the diagnosis. Similarly false positive tests in essential hypertension have been recorded. The hypertension in Cushing's syndrome, whether due to adrenal tumor or of pituitary origin, does not respond to benzodioxane. The hypertension in such cases is probably due to excessive secretion of cortical hormones.

Dibenamine and certain imidazoline derivatives have been tried instead of benzodioxane compounds. These substances have more powerful adrenergic blocking effects with a greater tendency to lower blood pressure in patients with essential hypertension.

EPINEPHRINE

PIPERIDO-METHYL-BENZODIOXANE

THE ADRENAL CORTEX

The cortex of the adrenal glands elaborates at least six hormones which are indispensable to the living organism. These hormones have essential effects in maintenance of normal water and electrolyte balance, carbohydrate metabolism, growth and sex characteristics, blood pressure, and rate of disintegration of lymphocytes (thereby probably influencing formation of anti-bodies).

The first observations in regard to changes in inorganic serum constituents as a result of adrenalectomy were made in 1926. At that time and shortly thereafter several workers reported increases in serum potassium and decreases in sodium and chloride levels as well as of plasma volume in adrenalectomized animals. Subsequently such changes were found to be characteristic in Addison's disease.

Dehydration in cortical insufficiency is associated with loss of sodium. An important feature of the lowered concentration of sodium chloride in the interstitial tissue is the redistribution of water between intracellular and extracellular compartments. Because of the cell membrane barrier, electrolytes inside the cells cannot migrate into the surrounding fluid and thereby readjust the osmotic balance, and consequently a shift of water into intracellular compartments takes place until osmotic equilibrium is restored. The decrease in volume of blood and interstitial fluid is accomplished by loss of water and salt through the kidneys and from the interstitial fluid to the cells. Release of water from the cells can be observed as a secondary diuresis when adrenalectomized animals are treated with cortical extract. Loss of water and electrolytes by vomiting may contribute to the severe dehydration and loss of salt. This parallels the events occurring in the development of severe diabetic acidosis but it should be mentioned that emesis is contributory to the final clinical picture only after dehydration has become pronounced.

Talbott and associates have investigated renal function in patients with Addison's disease and in patients with adrenal insufficiency secondary to pituitary pan-hypofunction. Their patients were well compensated and did not exhibit symptoms of severe cortical deficiency, nor did they show abnormalities in the common clinical tests for renal function. These investigators applied tests for clearance of inulin, creatinine, diodrast, glucose, sodium, chloride, and potassium and found general impairment of kidney function. The tubular excretory rate for diodrast was affected least, while glomerular filtration rate and tubular reabsorption of glucose were affected most. Administration of desoxycorticosterone tended to repair these excretory deficiencies, while this hormone did not affect excretion in the normal subject. Talbott and associates point out that the excretory anomalies in adrenal insufficiency are presumably functional since histological changes in the kidneys are not observed consistently. It may be argued that decrease of glomerular filtration rate may be the result of decreased blood flow. In Talbott's studies clearances of creatinine and diodrast gave values for glomerular filtration rates which were depressed out of proportion to the reduction in renal blood flow.

As a result of dehydration and lowered blood pressure, adrenal insufficiency is accompanied by retention of non-protein nitrogen in the blood. This does not differ from the extrarenal azotemia in hemorrhage, shock, or dehydration from any cause, and responds to therapeutic measures directed toward rehydration of the patient.

The changes in potassium level in plasma in cortical deficiency present several interesting aspects because similar changes occur occasionally in other conditions in which the adrenals presumably are not involved. The function of potassium in the organism is not clear. The action potential and impulse of nerve conduction depends upon changes in permeability of the neuronal surface as discussed in Chapter 17, the migration of potassium apparently being of major importance. A similar mechanism is postulated as underlying excitation of muscle fibers. Potassium may also play a role in phosphorylation. The relatively high concentration of potassium in the cell is said to be caused by the impermeability of the cell membrane to sodium and anions except those with which potassium is combined. Therefore, potassium ions tend to migrate into the extracellular fluid in conditions involving loss of sodium and water. Increased levels of potassium of the plasma are found in cases of severe vomiting such as in intestinal obstruction, and in cases of severe hemorrhage and shock. Apparently the increase in potassium concentration in the blood in cortical deficiency may be a secondary effect of the excessive loss of sodium ions resulting in their lower concentration in the blood and interstitial fluid. The increase in blood potassium level is accompanied by decrease in its excretion in the urine. In spite of these anomalous changes, it is possible that cortical hormones have a direct effect on the distribution of potassium. Ingle and associates have found that adrenalectomized animals with bilateral nephrectomy respond to the administration of cortical extract by showing a decrease in plasma potassium levels. The reduction in potassium level in plasma in normal subjects following injection of desoxycorticosterone also seems to be a direct hormonal effect; if sufficient amount of hormone is supplied the potassium concentration in the blood may drop to levels comparable to those in familial periodic paralysis, and symptoms of this disease appear.

The adrenal cortical hormones have specific effects on carbohydrate metabolism. Subjects suffering from cortical deficiency exhibit a "flat" glucose tolerance curve, low stores of glycogen, intolerance to insulin, and failure to show a rise in blood glucose concentration comparable to that of the normal organism following injection of epinephrine. On the other hand cortical extracts injected into normal animals produce increases in blood glucose levels and liver glycogen deposits. Diminished absorption of carbohydrate from the intestine in cortical insufficiency may be a contributory factor to the altered carbohydrate metabolism. Fenn has pointed out that passage of sugar into cells is associated with passage of potassium in the same direction.

Adrenalectomized animals show decrease in concentration of fatty acids and phospholipids and at least partial inability to increase the fat content of the liver under conditions which cause hepatic deposition of fat in normal animals. Nelson and his associates have demonstrated decreased utilization of intravenously injected sodium β-hydroxybutyrate in adrenalectomized rats.

Available evidence points to gluconeogenesis as the phase of carbohydrate metabolism affected by cortical hormones. The fasting adrenalectomized animal excretes less nitrogen than the normal. Increase in nitrogen elimination from these low levels takes place simultaneously with increases in blood glucose and glycogen deposits upon treatment with cortical extracts or some of the individual hormones. It has also been observed that diabetes in depancreatized animals can be ameliorated by removal of the adrenals, and that injection of cortical extract in partially depancreatized animals causes increase in the urinary loss of glucose. Failure of gluconeogenesis can be demonstrated in adrenalectomized animals by comparison with normal controls after administration of phlorhizin to both groups; the rate of excretion of glucose in the urine of the adrenalectomized animals is considerably less than that of the controls.

The mode of action of the cortical hormones has been studied by using liver and kidney slices in vitro. The conversion of alanine and glutamic acid to carbohydrate in kidney slice experiments is slower with kidney from adrenalectomized than from normal animals. Glucose, pyruvic acid, and lactic acid are converted to glycogen by liver slices at rates independent of the status of the adrenal glands in the animal. Such experiments tend to confirm the gluconeogenic effect of cortical hormones and indicate that the action consists of promotion of deamination of amino acids.

Clinically, cortical deficiency is associated with hypertrophy of lymphatic tissue, and lymphocytosis. On the other hand it is possible to produce lymphocytopenia in normal animals by injection of cortical extract or adrenocorticotropic hormone of the pituitary gland. It is believed that antibodies (γ-globulin) originate chiefly from the breakdown of lymphocytes which may explain susceptibility to infection in patients with cortical deficiency as a result of impairment of the normal rate of disintegration of lymphocytes. It has been suggested that leukemias and lymphatic neoplasms may be beneficially affected by administration of cortical hormones.

The adrenal glands have a high content of cholesterol and it is likely that cholesterol serves as the material from which the glands produce the various cortical hormones. It is possible that this process involves a conjugation between the steroid molecule and ascorbic acid. However, there is no evidence at present to prove the actual pathway followed in the natural synthesis of the steroid hormones. The content of cholesterol and ascorbic acid in the adrenal cortex of the rat decreases following non-fatal hemorrhage and shock. Under such conditions the cholesterol content of liver and brain remains unaltered. Such observations may be interpreted in favor of cholesterol being a cortical hormone precursor.

THE HORMONES OF THE ADRENAL CORTEX

The biologically active secretion of the adrenal cortex consists of steroid complexes which can be crystallized and amorphous material. At the present time approximately 30 different steroid compounds have been isolated from the adrenal cortex. More than 40 have been recovered from human urine. One fourth of these substances are active biologically, the activity varying greatly both qualitatively and quantitatively.

The general configuration and nomenclature of the steroids is discussed in Chapter 6, and the description of the cortical steroids with substitutions at C_{11} and C_{17} should be reviewed by the reader. The crystalline substances of special biological interest are:

> Corticosterone
> Desoxycorticosterone
> 11-Dehydrocorticosterone
> 17-Hydroxycorticosterone
> 11-Dehydro-17-hydroxycorticosterone
> 11-Desoxy-17-hydroxycorticosterone

Another steroid with biological activity has been isolated from the adrenal cortex of cattle. This hormone yields adrenosterone upon oxidation with periodic acid or chromic acid and splits off ascorbic acid upon hydrolysis in the absence of oxygen. Previous observations have shown that adrenal cortex is rich in ascorbic acid, and that this vitamin tends to disappear during excessive demands upon the gland. The steroid-ascorbic acid complex has not been isolated from the adrenal cortex of guinea pigs or humans, who derive their ascorbic acid from food, being unable to synthesize this vitamin. This is the first instance of a combination of a steroid hormone with a vitamin.

The interrelationship of the steroid hormones of the cortex both in regard to structure and to function increases in complexity when the steroid sex hormones are considered. In spite of the known correlation of biological activity concerning electrolyte and carbohydrate metabolism with specific configurations at positions 11 and 17 of the sterol ring structure, there is some overlapping of functions. Moreover, this overlapping of functions can be observed between cortical and sex hormones. For instance, very large doses of desoxycorticosterone will elicit mild estrus upon injection into females. Normal male urine contains substances with properties of cortical hormones. Venning and associates have demonstrated that these substances promote gluconeogenesis, and Dorfman and associates have shown that adrenalectomized rats can be protected against the effects of cold by injection with such excretory substances. One case has been reported of carcinoma of the adrenal cortex in a male who developed gynecomastia and a high concentration of estrogens in the urine.

Desoxycorticosterone (DOCA) has a most potent effect in causing retention of water and salt and increases the excretion of potassium and phosphorus. Excessive administration of this hormone results in abnormal retention of salt and water resulting in edema, increase in blood volume, and occasionally in failure of the heart. The hormone has a specific hypertensive effect which is apparent upon its administration to subjects with total deficiency of cortical function. It is likely that other substances in the normal adrenal cortex are able to counterbalance this effect because it cannot be elicited upon administration to normal subjects nor is it produced by adrenocortical extracts.

The adrenocortical hormones with an oxygen atom or hydroxyl group at C_{11} have the gluconeogenic properties described above. These hormones include corticosterone, 11-dehydrocorticosterone, 17-hydroxycorticosterone, and 11-dehydro-17-hydroxycorticosterone (Kendall's Compound E).

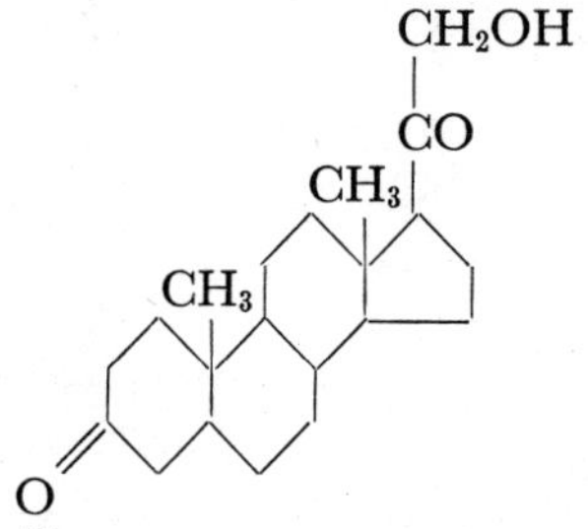

DESOXYCORTICOSTERONE

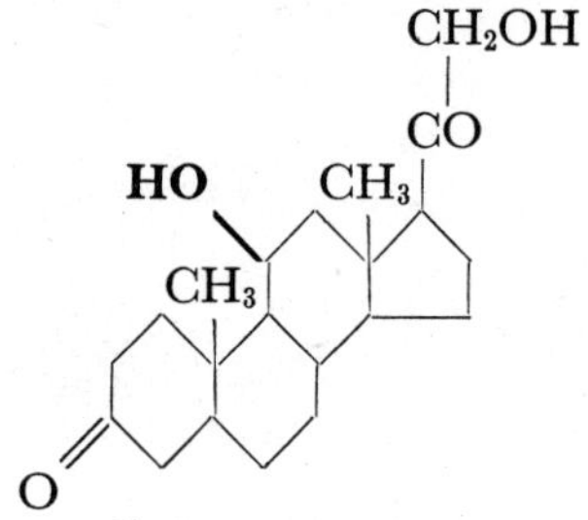

CORTICOSTERONE

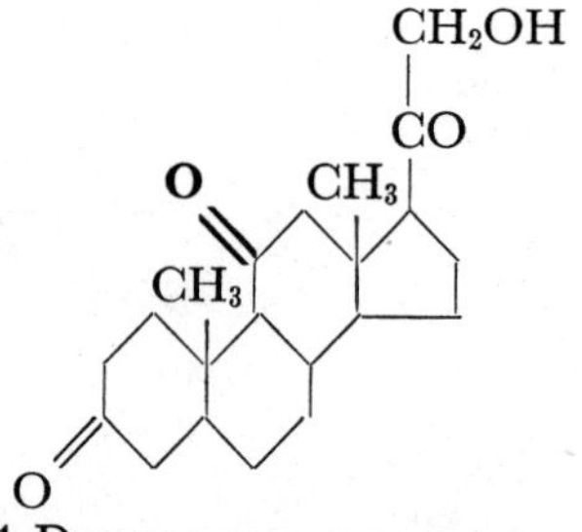

11-DEHYDROCORTICOSTERONE

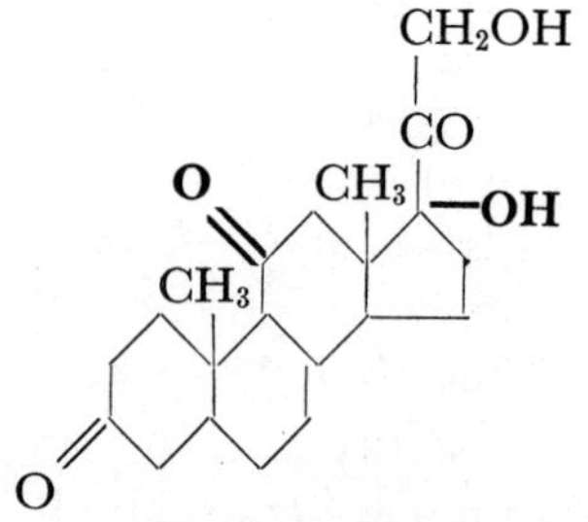

11-DEHYDRO-17-HYDROXYCORTICOSTERONE

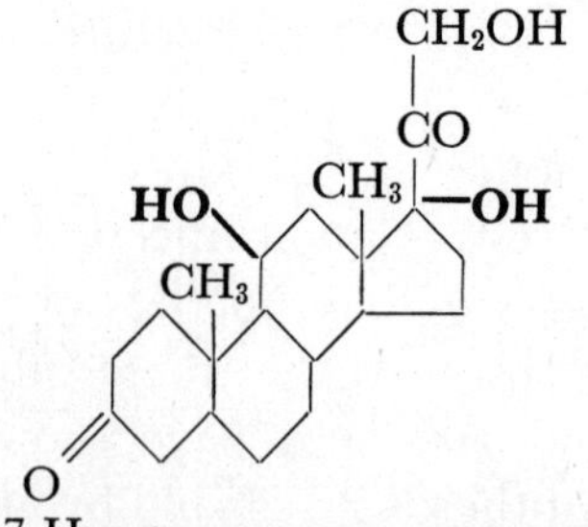

17-HYDROXYCORTICOSTERONE

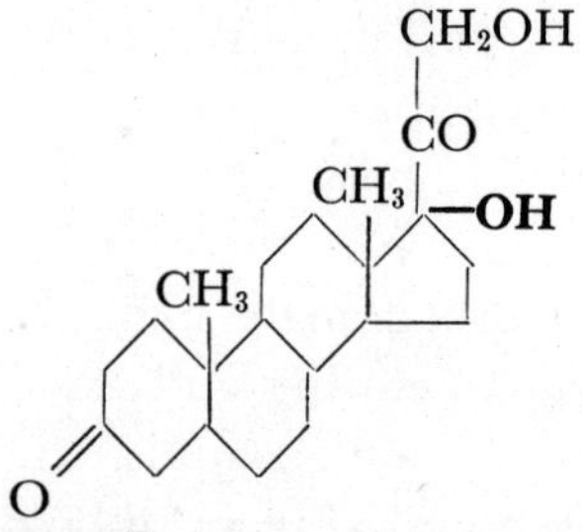

11-DESOXY-17-HYDROXYCORTICOSTERONE

Corticosterone and 11-dehydrocorticosterone bring about a slight salt retention effect while 11-dehydro-17-hydroxycorticosterone stimulates urinary excretion of sodium and thus contributes to a negative sodium balance. The same effect on salt balance is exerted by 17-hydroxycorticosterone so that it appears that introduction of a hydroxyl group at C_{17} induces effects which are opposite to those of desoxycorticosterone.

ADDISON'S DISEASE

This condition is usually produced by bilateral atrophic changes in the adrenal cortex or by destruction from tuberculous infection. Many other infections are able to affect the adrenal cortex but most of these infections do not induce sufficiently extensive damage to elicit the clinical picture of Addison's disease. The adrenals have outstanding ability to recuperate their function following injury by an acute infection. Sudden and extensive destruction of the glands may occur as a result of bilateral hemorrhage, usually associated with meningococcus infections. In such rapid destruction the clinical features are different from those of the much more slowly progressing changes in Addison's disease (see Waterhouse-Friderichsen syndrome). Addison originally described the disease as of slow and insidious onset, characterized by general languor and debility, with changes in the color of the skin, and feebleness of action of the heart. Patients with Addison's disease complain of loss of weight and appetite, gastro-intestinal changes with vomiting, constipation or diarrhea, occasionally diffuse abdominal pains, and changes in the color of the skin. The disease is usually associated with hypotension.

The development of crisis in Addison's disease is a dramatic intensification of the various pathological processes, and it is not uncommon that a crisis is the first event demanding medical attendance in the development of the disease. The patient in crisis is in shock and severe dehydration and immediate treatment is imperative to save his life.

The chemical changes which are demonstrable in Addison's disease are essentially those occurring in experimental animals subsequent to adrenalectomy. The serum exhibits decrease in sodium and increase in potassium concentrations. There is an increase in urinary elimination of sodium and acidosis may develop because urinary loss of sodium exceeds that of anions.

In Addison's disease laboratory findings (decrease in sodium and increase in potassium and total protein in serum, and higher hematocrit readings) vary greatly. During crisis these changes are well defined but at other times they may not be of sufficient magnitude to be interpreted unequivocally. A diagnosis may be made after using procedures which tend to intensify the physiological disturbances. Such tests, however, should be used with great caution as they may throw a comparatively well compensated patient into crisis.

In 1933, Harrop and associates suggested a salt deprivation test in questionable cases of Addison's disease. In this test the demonstration of excretion of sodium in the urine in excess of sodium intake, and a drop in sodium concentration in the serum, point toward the presence of Addison's disease. Modifications of this test were made by Cutler, Power, and Wilder, who recommended a diet containing a definite amount of sodium chloride and potassium. The concentration of chlorides in the urine after the patient has been on the diet for 48 hours is used as the index for the test. Robinson, Power, and Kepler developed two diagnostic procedures (the 'water test') which Levy, Power, and Kepler subjected to analysis in 1946. In the water test, the first procedure is based on determination of the rate of formation of urine under specified conditions. Patients with cortical deficiency appear unable to excrete ingested water at the normal rate and eliminate a large portion of the urine during the night, in contrast to normal persons who excrete most of their urine during the day. The test is negative (signifying the probable absence of Addison's disease) 'if the volume of any single hourly specimen voided during the morning is greater than the volume of urine voided during the night.' The second procedure involves measurement of the clearance of urea and chloride and the ratio of volume of day urine to that of night urine. An index is determined according to the following formula:

$$A = \frac{\text{Urea clearance}}{\text{Chloride clearance}} \times \frac{\text{Volume of day urine}}{\text{Volume of night urine}}$$

The clearance for this purpose is determined on the basis of urine collected during the water test between 10:30 p.m. and 7:30 a.m., the plasma urea and chloride concentrations being ascertained on blood obtained at 11 a.m. The value of A in Addison's disease is low, usually less than 30. According to Levy and associates positive tests in the first procedure may occur in a variety of conditions so that the test cannot be interpreted as establishing a diagnosis of cortical deficiency. Although a negative test in the first procedure is rare except in Addison's disease, it does occur, and in such cases diagnosis is difficult to establish by other procedures. In cases reported by Levy the administration of salt, desoxycorticosterone, or cortical extract did not appear to correct the factors which caused the water excretion to be abnormal. The water test has the advantage that it is safer than the provocative tests involving changes in normal intake of electrolytes. Negative water tests in suspected cases of cortical deficiency may be followed up by the other tests.

A large proportion of patients with Addison's disease exhibit abnormalities of carbohydrate metabolism. Most of them have fasting blood glucose levels somewhat below the average normal, and the glucose tolerance curve has a flat configuration frequently not attended by a rise in blood glucose concentration at any time during the test and often terminating in hypoglycemia which may be severe. Thorn and his associates found that the intravenous glucose tolerance test yields peak glucose values comparable to those of normals but that the patients tend to pass into severe degrees of hypoglycemia at the end of the test. These findings indicate abnormalities in intestinal absorption of glucose in cortical deficiency. The influence of the cortical hormones in gluconeogenesis has been discussed previously.

Severe hypoglycemic periods constitute one of the acute dangers in Addison's disease. In contradistinction to insulin shock in the treated diabetic, the hypoglycemia in Addison's disease does not tend to improve spontaneously, and the patient is apt to die in the absence of prompt treatment. The hypoglycemia may occur spontaneously or it may be precipitated by an acute infection. This effect in addition to the lack of response in the normal immune antibody mechanism may explain the fact that an acute infection, often of minor character, may be the precipitating factor in crisis. As is to be expected, these patients are very sensitive to insulin. Patients with diabetes and Addison's disease present a difficult problem, fortunately encountered only rarely. In such patients the cortical deficiency tends to ameliorate the severity of the diabetes as measured by the amount of insulin required, but the sensitivity to insulin remains. It is likely that some degree of liver damage is associated with depletion of liver glycogen stores in Addison's disease. Thorn and his co-workers have found the intravenous hippuric acid test to give abnormal results in these patients.

The urinary excretion of 17-ketosteroids in cortical deficiency has been discussed in Chapter 6. In total destruction of both adrenals, excretion of 17-ketosteroids by the female drops to zero while in the male the gonads may account for an excretion of a few milligrams in 24 hours.

Thorn has used the effect of cortical hormones on lymphocytic activity as a test for cortical deficiency. In the presence of normal cortical tissue, the injection of adrenotropic hormones of the pituitary gland stimulates the breakdown of lymphocytes, which is evidenced by an increased excretion of uric acid. He measures the change in uric acid excretion as compared with the excretion of creatinine which presumably remains constant. Thorn also finds a specific response in the circulating eosinophilic cells.

Many asthenic patients present symptoms resembling those of mild Addison's disease. Such patients should not be designated as suffering from cortical deficiency unless positive evidence is present in favor of the diagnosis. Certainly the empirical use of cortical extracts and specific hormones in unconfirmed cases should be condemned.

WATERHOUSE-FRIDERICHSEN SYNDROME

This condition is rare; the majority of recorded cases have occurred in infants although a number of patients have been in older childhood or in adult age. In infants the syndrome is produced most frequently by trauma at time of birth; in some instances congenital syphilis has been considered the cause. In older children and adults the disease is usually associated with severe sepsis, the majority of the cases involving the meningococcus although other bacteria such as streptococcus hemolyticus and viridans have been implicated.

It is interesting that in cases where the meningococcus has been isolated that a typical meningitis is generally absent. Occasionally increased intracranial pressure is present with symptoms of encephalitis. The disease tends to progress to a fatal termination so rapidly that time does not permit a purulent meningitis to develop. Instances of recovery from the disease are reported in recent literature. It is difficult to establish the accuracy of the diagnosis in such cases because the meningococcemia may well be responsible for the clinical picture without involving adrenal hemorrhage.

The pathological finding is extensive bilateral hemorrhage into the adrenal glands. Smaller adrenal hemorrhage may occur in many acute infectious diseases, purpura, neoplastic diseases, hemophilia, and other conditions but such hemorrhage is generally too insignificant to produce the Waterhouse-Friderichsen syndrome.

Treatment of the Waterhouse-Friderichsen syndrome is essentially the same as that employed in the crisis of Addison's disease. The chemical changes induced by cortical deficiency are generally lacking because of the rapid course of events.

CORTICAL TUMORS OR HYPERPLASIA

The association of the adrenal cortex and the pituitary gland in Cushing's syndrome is discussed in Chapter 12. It is important to remember that not all tumors of the adrenal gland are associated with abnormalities of endocrine function. Hyperplasia and tumors producing cortical hormones may induce a variety of manifestations. Cushing's syndrome places emphasis upon the characteristic type of obesity, hypertension, decreased glucose tolerance, polycythemia, striae, discoloration of the skin, and osteoporosis. Another group exhibits sexual changes predominantly, the form of these changes depending greatly upon the age at which the disorder develops. Important symptoms and signs are precocious physical and sexual development, hirsutism, impotence, amenorrhea, and occasionally pseudohermaphroditism and a tendency to sex reversal.

The group with predominant sexual changes is referred to as the adrenogenital syndrome. A great deal of overlapping of symptoms in the two major groups may occur.

In the adrenogenital syndrome disturbances in carbohydrate metabolism occur only occasionally and frank diabetes is rarely associated with the clinical picture. When hyperglycemia occurs the level of blood glucose is relatively unaffected by large doses of insulin. Ketosis is usually not present and diabetic coma has not been reported so that it is questionable how important it is from a therapeutic standpoint to control the blood glucose level within normal limits. The effect of cortical hormones on gluconeogenesis has been discussed previously. If the increased secretion of these hormones produce an increase in the rate of gluconeogenesis it is to be expected that subjects suffering from cortical hyperplasia or a hormone-producing tumor should be in negative nitrogen balance. This has been found generally to be the case. Another factor of importance may be that certain hormones of the adrenal cortex interfere wth peripheral utilization of glucose. 11-Dehydro-17-hydroxycorticosterone has been shown to increase glycosuria without a simultaneous increase in nitrogen excretion in adrenalectomized and depancreatized dogs. The excretion of 17-ketosteroids is usually markedly increased in cortical hyperplasia and tumors which secrete excessive amounts of hormones.

DISEASES OF ADAPTATION

Years ago Cannon clearly stated his views on the role of epinephrine in preparing an animal for a sudden effort or an emergency. In more recent years Selye and others have studied the action of adrenal cortical hormones in developing resistance to various forms of stress such as exposure to changes in environmental temperatures, prolonged effort, trauma, burns, fasting, and effects of various chemical and infectious agents. Selye has pointed out that the organism responds to various forms of stress in a manner which has many features in common. His attention was drawn to the adrenal cortex by the fact that this organ would show enlargement with histological signs of hyperactivity under prolonged conditions of stress while other organs tended to show involutional or degenerative changes. Originally the adrenal response was visualized as an 'alarm reaction' but later Selye and his co-workers developed the concept of the alarm reaction as simply the first stage of a much more prolonged 'general adaptation syndrome.' This syndrome is a defensive mechanism useful to the organism and represents the normal physiological response to various forms of stress. Derangements of this mechanism may result in 'diseases of adaptation' in which inadequate secretion or disturbances in quantitative relationship of pituitary and cortical hormone production are primary etiological factors. Diseases such as rheumatic fever, rheumatoid arthritis, cardio-vascular disorders, nephrosclerosis and others are viewed as diseases of adaptation.

SUPPLEMENTARY READING

Dorfman, R. I., Horwitt, B. N., and Fish, W. R.: Presence of a cortin-like substance (cold-protecting material) in the urine of normal men. *Science, 96:*496, 1942.

ELKINTON, J. R., WINKLER, A. W., and DANOWSKI, T. S.: Transfers of cell sodium and potassium in experimental and clinical conditions. *J. Clin. Investigation, 27:74*, 1948.

FENN, W. O.: The role of potassium in physiological processes. *Physiol. Rev., 20:377*, 1940.

GUTTMAN, P. H.: Addison's disease. A statistical analysis of 566 cases and a study of the pathology. *Arch. Path., 10:742*, 1930.

HARROP, G. A., NICHOLSON, W. M., SOFFER, L. J., and STRAUSS, M.: Extracellular and intracellular water loss during suprarenal insufficiency in the dog. *Proc. Soc. Exper. Biol. & Med., 32:1312*, 1935.

LEVY, M. S., POWER, M. H., and KEPLER, E. J.: The specificity of the "water test" as a diagnostic procedure in Addison's disease. *J. Clin. Endocrinol., 6:607*, 1946.

LOWENSTEIN, B. E., and ZWEMER, R. L.: The isolation of a new active steroid from the adrenal cortex. *Endocrinology, 39:63*, 1946.

NELSON, N., GRAYMAN, I., and MIRSKY, I. A.: The utilization of acetone bodies. III. The influence of adrenalectomy. *J. Biol. Chem., 132:711*, 1940.

Pituitary-Adrenal Function. Am. A. Adv. Sc., 1950.

ROBINSON, F. J., POWER, M. H., and KEPLER, E. J.: Two new procedures to assist in the recognition and exclusion of Addison's disease: A preliminary report. *Proc. Staff Meet. Mayo Clin., 16:577*, 1941.

SOFFER, L. J.: *Diseases of the Adrenals*. Lea & Febiger, 1946.

Symposium on Steroids in Experimental and Clinical Practice. The Blakiston Co., 1951.

TALBOTT, J. H., PECORA, L. J., MELVILLE, R. S., and CONSOLAZIO, W. V.: Renal function in patients with Addison's disease and in patients with adrenal insufficiency secondary to pituitary pan-hypofunction. *J. Clin. Investigation, 21:107*, 1942.

THORN, G. W.: *The Diagnosis and Treatment of Adrenal Insufficiency*. American Lecture Series, Charles C Thomas, Publisher, 1951.

THORN, G. W., and CLINTON, M., JR.: Metabolic changes in a patient with Addison's disease following the onset of diabetes mellitus. *J. Clin. Endocrinol., 3:335*, 1943.

THORN, G. W., KOEPF, G. F., LEWIS, R. A., and OLSEN, E. F.: Carbohydrate metabolism in Addison's disease. *J. Clin. Investigation, 19:813*, 1940.

VENNING, E. H.: Evaluation of adrenal cortical function in man. *Med. Clin. North America*, p. 89, Jan., 1948. W. B. Saunders Company.

VENNING, E. H., HOFFMAN, M. M., and BROWNE, J. S. L.: The life-maintaining and gluconeogenic properties of the cortin-like material excreted postoperatively. *J. Biol. Chem., 148:455*, 1943.

Chapter 16

DISORDERS OF THE BONES

BONES are made up of an organic matrix and inorganic material, largely calcium phosphate. The rigidity of the bones is due to the inorganic component which normally constitutes approximately 45 per cent by weight of the dry bone. About 25 per cent of the bone is water and the remaining 30 per cent is organic material, forming the osteoid framework in which the inorganic material is deposited. The inorganic constituent is mainly a double salt of calcium combined with phosphate and carbonate according to the general formula: $(Ca_3(PO_4)_2)_n \cdot CaCO_3$. The value of n varies between 2 and 3, the highest value being found in early life.

Besides the calcium and phosphate and carbonate, bone contains a small amount of magnesium phosphate and other minerals in traces. Occasionally the inorganic constituents of bone include unusual elements of chemical behaviour similar to the normal constituents. Such, for instance, are lead and radium.

The interpretation of the altered biochemical conditions which are found in bone disorders depends upon an understanding of the normal calcium and phosphorus metabolism including the enzymic and hormonal factors controlling these metabolic processes. Abnormalities in the bone marrow also are occasionally reflected in detectable biochemical changes.

CALCIUM AND PHOSPHORUS METABOLISM

Calcium is supplied in certain foods such as milk, beans, and spinach and is absorbed in the small intestine. The average daily requirement for maintenance of normal calcium balance is approximately 0.5 gms., but more must be ingested because only a part of it is assimilated. Conditions prevailing in the intestinal tract largely govern the amount of calcium absorbed. A slightly acid reaction favors absorption because acid increases the solubility of calcium salts, alkali having the opposite effect. Proteins seem to aid in the absorption of calcium because soluble calcium combinations with certain amino acids are formed as digestion of the protein occurs. A high fatty acid content in the intestinal tract such as occurs in obstructive jaundice, steatorrhea, etc., tends to lower the calcium absorption through formation of insoluble calcium soaps; a comparable effect may take place if the phosphorus intake is high in proportion to the calcium because of the formation of insoluble calcium phosphate.

Certain vitamins influence the utilization of calcium. Dietary deficiency of vitamin D results in bone disorders of major clinical importance. There is, however, no unequivocal proof that vitamin D increases the absorption of calcium from the intestinal tract in the normal organism.

Phosphorus is adequate in amount if the diet is well balanced. The phosphoprotein of the diet supplies a fairly large share of the minimum requirements. Occasionally animals may develop phosphorus deficiencies if maintained upon phosphorus-poor soil, and it has been shown that milk production of cows is increased when phosphate is put on the pasture land.

Calcium is excreted in both the feces and the urine, the urinary calcium being the smaller part of the total excretion under normal conditions. Part of the calcium in the feces is derived from endogenous excretion in the bile by way of the intestine and part of it is unabsorbed from the food. If the normal calcium balance is disturbed it is frequently reflected in the excretion of calcium in the urine. For this reason crude quantitative tests for urine calcium can be used as a guide in the therapy of hypoparathyroidism.

BLOOD CALCIUM

The calcium in the blood is in equilibrium with the calcium deposits in the body, namely, bone and teeth. Blood calcium is subject to some minor temporary fluctuations after ingestion of large amounts of calcium salts. Practically all is present in the plasma or in the serum. In laboratory procedures it is customary to determine the calcium concentration in serum because the commonly used anti-coagulants precipitate calcium to prevent clotting. The calcium is partly combined in a diffusible form and this fraction is nearly all ionized. The other part of the calcium is in a non-diffusible, non-ionized state because of being in combination with protein. The solubility equilibrium between dissolved and non-dissolved calcium determines the ionized calcium level. The calcium ion concentration can be estimated by both chemical and biological assay. McLean and Hastings used the physiological effect on a frog's heart, and they expressed their results by the following equation:

$$\frac{(Ca^{++}) \times (Prot^-)}{(CaProt)} = K$$

This relationship of calcium concentration to protein concentration indicates that a good estimate of ionized calcium in the serum can be obtained if the total concentrations of calcium and protein are known. This relationship is used in the laboratory for the practical, approximate estimation of ionized calcium.

If the ionized calcium is in actual equilibrium with the non-dissolved calcium in storage, the total normal calcium concentration should vary with the concentration of the plasma proteins. If the plasma protein concentration is within normal limits, the normal total calcium concentration falls within 9 to 11 mg. per 100 cc. It cannot be emphasized too strongly that these normal limits for calcium change with the protein concentrations, and that the clinician must be cautious in the interpretation of apparently abnormal total calcium values until he has made sure that the corresponding values for the ionized calcium also are outside their normal range. Approximately 55 per cent of the total calcium of plasma is in the ionized form.

PHOSPHATASE

The development of bone is a complicated process consisting essentially of the formation of osteoid organic tissue and the deposition of mineral salts in this tissue. Undoubtedly the calcium, in the form of various salts from the absorption of food, undergoes a number of intermediary transformations through organic structures before it is laid down as the characteristic phosphatase-carbonate complexes in the bone. It is likely that in some way phosphate ions are liberated at the site of ossification from organic intermediates. Thus the concentration of phosphate ions is increased and, as the solubility product of calcium and phosphate ions limits the amount which can stay in solution, it follows that insoluble calcium salts are formed and are deposited in the osteoid tissue. It is believed that the conversion of phosphorus from the organic to the inorganic form is under the control of enzymes called *phosphatases*. Phosphatases may be produced by osteoblastic cells, but ossification is not just a simple matter of interaction of phosphatase from these cells with intermediate phosphorus compounds because phosphatase is found in other tissues without causing deposition of calcium.

From a clinical standpoint it is not yet possible to determine the degree of phosphatase activity at the site of ossification but increased activity is reflected by an elevation of the phosphatase content of the blood. As in all enzyme determinations the quantitative effect of the enzyme is measured by use of a substrate under standardized conditions. Two methods are commonly used. The Bodansky method is based on the rate of conversion of sodium glycerophosphate to inorganic phosphate and the King and Armstrong method measures the rate of liberation of phenol from disodium phenyl phosphate. Because of the arbitrary conditions under which these 2 tests are performed, the units expressing the phosphatase activity are different. One *Bodansky unit* corresponds to approximately 2 *King and Armstrong units*.

If the ability of blood to split organic phosphate complexes is determined over a wide range of pH, it will be found that there are two pH values for optimum activity. These are at approximately 5 and 9 on the pH scale, and it is, therefore, assumed that blood contains two distinct phosphatases, called the *acid phosphatase* and the *alkaline phosphatase* respectively. The alkaline phosphatase is usually studied in disorders of bones while an acid phosphatase is of interest because of its specific behaviour in metastatic carcinoma of the prostate.

VITAMIN D

This oil-soluble vitamin is necessary for normal bone development. While it may be questionable if increases in the vitamin D intake in the normal organism influence the rate of absorption of calcium from the intestinal tract, with a deficiency of vitamin D normal absorption will not take place no matter how abundantly calcium and phosphorus are supplied. Besides this regulatory effect on absorption, vitamin D has a specific function in assisting the deposition of the calcium salts in the osteoid tissue. Calcium is mobilized from the bones by extremely large doses of vitamin D which resembles the action of the parathyroid hormone in this respect.

A number of compounds are known with vitamin D properties. They are steroid derivatives obtainable in the active form from natural sources such as fish oils, etc., or by irradiation of other steroids such as ergosterol. The various steroids with vitamin D activity are designated D_1, D_2, D_3, etc. Fish oil yields D_3:

VITAMIN D_3

The distinguishing feature of all vitamin D structures is that ring B is open with an additional double bond in the open ring giving three conjugated double bonds. The structure of vitamin D_2, *calciferol,* is similar to D_3 except for the C_{17} side chain, which is that found in ergosterol. One of the irradiation products of the vitamin D series is *dehydrotachysterol* (A. T. 10) which acts very similarly to the parathyroid hormones.

RICKETS

This disease of childhood is the result of a deficiency of vitamin D. Its prevention or cure depends on correction of the fundamental deficiency by administration of adequate amounts of vitamin D or exposure to sunlight. Ultra-violet radiation converts 7-dehydrocholesterol in the skin into antirachitic vitamin D_3. A dietary intake of calcium and phosphorus less than the minimal requirements tends to produce the same clinical picture of severe rickets regardless of the amount of vitamin D ingested. As stated previously, the condition cannot be ameliorated by large amounts of calcium and phosphorus in the absence of vitamin D.

In rickets the bones are deficient in the inorganic bone salts. Such bone salts as are deposited are normal in their composition, there being no change from the normal proportion of calcium and phosphorus. The serum concentration of calcium is usually close to the normal, but the serum phosphorus content is lower than the 5 mg. per 100 cc. which is normal for a child. High values of alkaline phosphatase in the blood are the rule, possibly as a reflection of increased attempts on the part of the bone-forming cells to produce normal ossification. It should be borne in mind that normal alkaline phosphatase values in infants may be as high as 12 Bodansky units, while in normal adults the value lies between 1.5 and four units. The phosphatase in blood gradually returns to the normal range after administration of vitamin D.

Osteomalacia is a manifestation of vitamin D deficiency in the adult. In contradistinction to infantile rickets the proportion of calcium to phosphorus in the bone salts is altered, the calcium content being proportionally lower. Osteomalacia frequently is attended by a lowering of the calcium concentration of the blood so that tetany may be part of the clinical picture.

Celiac rickets is a childhood disorder exhibiting defects in the metabolism of fats with resulting derangement of the calcium absorption. The underlying pathology is probably a primary failure to absorb vitamin D from the intestinal tract. A large part of the ingested calcium is excreted in the fatty stools as calcium soaps. In the adult, *idiopathic steatorrhea*, or *non-tropical sprue*, is a condition similar in fundamental pathology to celiac rickets. In these conditions the calcium and phosphorus concentrations of blood are generally low and tetany is a common symptom.

PARATHYROID DISORDERS

Calcium ions and phosphorus ions together in the same medium will combine to form calcium phosphates of varying compositions. These phosphate salts are very insoluble and the small degree to which they can dissolve depends on the product of their ion concentrations, expressed by a simplified equation:

$$(Ca\text{-ions}) \times (Phosphate\text{-ions}) = K$$

If the product of the two concentrations is equal to K the solution is saturated, if greater than K a certain amount of phosphate must be precipitated. The equation also makes it plain that the concentrations of the 2 ions must vary inversely and, therefore, increases in the calcium ion concentration in the plasma are usually associated with decreases in the phosphorus concentration and vice versa. The actual numerical expressions of the concentrations of calcium and phosphate ions in plasma do not conform to constants determined in a pure solution because plasma contains many components which influence the ionic balance. The ranges of calcium and phosphorus concentrations among other factors depend upon the activity of the parathyroid glands. Increased parathyroid activity produces elevation of the calcium levels and depression of the phosphorus, while a hypoparathyroid state has the opposite effect.

Hyperparathyroidism (von Recklinghausen's disease) is characterized by an elevation of the blood calcium level and an accompanying reduction in blood phosphorus concentration, together with an increase in the amounts of calcium and phosphorus excreted in the urine. Most frequently the disease is associated with a solitary adenoma of one of the parathyroid glands, and the surgical removal of the adenoma reverses the abnormal changes in the calcium and phosphorus balance. Surgery of this nature occasionally necessitates the administration of parathyroid hormones for a period of time following the operation due to a secondary hypoplasia of the remaining glands. The changes in calcium balance described can be produced experimentally by injection of parathyroid extracts. The urinary phosphorus excretion rises rapidly after injection of the hormones, and it has been proposed that the initial effect is a lowering of the renal threshold for phosphates with a secondary rise of blood calcium derived mainly from the bone. After experimental administration of the parathyroid hormone it can be shown that there is an increase in certain other urinary excretion products such as water, sodium, potassium, etc. It has been suggested at various times that the action is due to a stimulation of osteoclasts or possibly to the removal of calcium from the bone by a direct combination with the hormone. The exact mechanism is not understood at present. The increase of calcium in the serum of patients with hyperparathyroidism is often not large. In some cases the calcium concentration may be only slightly higher than 11 mg. per 100 cc., and in suspected cases it is advisable to determine the calcium level at intervals over quite a period of time. Similarly a low phosphorus level is not an absolute rule. The phosphatase of the blood is quite uniformly increased, frequently to very high values.

In von Recklinghausen's disease the bones eventually show marked osteoporosis with the characteristic cystic areas of decalcification which have given the name *osteitis fibrosa cystica* to the disease. Deposits of calcium in the kidneys may give rise to renal calculi which may be the first subjective manifestation of the malady. Renal impairment with nitrogen retention is seen frequently in untreated hyperparathyroidism; presumably the damage is caused by calcium precipitates in the kidney substance. As a complicating factor, kidney damage may induce parathyroid hyperplasia. As a matter of fact, a number of diseases with bone manifestations have been reported to be associated with hypertrophic changes of the parathyroids. Rigid biological studies are not always available to support some of these concepts.

Renal damage in the course of hyperparathyroidism may confuse the chemical picture as the phosphorus level may undergo a secondary rise due to impairment of its excretion through the kidneys. The resulting depression of the abnormally elevated calcium concentration may lower it toward a more normal level. The phosphatase remains high, however, and the characteristic x-ray findings, pertaining to the bones, usually leave little doubt as to the diagnosis.

Hypoparathyroidism as a clinical entity is encountered much more frequently than hyperparathyroidism. Most cases are due to the unintentional removal of the parathyroid glands during thyroidectomy. Idiopathic hypoparathyroidism is seen occasionally.

Hypoparathyroidism results in a lowering of the blood calcium and an increase in the phosphorus levels. The upper normal limit for serum phosphorus in adults is 4 mg. per 100 cc. As the calcium concentration drops, the clinical symptoms of the disorder are correlated with this decrease. Actually the ionized calcium is the determining factor, but in a patient with spontaneous parathyroid deficiency both ionized and unionized calcium levels presumably follow parallel changes.

The symptomatic effect of a lowering of the blood calcium concentration is due to an increase in neuromuscular excitability. As a rule, patients with calcium levels below 7 mg. per 100 cc. show fibrillary twitchings of the muscles followed by the clonic and tonic muscular contractions of *tetany*. In the range between normal calcium values and those concentrations associated with manifest tetany, the patients show increased neuromuscular response to stimuli, and this state is referred to as *latent tetany*.

The urinary calcium excretion is low in hypoparathyroidism. The excretion of phosphorus may also be low but this finding is not uniformly present. When the disorder is treated by administration of parathyroid hormone (*parathormone*) the manifestations of hyperirritability of the neuromuscular system subside and the chemical changes in blood and urine are reversed. Continuous administration of parathormone eventually results in a more or less refractory state. In recent years *dihydrotachysterol* (A. T. 10) has been used, as its effect is similar to the parathyroid hormones and the patients do not become refractory to it. A. T. 10 has the additional advantage of being effective if administered orally. Treatment of hypoparathyroidism is facilitated by administration of high calcium, low phosphorus diets.

Gastric tetany is a term used to characterize the tetanic convulsions observed in severe alkalosis. It is thought that this condition is brought about by a marked depression of the ionized calcium. Bodlander's equation:

$$[Ca^{++}] = K\frac{[H^+]}{[HCO_3^-]}$$

gives an expression of the changes to be expected in the concentration of ionized calcium from a shift in acid-base balance. The equation shows that an increase in the bicarbonate fraction with the associated decrease in hydrogen ions can be responsible for a lowering of the concentration of ionized calcium even if the total concentration is normal.

NEOPLASTIC CHANGES IN BONE

Bone tumors do not necessarily give rise to demonstrable biochemical changes. Some of the pathological conditions considered up to this point have been noteworthy in this respect that formation of bone has been a prominent feature even if the osteogenesis is an attempt at repair incidental to the primary destruction of bone. It is to be expected that neoplastic changes involving the proliferation or destruction of osseous tissue will result in changes in the values of calcium, phosphorus, and phosphatase in the blood. On the other hand, benign tumors usually do not involve bone-forming cells and, therefore, do not result in demonstrable biochemical changes.

Alkaline phosphatase is probably formed by the osteoblasts; thus its concentration in the blood may be an index of the osteoblastic activity. In agreement with this is the fact that fluctuations in the blood phosphatase follow closely the clinical changes when bone tumors are treated. Removal of a malignant growth associated with marked osteoblastic activity is attended by a decrease in the abnormal phosphatase levels and a coincidental increase is often observed with recurrence of the malignancy. In lesions of strictly osteoclastic nature, where bone destruction is the dominant feature without attempts at repair, the blood phosphatase is usually normal.

Osteogenic sarcoma may be manifested in various forms. It is unusual for the neoplastic changes to produce detectable alterations in the calcium and phosphorus levels. In the osteoblastic types the alkaline phosphatase may reach very high values, while in the strictly osteolytic processes the blood phosphatase is usually not affected, or only to a very minor degree. *Ewing's endothelial tumor* is not reflected in any increase in the blood phosphatase while *giant cell tumors* may occasionally show slight increases.

Metastatic carcinoma in bone frequently behaves in the same manner as the primary tumors from the standpoint of demonstrable biochemical changes. In most cases the levels of calcium and phosphorus remain within normal limits. At times a minor elevation of the calcium is found with associated normal phosphorus. On rare occasions the calcium concentration may rise considerably. The phosphatase value is generally correlated with the relationship of osteoblastic and osteoclastic activity, and metastatic bone tumors with marked osteoblastic features may exhibit phosphatase values as high as those seen in the primary tumors.

Metastatic lesions of the bone from *carcinoma of the prostate* have a special interest. They generally conform to the behaviour of osteoblastic tumors by increasing the blood phosphatase. Besides the increase in alkaline phosphatase there is an associated increase in the acid phosphatase, the source of which apparently is the metastatic prostatic cells. It can be shown by special staining techniques that the acid phosphatase content is very high in these cells. However, this abundant supply of acid phosphatase does not result in increase in the blood as long as the neoplastic growth is confined within the capsule of the prostate. It was originally thought that an elevated acid phosphatase level was diagnostic of disseminated prostatic carcinoma. This is not quite true as other conditions may cause such an increase, however, in suspected malignant lesions of the bone high acid phosphatase values strongly indicate that the prostate is the primary site of the neoplasm.

Multiple myeloma is a neoplastic process arising in the bone marrow. The osseous tissue surrounding the tumor is gradually decalcified and regeneration of bone is slight or absent; therefore, the disease is not accompanied by a rise in blood phosphatase above normal levels.

Certain chemical features are characteristic of the disease. It has been known for a long time that a specific protein, the Bence-Jones protein, occurs in the urine of patients with multiple myeloma. This protein precipitates at temperatures between 40° and 60° C. and redissolves at higher temperatures. At the boiling point other urinary proteins are precipitated and they can, therefore, be separated from the redissolved Bence-Jones protein by filtration at the high temperature. If the urine is observed while cooling the Bence-Jones protein will be seen to reappear as a precipitate in the same temperature range as that in which it was originally precipitated.

The presence of Bence-Jones protein is not a satisfactory diagnostic test for multiple myeloma as it is occasionally observed in other malignancies. It is extremely likely, however, that such neoplastic processes must have invaded the bone marrow to elicit the urinary excretion of the characteristic protein. It is also important to note that Bence-Jones protein is present in the urine in approximately 2/3 only of patients with multiple myeloma, so that its absence in the urine does not rule out the diagnosis. However, some investigators believe that careful search in 24 hour urine specimens will reveal the presence of Bence-Jones protein in a much higher percentage of cases.

The hyperproteinemia commonly observed in multiple myeloma is a very interesting phenomenon. The increase in protein is almost exclusively confined to the globulin fraction, and serum globulin values may go as high as 10 gm. per 100 cc. of serum. If the blood proteins are subjected to electrophoretic separation as in the Tiselius apparatus, it can be shown that the increase in their concentration can be assigned at least in part to a specific fraction of the globulins. It would be tempting to explain the increased globulin fraction as due to the presence of Bence-Jones protein in the blood, but this specific substance is probably only a part of the increase. It should be remembered that many types of neoplastic growths may be attended by higher values of the blood globulin fraction, although of considerably less magnitude than the above changes.

Large increases in the calcium concentration of the serum are frequently found in multiple myeloma. Unlike the corresponding situation in hyperparathyroidism this finding is not generally associated with a marked increase of urinary calcium, although mild hypercalcinuria may occasionally be observed. The high blood calcium should be interpreted in relation to the hyperproteinemia. If the ionized calcium fraction is calculated on the basis of McLean and Hastings' equation, it will be found frequently that the increase in calcium level is almost entirely in the non-diffusible form, and that the ionized calcium falls within normal limits. This may explain the relative absence of excessive urinary calcium.

Renal impairment is a feature of importance in multiple myeloma as evidence of retention of urinary excretory products is present in approximately 7 out of 10 patients. The actual cause of the kidney damage has not been determined. It has been suggested that the Bence-Jones protein might be the cause of the nephritic changes, but such changes have been observed in cases with no evidence of the specific protein in the urine. Uric acid concentration of the blood increases in patients with renal failure but occasionally this increase may be observed to exceed markedly the rate of increase in the concentration of the other urinary excretion products in the blood. This may indicate a special involvement of uric acid in the neoplastic process, possibly associated with excessive breakdown of nucleoproteins, but definite experimental proof of the actual mechanism has not been presented.

PAGET'S DISEASE

This disease is frequently referred to as *Osteitis deformans* because of its tendency to produce extensive deformities in the bones. The etiology is obscure but the histological picture of the bone is characteristic. In the early stages of the disease the bones become soft from removal of inorganic constituents resulting in deformities. As the condition progresses new lamellar bone is formed causing a partial rehardening of bones, thickening of the skull, etc. This new bone is spongy in character and the inorganic content is lower than in normal bone.

The calcium and phosphorus concentrations in the serum do not usually change, but the increased osteoblastic activity results in phosphatase levels that may at times be extremely high.

ARTHRITIS

The hypertrophic and rheumatoid arthritides are not associated with characteristic chemical findings. Occasionally abnormal values of the blood calcium and phosphorus may be encountered in patients under treatment with large doses of irradiated vitamin D compounds. The vitamin in these large doses acts as does parathormone and the chemical changes are similar to those observed during administration of excessive amounts of this hormone. It has been thought that certain diseases besides rheumatoid arthritis, such as rheumatic fever, lupus erythematosis, etc., belong to a special group, the collagen diseases, and that there may be a common hormonal disturbance as the etiological background for these diseases. During pregnancy the inflammatory manifestations of rheumatoid arthritis tend to subside. The same observation has been made during attacks of hepatocellular jaundice. The observation that these conditions are associated with higher levels of steroids including the glycocorticoids led Hench and Kendall and associates to try Kendall's compound E in the treatment of rheumatoid arthritis. The spectacular effects are history now. Similar results are obtained by injection of ACTH. Upon discontinuation of treatment with either substance, the arthritic manifestations reappear rapidly with symptoms in the same joints as prior to treatment. There is no evidence at present that rheumatoid arthritis is actually produced by a deficiency of the hormones used therapeutically. The injection of ACTH may stimulate production of a cortical hormone as yet unknown, and the benefits from compound E (cortisone) may be similarly associated with an unknown hormone metabolically related. So far there are no demonstrable endocrine abnormalities present in rheumatoid arthritis. Particularly, the adrenal production of C_{11}-oxysteroids appears normal.

Gout is associated with elevated blood uric acid levels and deposits of urates in the form of tophi in cartilaginous tissue mostly involving the joints of the fingers and toes. The etiology remains undetermined although recent investigations implicate certain hormonal abnormalities. The combined use of colchicine and ACTH produces rapid improvement in acute attacks of gout. Such attacks can be precipitated by endocrine means. The retention of uric acid as such does not cause attacks of gout as the condition is not seen in other diseases causing elevated blood uric acid levels.

The hyperuricemia of gout appears to be an inherent characteristic which, although present before the onset of the disease, does not reflect itself in abnormally high plasma uric acid levels until puberty in the male and menopause in the female. Normal males and females show corresponding increases in plasma uric acid concentration but to a lesser extent. The 11-oxysteroids are potent regulators of uric acid metabolism and disturbances in metabolism of these hormones have been considered as etiological factors in gout. It has also been suggested that an abnormal male sex hormone, produced by the adrenal cortex, may be involved. Whatever the actual mechanism the administration of ACTH has important therapeutic benefits. However, relapses occur shortly after the withdrawal of the hormone unless colchicine is used simultaneously.

OTHER BONE DISORDERS

Certain bone diseases may be observed in which an unusual relationship between inorganic and organic constituents exists. In *osteogenesis imperfecta* (*fragilitis ossium*) the inorganic content is very low. Marble bone disease (*Albers-Schönberg disease*) shows increased bone density but is not necessarily associated with a disturbance in the inorganic/organic ratio. Changes in calcium, phosphorus, and phosphatase levels in the blood are occasionally associated with these diseases, but the findings are not consistent enough to be of diagnostic importance.

SUPPLEMENTARY READING

ALBRIGHT, F., BAUER, W., COCKRILL, J. R., and ELLSWORTH, R.: Studies on the physiology of the parathyroid glands. II. The relation of the serum calcium to the serum phosphorus at different levels of parathyroid activity. *J. Clin. Investigation, 9:*659, 1930-31.

ALBRIGHT, F., BLOOMBERG, E., DRAKE, T., and SULKOWITCH, H. W.: A comparison of the effects of A. T. 10 (dihydrotachysterol) and vitamin D on calcium and phosphorus metabolism in hypoparathyroidism. *J. Clin. Investigation, 17:*317, 1938.

BODANSKY, A., and JAFFE, H. L.: Phosphatase studies. III. Serum phosphatase in diseases of the bone: interpretation and significance. *Arch. Int. Med., 54:*88, 1934.

CANTAROW, A.: Bence-Jones proteinemia in multiple myeloma. *Am. J. Med. Sc., 189:*425, 1935.

GUTMAN, A. B., and KASABACH, H.: Paget's disease (osteitis deformans); Analysis of 116 cases. *Am. J. Med. Sc., 191:*361, 1936.

GUTMAN, A. B., and GUTMAN, E. B.: An "acid" phosphatase occurring in the serum of patients with metastasizing carcinoma of the prostate gland. *J. Clin. Investigation, 17:*473, 1938.

HENCH, P. S.: Therapeutic "information please": Arthritis. *J.A.M.A., 132:*974, 1946.

HUGGINS, C., and HODGE, C. V.: Studies on prostatic cancer: I. The effect of castration, of estrogen and of androgen injection on serum phosphatase in metastatic carcinoma of the prostate. *Cancer Research, 1:*293, 1941.

KING, E. J., and ARMSTRONG, A. R.: Convenient method for determining serum and bile phosphatase activity. *Canad. M.A.J., 31*:376, 1934.

McLEAN, F. C., and HASTINGS, A. B.: Clinical estimation and significance of calcium-ion concentrations in the blood. *Am. J. Med. Sc., 189*:601, 1935.

STEARNS, G.: The significance of the retention ratio of calcium: phosphorus in infants and in children. *Am. J. Dis. Child., 42*:749, 1931.

SULLIVAN, T. J., GUTMAN, E. B., and GUTMAN, A. B.: Theory and application of the serum "acid" phosphatase determination in metastasizing prostatic carcinoma of the prostate gland. *J. Urol., 48*:426, 1942.

Chapter 17

THE NERVOUS SYSTEM

THE anatomical and functional element of the nervous system is the neuron, the neuroglial cells serving as supporting tissue. A neuron consists of a cell body and 2 types of protoplasmic extension, the axon and the dendrite, which differ somewhat in structure. The axon is highly specialized structurally, is of uniform thickness, and serves functionally to conduct the nerve impulse from the cell body outward. The dendrites are usually less specialized, being arborized extensions of the cell body, which by their presence is able to increase greatly the receptive surface at the synapse.

Two types of axons are generally recognized on the basis of presence or absence of a protein-lipoid covering called the myelin sheath, viz.; myelinated or unmyelinated fibers. This sheath is not part of the neuron itself, but is an accessory structure. Both types of axons are found in the central and peripheral nervous systems but differ in one important respect in their localization. The myelin of peripheral nerve is ensheathed with a nucleated membrane called the neurilemma which plays an important role in regeneration of injured axons, this sheath being lacking about myelinated fibers of the brain and spinal cord. Here the myelin is surrounded by a neuroglia membrane which apparently does not possess the regenerative capacity of the neurilemma. Myelin is absent on dendrites where the synapse occurs. Fibers of $1-1.5\mu$ are commonly regarded as lacking a myelin sheath. Such naked fibers of the peripheral nervous system possess a nucleated sheath comparable to the neurilemma in structure and potentialities of regeneration, but these features are lacking in non-myelinated fibers of the central nervous system. Recent studies by improved methods indicate that the so-called unmyelinated fibers actually possess a thin myelin sheath, too thin to be observed by the ordinary microscope.

Stimulation of nerve fibers may be accomplished by various means. If the local excitatory state is of sufficient magnitude, it initiates an impulse which travels along the nerve fiber. Nerves have the property in common with other irritable tissues that subthreshold stimuli may be summated so that a nerve impulse may result from a series of stimuli of which each one is inadequate to elicit this response. Conduction rates of the nerve impulse vary enormously according to the diameter and condition of the nerve. Large mammalian afferent and motor fibers conduct the impulse at approximately 100 meters per second, whereas conduction in the smallest non-myelinated fibers may be as low as 0.2 meters per second. The energy for transmission is supplied by the nerve fiber over which the impulse travels. If the conductivity is depressed in a section of nerve as by cooling or application of an anaesthetic, the impulse is reduced in both velocity and amplitude while traversing this sector, but increases again to its initial characteristics upon reaching intact nerve tissue. Following the passage of an impulse the fiber passes into a refractory state during which it is unable to respond to another stimulus regardless of its strength. The duration of this state is known as the absolute refractory period, which is followed by a relative refractory period during which the strength of a stimulus necessary for excitation is above the normal excitatory threshold, but gradually decreases until the original state is re-established. Apparently a nerve has to regenerate its conduction mechanism during the refractory state; it is not merely a matter of exhaustion at the point of local excitation because the refractory nerve cannot be stimulated anywhere along its length.

THE MECHANISM OF THE NERVOUS IMPULSE

For many years the only means of studying the transmission of nerve impulses consisted of measurements of electrical changes in normal and injured nerves. The neuron in the resting stage is characterized by positive and negative electrical charges in apposition along its surface membrane. An impulse is initiated by a disturbance in the distribution of these charges, and the propagation of the disturbance is associated with the relative change in the adjacent charges traveling along the nerve fiber. The maximum change in electrical potential in a nerve as a result of excitation is called the *main action potential* or *spike potential*. Such potentials can be measured with delicate electrical instruments under certain conditions. Various devices such as the encephalograph and electrocardiograph are designed to record the pattern of electrical impulses from groups of nerves and muscles under normal and abnormal conditions. Recording of electrical potentials, however, gives information as to the electrical characteristics of the nerve impulse only; it contributes little to an understanding of the underlying chemical mechanism. Therefore, further successful studies must be concerned with details of metabolic processes in nervous tissues during rest and excitation, must account for the sources of energy which obviously must be available, and must explain the way in which impulses are transmitted to a second neuron or to an effector cell.

Early in the century it was suggested that transmission of a nervous impulse from the nerve ending to the effector cell is mediated through the liberation of a chemical compound, probably adrenaline, at the sympathetic nerve endings. Later Loewi discovered that in the perfusion fluid from a frog's heart during vagus stimulation, a substance accumulates capable of eliciting the vagus effect in a second heart. This substance was identified as *acetylcholine.* Subsequent attempts to explain the transmission of nerve impulses to the neuromuscular junction and across the ganglionic synapse by the action of a chemical substance encountered difficulties because of (1) rapidity of the transmission of the impulse; and (2) evidence from electrical phenomena of nerve conduction that there is no fundamental difference in transmission of impulses along the axon and across the synapse.

Potassium appears to play an important role in the conduction mechanism of nerve, because nerve at rest contains exceptionally large amounts of potassium, which is rapidly dissipated into the surrounding fluid after stimulation or upon deprivation of oxygen. Restoration of potassium distribution takes place when the nerve is at rest or is re-supplied with oxygen if the potassium diffusion originally is caused by asphyxiation. As already stated, the resting nerve has an electrically polarized membrane, and conduction of an impulse depends upon establishment of a point of depolarization which 'travels' along the axon. The depolarization is accompanied by increase of permeability of the membrane and release of potassium to the surrounding fluid, the opposite chain of events taking place during recovery. Increasing the concentration of potassium in the fluid surrounding a nerve decreases its action potential. Excitability may be lost entirely at sufficiently high concentrations of potassium and may be restored if the excess potassium is removed from the surrounding fluid. Cole and Curtis have calculated that the decrease in electrical resistance in the polarized membrane during transmission of an impulse is from 1,000 ohms to approximately 25 ohms per square centimeter, giving a measure of the extent to which the permeability of the axon membrane is increased for all ions including potassium. The changes in permeability may be explained as produced by the appearance and removal of acetylcholine in an intracellular process rather than that this substance is responsible for transmission of impulses from one nerve to another through an extracellular reaction. In other words, nerve impulse transmission depends on the propagation of a disturbance in an electrically polarized membrane whether this disturbance is transmitted along the axon or across a synapse to another nerve unit, while the acetylcholine comprises part of the energy system of the nerve.

Nachmansohn used the electric organ of the electric eel as material for the study of the role of acetylcholine as a chemical mediator in the transmission of the impulse from nerve to muscle. The electrical tissue consists of units of modified muscular elements, the electrical plates, in which each can develop an action potential of approximately 0.1 volt. The high voltage in these eels is produced by the arrangement of hundreds of individual tissue elements in series. The voltage of each unit is approximately the same as in ordinary nerves. It has been found that an enzyme, *cholinesterase,* is active in the hydrolysis of acetylcholine. It may be assumed that there is a direct proportionality between the rate of break-down of acetylcholine and the concentration of cholinesterase. By studying the relationship of cholinesterase concentration and the voltage and number of electric plates, Nachmansohn was able to demonstrate a close relationship between these factors. Cholinesterase is concentrated along the neuronal surface. The giant axon of the squid is easily utilized to demonstrate this because the axoplasm may be separated from the sheath and is practically free of cholinesterase, the entire enzymic activity remaining in the sheath. Motor end plates exhibit an exceptionally high concentration of cholinesterase and it has been shown that this holds true for synapses also. However, the distribution of cholinesterase along the axon is such that the difference between the axon and the synapse or motor end plate is only sufficient to permit an uninterrupted transmission of an impulse. Nachmansohn's experiments on the electric organ reveal that the rate of acetylcholine hydrolysis is adequate to split several milligrams of acetylcholine in 1/1,000 of a second, so that the time factor in transmission of neuron impulses is compatible with acetylcholine hydrolysis being part of the conduction mechanism. Cole and Curtis demonstrated a drop in resistance in the giant axon of the squid during passage of a nerve impulse and their experiment, as well as those of others, supports the view that the relationship between acetylcholine metabolism and voltage along the axon is due to the effect of the ester on surface permeability.

The question of sources of energy in nerve tissue is particularly interesting. For a long time it was impossible to demonstrate production of heat in a nerve as associated with transmission of impulses. Hill determined a rise of $7/10,000°$ C. in temperature of a nerve as the result of maximal stimulation for 10 seconds. Therefore, the energy and metabolic changes in ordinary nerves are too small to permit adequate quantitative studies being made. Nachmansohn found that these changes of heat in relation to the discharge of the electric organ were of sufficient magnitude for closer investigation. His result indicates that the energy is obtained from energy-rich phosphate bonds by a mechanism similar to that operating in muscle with transfer of phosphate to creatine through adenosine triphosphate. When the amount of acetylcholine split during an electrical discharge is calculated on the basis of the cholinesterase present, the amount of acetylcholine and of phosphocreatine transformed are of the same order of magnitude. However, the energy required per mole to acetylate choline is considerably less than that derived from 1 mole of phosphocreatine, so a significant amount of heat is unaccounted for. Brain tissue contains *cholineacetylase* which under anaerobic conditions in cell-free solution in the presence of adenosine triphosphate is able to acetylate choline. This is additional evidence in favor of phosphate bonds as the energy source in nerve tissue.

Cholineacetylase requires for its action the presence of potassium in a concentration approximately equal to that in the brain. Certain amino acids have an activating effect on the enzyme. Recently particular attention has been given to glutamic acid which increases the rate of formation of acetylcholine by nerve in vitro. Administration of glutamic acid (in the naturally occurring form) decreases the frequency of psychomotor and petit mal attacks, but does not have any effect on grand mal seizures. This amino acid is said to increase physical and mental alertness in mentally retarded subjects, and to cause rats to acquire increased ability to solve intricate maze problems. The processes underlying the production of nerve action potentials also help to explain the effects of certain substances of pharmacological importance. Bullock, Nachmansohn, and Rothenberg have shown that physostigmine (eserine) is a strong inhibitor of cholinesterase and that the nerve action potential can be abolished by sufficiently high concentration of physostigmine. The inhibitory action is reversible both in vitro and in vivo. This action of physostigmine is easily understood if acetylcholine is a depolarizing agent and if regeneration of conductivity depends upon repolarization following removal of acetylcholine by enzymic hydrolysis.

Prostigmine resembles physostigmine in its action. Acetylcholine and prostigmine are quaternary ammonium salts while physostigmine is a tertiary amine. It appears that the quaternary ammonium salts cannot penetrate the lipoid membrane of nerve while this can be accomplished by an undissociated tertiary amine such as physostigmine. These properties explain the inability of prostigmine and acetylcholine to affect nerve conduction if they are applied to the axon, while a typical reaction is elicited in contact with unmyelinated fibers. The specific effect of injected acetylcholine on the synapse apparently may be accounted for by its structural characteristics.

Attention has recently been directed to electrical potentials which occur at oil-salt solution interfaces, explaining these potentials by the preferential solution of organic bases in the oil phase, and a resulting arrangement of ions in a double layer. Lecithin and cholesterol in benzyl alcohol in contact with a salt solution give rise to relatively strong electrical potentials in the presence of small amounts of acetylcholine. Epinephrine exerts the same type of effect in a similar system where triglycerides have been substituted for lecithin and cholesterol. Such considerations have been applied to explain the action at cholinergic and adrenergic nerve endings.

Stimulation of the sympathetic nerve fibers to a frog's heart produces a substance in the perfusion fluid capable of causing sympathetic effects on another heart. It has also been shown that stimulation of sympathetic nerve fibers in an organism has remote effects of adrenergic nature on organs which have been isolated from all postganglionic fibers. The effect can be elicited after adrenalectomy. These findings led Cannon and Rosenblueth and others to conclude that the activation of the effectors by the postganglionic sympathetic nerve impulses is elicited by the release of *adrenalin* at the myo-neural junction. Cannon and Rosenblueth's experiments earlier had led them to conclude that the substance liberated by adrenergic excitor terminals was related chemically to adrenalin and that it could be secreted with either purely excitatory or purely inhibitory properties, corresponding to its formation in an excited or an inhibited effector. Two hypothetical forms of the unknown substances produced were designated sympathin E and sympathin I. Sympathin E liberated in blood vessels under certain experimental conditions affects the small intestine in an inhibitory manner (relaxation), thus demonstrating that the same substance can initiate both excitory and inhibitory actions. Demethylated adrenalin (nor-adrenalin) has been suggested as being sympathin E, but further experiments have tended to refute this possibility.

SYMPATHOMIMETIC AMINES

In recent years a number of sympathomimetic amines have become of considerable pharmacological importance. The pharmacological properties of several homologous series of amines have been investigated, such as the primary aliphatic amines (2 aminoheptane), and the aromatic amines, particularly those containing β-phenylethylamine and phenylisopropylamine structures.

The most prominent effects of the various sympathomimetic amines are similar to those of adrenalin. In contrast to adrenalin, their effects are of long duration and can be obtained by either oral or topical administration. Ephedrine typically shows these properties. Those compounds which contain a phenylisopropylamine structure, such as amphetamine, stimulate the central nervous system and are being used as analeptic and antidepressant drugs.

Dibenzyl-β-chloroethylamine hydrochloride has sympatholytic properties. Other substances with similar properties may become useful therapeutic agents in peripheral vascular disease.

CEREBROSPINAL FLUID

The composition of this fluid differs considerably from that of plasma. Deviations from the normal in respect to some of the components can be determined by procedures similar to those used for the same substances in the plasma. Comparison of the cerebrospinal fluid with plasma leads to the conclusion that the former is not a simple ultrafiltrate of the latter. Thermodynamic considerations indicate that work must be performed by the secretory cells to offset the opposing hydrostatic pressure between the capillary blood and the cerebrospinal fluid.

Normal spinal fluid usually contains 0.015 to 0.04 per cent protein. These figures apply to specimens obtained by lumbar puncture. Fluid from the cisternae or the ventricles usually has a lower protein content than lumbar fluid. This difference may be attributed to the rather sluggish circulation of the cerebrospinal fluid, with stasis in the lower part of the spinal canal. If there is mechanical obstruction to the flow this stagnation is intensified and the protein content of the fluid increases. Therefore, higher-than-normal protein concentrations in fluid from lumbar punctures have diagnostic significance in suspected lesions with obstructive features.

Brain tumors may cause an increase in the protein content of the spinal or ventricular fluid, but such findings are inconstant and do not often contribute to localization of the tumor. Attempts have been made to correlate distinct cellular types of tumors with protein levels in the cerebrospinal fluid. For instance, glioblastomas as compared statistically with oligodendrogliomas show increased protein levels, but such data are practically useless in individual diagnostic problems.

Because of the low protein concentration of cerebrospinal fluid and the much higher concentration in plasma, the admixture of a small amount of blood with the former will cause a relatively large increase in the protein level. The clinician should not place reliance on such protein values unless the fluid is obtained uncontaminated with blood from puncture trauma.

Cerebral hemorrhage may produce a bloody cerebrospinal fluid. If the hemorrhage does not communicate directly with the fluid system direct evidence of blood is not to be expected, but a gradual increase of protein concentration may result from seepage from the clot. In such cases the lumbar fluid may also show *xanthochromia* because of transport of pigments from the site of injury by phagocytic cells.

Elevated protein levels are encountered in pathological conditions associated with irritation of the lining membranes of the central nervous system. Such changes are produced by inflammatory processes of bacterial or other origin. In acute purulent meningitis the protein of the spinal fluid may reach very high levels, exceeding occasionally one gram per 100 cc. Puncture fluid from such patients is cloudy and contains a large number of cells, so that protein determinations actually are of little interest from a diagnostic standpoint. Virus infections in the central nervous system produce smaller increases in protein concentration than bacterial infections. In general, the cytology of spinal fluid in virus infections is of much more diagnostic importance than the chemical changes.

Acute syphilitic meningitis may develop at any stage of a syphilitic infection; it is most commonly observed during the second stage. In chronic (tabetic or paretic type) syphilitic infection of the central nervous system approximately ½ of the patients show spinal fluid protein levels exceeding the upper normal limit. The *Lange colloidal gold test* is particularly useful in the study of such fluids, the characteristic curves probably being determined by qualitative as well as quantitative changes in the protein.

Some conditions of unknown etiology in the central nervous system are associated with increases in protein level in spinal fluid. One-fourth to ½ of patients suffering from multiple sclerosis show significant increases in protein concentrations. Syringomyelia may be associated with elevated protein levels which occasionally may be quite high. Degenerative changes in the spinocerebellar tracts (Friederich's ataxia) usually do not cause any demonstrable abnormalities in the spinal fluid.

Various pathological changes in nervous tissue induce increased protein levels. In the diabetic with neurological changes it is quite common to find the protein concentration of cerebrospinal fluid increased from 50 to 100 per cent.

The *glucose* concentration in the cerebrospinal fluid is normally less than that of blood, being approximately 45 to 80 mg. per 100 cc. In infections with microorganisms that consume glucose readily the glucose content approaches zero. Tuberculous infections in the central nervous system also tend to produce a reduction in the glucose level but not as marked as that seen for instance in meningococcic and pneumococcic meningitis. In tuberculous meningitis the glucose concentration is often approximately 20 to 30 mg. per 100 cc. It is important to keep in mind that fluctuations in blood glucose are reflected in the spinal fluid glucose so that a determination of glucose concentration should be done on blood obtained at the time of the tapping of the spine. If this is omitted the wide range of blood glucose in uncontrolled diabetes may result in spinal fluid glucose values that cannot be interpreted correctly.

The average normal concentration of *sodium chloride* in cerebrospinal fluid is approximately 720 ± 20 mg. per 100 cc. Diseases, such as acute infections, which are attended by low plasma chloride levels also exhibit low chloride concentration in the spinal fluid. Very low values (e.g., 550 mg. per 100 cc.) are frequently present in tuberculous meningitis. Such low values associated with glucose concentrations of about 25 mg. per 100 cc. and elevated levels of protein, are highly suggestive of cerebrospinal tuberculosis.

The total volume of cerebrospinal fluid in the normal adult is approximately 130 cc., and its pressure in the recumbent position is about 110-130 mm. of water. The volume and pressure can be affected by injection of fluid intravenously. A transient rise in pressure may be occasioned by injection of large volumes of isotonic fluid. More prolonged increases in pressure are produced if the intravenous fluid is hypotonic. Certain conditions such as acute encephalopathy in hypertensive patients may require drastic measures in treatment. A satisfactory temporary decrease in intracranial pressure may be affected through intravenous injections of hypertonic solutions. The solute should preferably be a substance which does not ordinarily pass into the cerebrospinal fluid or otherwise a secondary rise in pressure may occur later. Suitable substances are sucrose and magnesium sulfate.

METABOLIC CHANGES IN NERVOUS DISORDERS

Knowledge of biochemical processes in the nervous system is fragmentary and only rarely does such knowledge permit explanation of abnormal phenomena pertaining to motor and sensory functions as well as to psychiatric disorders. A few conditions will be described briefly in which biochemical abnormalities seem to have definite correlation with the symptoms of the disease.

The normal supply of oxygen to the central nervous system as judged by the blood flow is not much in excess of requirements. Therefore, disturbances in volume of blood supply or in oxygen tension or content promptly cause demonstrable functional changes. The nervous system is unable to utilize proteins and fats so that energy is supplied by carbohydrates. The stores of carbohydrate in the form of glycogen are small so that normal metabolic needs depend on an uninterrupted supply of carbohydrate through the blood stream. Hypoglycemia of sufficient severity such as in insulin shock produces typical nervous manifestations, and if the supply of glucose is not restored rather promptly, permanent damage to the nervous tissue may result. Such irreversible damage has been reported in experimental animals subjected to prolonged insulin hypoglycemia. These findings are of considerable practical importance in the management of insulin shock therapy in schizophrenic patients.

Deficiencies in enzyme systems which normally participate in carbohydrate metabolism may conceivably affect the nervous system. Various forms of polyneuritis have been associated with lack of thiamine. It has been demonstrated in thiamine-deficient pigeons that pyruvic acid accumulates in the brain and that catabolism of pyruvate in brain slices from such birds can proceed if thiamine is added. The beneficial effects of administration of niacin on psychotic manifestations in pellagra may be mentioned as another example of a deficiency of an enzyme system as a presumptive etiological factor in a nervous disorder.

Many chemicals and drugs have definite effects on the nervous system; some of these substances exert their action almost exclusively on certain specific functions presumably by interfering with chemical processes characteristic of such functions. Chemical data pertaining to these phenomena are generally lacking, most of the observations falling in the field of empirical toxicology or pharmacology.

The conduction mechanism involved in muscular contraction may be similar to that involved in transmission of nervous impulses. Familial periodic paralysis is characterized by attacks at irregular intervals during which the muscles do not react to direct or indirect stimulation. An attack may be promoted by any procedure which leads to a marked fall in the concentration of serum potassium. Injections of large doses of glucose or insulin may initiate an attack so that it does not appear to have any specific relation to carbohydrate metabolism, but a lowering of potassium levels in the serum takes place in either event. Recovery from an attack can be accomplished by injection of potassium chloride. Excessive amounts of potassium injected intra-arterially produce a powerful muscular contraction followed by tetanus. These observations tend to confirm the similarity in conduction mechanism in muscle and nerve and its dependence upon the relative concentration of potassium ions inside and outside the fibers.

Myasthenia gravis is characterized by rapid onset of fatigue and muscular weakness. The disease is not associated with any demonstrable changes in the nervous system and it is thought that the disorder is localized at the point of transmission of the impulse from the nerve terminals to the muscle fibers. The course of the disorder has been sought in faulty metabolism of acetylcholine and remarkable improvement can be observed in patients after administration of prostigmine which presumably acts by inhibiting cholinesterase. A certain amount of evidence is available which tends to prove the presence of a curari-like substance as the agent blocking the transmission of the nerve impulse. Curari abolishes the response of muscles to indirect, but not direct stimulation. Prostigmine has anti-curari effect. Other drugs, such as potassium salts, the sympathomimetic amines, and guanidine are valuable in the treatment of myasthenia gravis. These drugs have anti-curari effects but do not markedly inhibit cholinesterase.

SUPPLEMENTARY READING

BOELL, E. J., and NACHMANSOHN, D.: Localization of choline esterase in nerve fibers. *Science, 92:*513, 1940.

CANNON, W. B.: *Chemistry and Medicine.* University of Minnesota Press, 1940.

CANNON, W. B., and ROSENBLUETH, A.: *Autonomic Neuro-Effector Systems.* Macmillan, 1937.

FLEXNER, L. B.: The chemistry and nature of the cerebrospinal fluid. *Physiol. Rev., 14:*161, 1934.

FULTON, J. F.: *Physiology of the Nervous System.* W. B. Saunders Co., 1949.

HERTZ, H.: Action potential and diameter of isolated nerve fibers under various conditions. *Acta. Physiol. Scandinav., 13:* Supplementum 43, 1947.

HIMWICH, H. E., FAZEKAS, J. F., BERNSTEIN, A. O., CAMPBELL, E. H., and MARTIN, S. J.: Syndromes secondary to prolonged hypoglycemia. *Proc. Soc. Exper. Biol. & Med., 39:*244, 1938.

KERR, S. E.: The carbohydrate metabolism of brain. VI. Isolation of glycogen. *J. Biol. Chem., 123:*443, 1938.

LAWRENCE, R. D., MEYER, A., and NEVIN, S.: The pathological changes in the brain in fatal hypoglycemia. *Quart. J. Med., 11*:181, 1942.

MERRITT, H. H., and FREMONT-SMITH, F.: *The Cerebrospinal Fluid.* W. B. Saunders Co., 1937.

MINER, R. W. (editor): The physico-chemical mechanism of nerve activity. *Ann. New York Acad. Sci., 47*:375, 1946.

MURPHY, F. D., HERSHBERG, R. A., and KATZ, A. M.: The effect of intravenous injections of sucrose solution (50%) on the cerebrospinal fluid pressure, the blood pressure and clinical course in cases of chronic hypertension. *Am. J. Med. Sc., 192*:510, 1936.

NACHMANSOHN, D.: Role of acetylcholine in mechanism of nerve activity. In: *Vitamins and Hormones, 3*:337, 1945.

NACHMANSOHN, D.: Chemical mechanism of nervous action. In: Green, D. E.; *Currents in Biochemical Research.* Interscience Publishers, Inc., 1946.

QUASTEL, J. H.: Respiration in the central nervous system. *Physiol. Rev., 19*:135, 1939.

ZIMMERMAN, F. T., BURGEMEISTER, B. B., and PUTNAM, T. J.: Group study of effect of glutamic acid on mental functioning in children and adolescents. *Psychosom. Med., 9*:175, 1947.

Chapter 18

NUTRITION

ADEQUATE nutrition depends upon a dietary intake comprising sufficient quantities of all substances essential for the various physiological processes in the body. The formulation of an ideal diet is not yet possible because it would require knowledge of all indispensable ingredients (a knowledge which certainly cannot be presumed at present), and of the availability of the essential food materials to permit them to be used in the correct proportions.

Foods supply energy, essential organic structures and inorganic ions, and a special group of substances, the vitamins, which in small amounts promote metabolic processes. Knowledge of dietary requirements has been obtained largely through feeding experiments on animals using diets lacking the particular substance under investigation but adequate in all other regards. Since nutritive requirements vary in different species, experimental findings can apply with certainty only to the species used. However, clinical observation on human subjects disclosing lesions similar to those observed in animals in deficiency states and the curing of such lesions by the administration of specific substances furnishes strong evidence of the etiological background.

It is not possible to determine minima for the nutritional adequacy of all food factors because each may be dependent upon the intake of the others. For instance, animals maintained on diets deficient in certain of the members of the vitamin B complex will show variations in rate of growth depending upon the type of carbohydrate fed. Furthermore, changes in the diet may affect the bacterial flora of the gastro-intestinal tract, thus influencing the synthesis of essential food factors, which in turn may alter the minimum dietary requirements. Other examples of interdependence of nutritional compounds may be found in the ratio of calcium to phosphorus in the diet, removal of assimilable calcium by precipitation in an insoluble form (such as calcium oxalate), or in the influence of pH and protein intake on assimilation of other nutrients. Recent investigations indicate that certain substances occurring naturally in the diet may have an inhibitory action on the utilization of essential food factors. This action seems to depend on close chemical similarity between the inhibitor and the essential food factor.

A healthy person with a good appetite, who is able to control his weight without undue restriction in total caloric intake, presents no nutritional problem if he has access to food in abundance both as to amount and variety. Under such conditions addition to the diet of special food factors such as the vitamins does not contribute measurably to maintenance of health. However, the clinician should be alert to the fact that severe restriction in diet necessary for treatment of obesity, or of other pathological conditions, may induce deficiency states unless supplementary feeding of certain essential factors is prescribed.

Adequate nutrition may be affected by inclusion in the food of toxic substances which may influence normal processes in the organism. A few of these toxins are of natural origin but many of them are added in the processing and preservation of food. Lead and arsenic are poisons commonly encountered in traces in food.

ENERGY

The energy content of food is measured in Calories, one Calorie being the amount of heat required to raise the temperature of 1,000 grams of water from 15° to 16° C. If the food undergoes complete oxidation in its metabolism, the energy content available to the organism is equal to that developed by complete combustion in a calorimeter. Carbohydrates and fats therefore yield 4.1 and 9.3 Calories per gram respectively, as they are completely metabolized to carbon dioxide and water. It has been found that the physiological heat value of proteins is equal to that of carbohydrates (4.1 Cal.) which is less than the heat per gram developed by calorimetric combustion (5.3 Cal.). This difference is due almost entirely to the residual energy contained in the nitrogenous excretory products.

Minor variations in elementary composition are responsible for slight deviation in caloric value of foods of a given type so that the heat equivalents stated above are averages only. For practical purposes the energy content of fats, proteins, and carbohydrates is calculated as 9.0, 4.0, and 4.0 Calories per gram respectively.

RESPIRATORY QUOTIENT (R.Q.)

This is defined as the ratio between the volume of carbon dioxide expired and the volume of oxygen inspired measured over several minutes. The following equation represents the complete combustion of glucose:

$$C_6H_{12}O_6 + 6O_2 \rightarrow 6CO_2 + 6H_2O.$$

This equation indicates that the amount of oxygen necessary for the completion of the reaction is equivalent to the carbon content of the glucose molecule because it already contains oxygen and hydrogen in the correct proportions to form water. The volumes of CO_2 and O_2 entering into the calculation of the respiratory quotient thus are the same, so that the R.Q. is unity. Fats do not contain sufficient oxygen to transform their hydrogen content into water. Therefore, in the complete oxidation of fats enough oxygen must be supplied for conversion of all the hydrogen into water, as well as for conversion of the carbon to carbon dioxide. During catabolism of fats the volume of expired CO_2 in proportion to inspired O_2 is approximately 7 to 10 so that the R.Q. is 0.7. The R.Q. of protein is approximately 0.8. The R.Q. is used as an indication of the relative proportions of various types of foods being metabolized.

BASAL METABOLIC RATE

This is the amount of heat dissipated per square meter of body surface by a subject at complete rest in the post-absorptive state, which means the least possible muscular, mental, and digestive activities. The determination of the B.M.R. should be performed at a room temperature of 20° C., since heat dissipation is affected by the temperature of the surroundings. At temperatures above 20° C. physical processes of body heat regulation increase, while at temperatures below 20° C., chemical regulation operates through elevation in rate of metabolic processes. Methods involving the direct measurement of heat produced by a subject under basal conditions are difficult and cumbersome to use for clinical purposes. Approximate B.M.R. calculations may be made from determinations of oxygen consumption. In the post-absorptive state the average normal respiratory quotient is 0.82 approximately. The corresponding energy value is 4.8 Calories per liter of oxygen, corrected for temperature and pressure. The basal metabolic rate varies with the age, sex, and size of normal subjects. Basal metabolism is proportional to body surface, and heat production under basal conditions may therefore, be expressed in terms of calories per square meter of body surface. Clinicians usually prefer to express basal metabolic rates in percentage deviation from the estimated standard. Such deviations are within plus or minus 15 per cent in the normal subject.

SPECIFIC DYNAMIC ACTION (S.D.A.)

A subject at rest fed a diet with a caloric content equal to his basal metabolic needs will lose weight because the ingestion of food raises the metabolic rate above its basal level. This effect of food is called its specific dynamic action. Various foods show differences in the value of their S.D.A., proteins producing the most extensive effect, namely an increase of approximately 30 per cent in heat production above that of the basal level. The corresponding values for fats and carbohydrates are approximately 4 and 6 per cent respectively. The heat represented by the S.D.A. of protein is waste and only contributes to the maintenance of body temperature; it cannot be converted to work in the various tissues of the organism. The energy liberated through the specific dynamic action of fats and carbohydrates, however, may be used for performance of work because the S.D.A. of these food substances, when fed exclusively during exercise, can be shown not to participate in the waste heat to be diverted from the body. A diet containing protein preponderantly is, therefore, not as efficient in sustaining heavy muscular work as a diet with the same caloric content made up of fats and carbohydrates.

The mechanism of the specific dynamic action is not entirely understood. The liver appears to be the site where the heat from the S.D.A. of proteins is developed since the effect can be abolished in hepatectomized animals. It is most likely that energy exchanges involved in the metabolism and excretion of nitrogen are responsible for the specific dynamic action. At present it is believed that the S.D.A. effect is entirely ascribable to 6 amino acids, glycine, alanine, leucine, tyrosine, phenylalanine, and glutamic acid.

FATS, CARBOHYDRATES, AND PROTEINS IN THE DIET

These furnish practically all caloric needs. Desire for food is desire for caloric energy which can be satisfied by any combination of palatable foods. The organism does not present a conscious craving for specific fats, carbohydrates, or proteins containing molecular components essential for health.

It is assumed that the reader will refresh his memory by reviewing the general discussion of the metabolism of fats, proteins, and carbohydrates in Chapters 6, 7, and 8. The following material will be confined to remarks on the essential nature of certain of the food components.

Early workers in the field of nutrition considered *fats* as a source of calories only. Subsequently, the importance of fats as carriers for the oil-soluble vitamins was discovered. The knowledge that certain unsaturated fatty acids are essential for normal nutrition and that they cannot be synthesized in the body, was obtained from observations on young laboratory animals maintained on low fat diets for extended periods. It is seldom possible to find patients who have been living on diets so low in fat that their nutritional state is comparable to that of fat deficient experimental animals. Evidence for human need of essential unsaturated fatty acids must, consequently, be indirect.

The deficiency in animals of essential fatty acids is manifested by cutaneous lesions and retardation of growth. At the present time, *linoleic* and *arachidonic* acids are the only 2 unsaturated fatty acids known to effect complete cures of the abnormalities. Either one can be substituted for the other. *Linoleic acid* and a few other unsaturated acids will stimulate renewed growth in fat deficient animals, but do not cure the skin lesions.

Clinical evidence is accumulating that cutaneous disorders in human subjects may be influenced by the composition of fats in the diet. A small number of children on fat-deficient diets have been observed to be more susceptible to impetigo, and the course of this malady appears to be abnormally severe in such patients. A number of cases have been reported in which dermatological abnormalities have been associated with idiopathic steatorrhea. In some of these cases it has been shown that the lipid content of the blood did not change in regard to the various fat fractions except that the iodine number became abnormally low. This may indicate that these patients are able to synthesize fatty acids from other food but that they have no way of maintaining normal concentrations of unsaturated fatty acids when intestinal absorption fails.

Proteins in food constitute the source of amino acids necessary for building and repairing tissues. The essential nature of certain of the amino acids has been discussed in Chapter 7. The classification of these acids as essential is based largely on animal experiments and there is no complete agreement at present as to their exact number or the amounts required by man. The essential need of certain amino acids for individual species also depends on the age of the animal, as some of the amino acids seem to be more indispensable for growth than for maintenance of tissues. A peptide-like material, *strepogenin,* is found in unaltered proteins or in incomplete hydrolysates; this factor seems to improve growth in mice over the rate observed if they are maintained on mixtures of amino acids.

The daily requirements of protein depend on the total caloric intake. If enough calories are available in the ingested fats and carbohydrates, the amino acids absorbed can be used for building of tissue rather than for fuel. Conversely, with insufficient caloric intake, the body must draw upon the energy contained in the amino acids.

It has been stated that the content of glucose-forming amino acids in the average food is sufficient to form 58 grams of glucose per 100 grams of protein, but quantitative studies to support this figure are not available. Possibly the diabetic patient may obtain a fairly large amount of carbohydrate by gluconeogenesis from proteins, and in spite of the questionable accuracy, dietitians use the above figure in calculating total available carbohydrates in diets. It seems likely that the percentage of amino acids converted to carbohydrate in the normal organism depends on the amount of glucose available from ingested carbohydrates.

The lowest protein intake compatible with normal physiological processes in the body would need to contain all essential amino acids in the proper proportions. Such an ideal distribution of amino acids in food proteins is hardly to be expected, so that a person must take in a liberal amount of protein to satisfy his requirements for all the essential amino acids. It is generally considered that 1 gram of protein per kilogram of body weight will supply the average adult with adequate amounts of all necessary amino acids. Children are thought to need a protein intake about twice this figure, but some workers feel that this allowance is much too generous. Physiological states which place additional demands upon protein synthesis in the body increase the need for dietary protein intake. This applies, for instance, during pregnancy and lactation.

Carbohydrates constitute the most immediate source of fuel in the organism. The metabolic 'turnover' is rapid and stored carbohydrates in the form of liver and muscle glycogen, and blood and extra-cellular glucose are capable of supplying ordinary demands for less than 24 hours. Carbohydrate does not contain essential components comparable to the essential amino and fatty acids of proteins and fats. Dietary deficiencies associated with carbohydrate intake are normally produced either by starvation or, indirectly, by the removal of indispensable accessory food factors during processing of the carbohydrate foods. Beriberi is an outstanding example of this type of deficiency.

There are differences in the nutritional value of various carbohydrates which otherwise furnish equivalent amounts of caloric energy to the organism. This is well illustrated by the growth rate and health of experimental animals on various carbohydrate diets if the animals are kept on insufficient amounts of some of the vitamins of the B complex. Sucrose apparently demands the greatest intake of the vitamins concerned while the relatively insoluble carbohydrates, such as starch, demand the smallest requirements. Elvehjem and Krehl state that dextrin, starch, lactose, glucose, and sucrose increase vitamin requirements in about this order. It is quite likely that the less soluble carbohydrates produce a more favorable environment for bacterial synthesis of vitamins in the intestinal tract, and thus lower the minimum which must be supplied in the diet to prevent deficiency states.

MINERALS

Available evidence indicates that at least 10 mineral elements are essential to life, namely sodium, potassium, calcium, iron, copper, magnesium, phosphorus, sulfur, chlorine, and iodine. Among the so-called 'trace elements,' manganese, cobalt, zinc, and fluorine are considered essential, but little is known about their specific functions.

The average daily intake of *calcium* in the adult is approximately 1 gram, which is about twice the minimum daily requirement. However, complete assimilation in the intestinal tract may be retarded by a number of factors such as the presence of ions which form insoluble calcium salts (oxalate, high concentration of phosphates, fatty acids, etc.), high pH, lack of amino acids, and deficiency of vitamin D. Children should have an intake of at least 1 gram of calcium daily. Pregnant women require about 1.5 grams per day during lactation. One liter of cow's milk contains approximately 1.2 grams of calcium.

A well balanced diet ordinarily contains *phosphorus* in excess of the amount required by the organism. Such cations as calcium, iron, and manganese which form insoluble phosphate compounds may interfere with phosphorus absorption, and conversely, excessive amounts of phosphates in food have been shown to hinder iron absorption. It has been stated that adults need approximately 10 mg. and infants about 50 mg. of phosphorus per kilogram of body weight. Recent studies by McKay and associates, on a small number of pre-school children revealed that phosphorus retention ranged from 6 to 16 per cent of the intake, indicating ample supply. They calculated phosphorus requirements to be from 3.5 to 10.8 mg. per kilogram of body weight. Phosphorus is present in food in inorganic form chiefly as calcium and sodium phosphates, and in organic form as phosphoproteins and phospholipids. Deficiency of phosphorus leads to limitation of growth and of ossification, and to muscular weakness. Symptoms of phosphorus deficiency may be seen in farm animals fed upon fodder from soil low in this mineral. Such symptoms include failure of estrus and of secretion of milk.

Sodium is obtained chiefly from fruit and vegetable sources and from the additional table salt used in cooking. *Potassium* and *magnesium* are also obtained from plant products. Because of the wide distribution in foods of these elements, deficiencies are not ordinarily encountered. A temporary deficiency of sodium chloride, because of excessive perspiration, may result from exposure to high temperatures.

Iron is needed for the synthesis of hemoglobin. Foods containing liberal amounts of iron are meats, liver, kidney, colored fruits and vegetables, and egg yolk. Milk contains very small amounts of this mineral. Children require approximately 0.5 mg. of iron per kilogram of body weight. The recommended dietary allowance in adult men and women of average weight is stated by the Food and Nutrition Board of the National Research Council to be 12 mg. per day. It is controversial what forms of iron in food are assimilable, certain investigators claiming that iron in the hemoglobin of meats is not utilizable and that iron must be absorbed in an ionizable form. Ferric iron tends to be reduced to the ferrous state in the intestinal tract and this form is probably the one in which iron enters the blood stream.

Over half of the iron in the body is present in hemoglobin; less than $1/4$ is stored, and the balance is mostly in the form of iron-containing oxidases, cytochrome, and myoglobin. Catabolism of hemoglobin releases a certain amount of iron which is stored temporarily in the spleen, liver, and bone marrow, to be used again in the synthesis of hemoglobin. A large proportion of the iron of a newborn child is stored and is generally adequate for hemoglobin synthesis for from 4 to 6 months. If the infant is nourished by milk exclusively beyond this period, it will develop iron-deficiency anemia.

Sulfur is obtained from the sulfur-containing amino acids, cystine and methionine. A well balanced diet containing adequate amounts of protein will invariably supply all the organism's demand for sulfur. Glutathione, thiamine, and biotin, are important physiological substances containing sulfur.

Iodine is important for the normal functioning of the thyroid gland. The significance of supplementing the iodine of the food in the endemic goiter-areas in the world is well known. The minimum prophylactic daily dose of iodine has not been determined with certainty, but is less than 0.3 mg.

Copper in minute amounts appears to be necessary for the formation of hemoglobin although the hemoglobin molecule does not contain copper. Copper occurs in hemocuprein in the erythrocytes and in hepatocuprein in the liver.

Some of the oxidases are copper-protein complexes. The essential role of copper in normal nutrition has been proved in experiments on animals. It is probable that these observations are applicable to man, but the evidence is inconclusive at present.

Among the 'trace elements' *fluorine* has attracted a great deal of attention in recent years. Beyond much doubt there is a direct relationship between the incidence of dental caries and deficiency of fluorine in the water and soil. Possibly some factor other than fluorine in natural drinking water may be implicated in the inhibitory influence on dental caries. Addition of fluorine to the diet is probably without significance in the health of teeth after calcification is completed.

VITAMINS

These organic dietary substances are essential for specific physiological processes. Only minute quantities are necessary for their activities but these minimum amounts must be present in the organism to prevent development of deficiency states with characteristic pathological features. The role of certain of the vitamins as co-enzymes has been discussed previously. Originally the vitamins were divided into water-soluble and fat-soluble substances. In order of discovery, they were designated by letters A, B, C, etc., and also by the main clinical manifestation associated with deficiencies in the diet. This nomenclature is still in common use despite the fact that the chemical structures of most of the vitamins are known.

Vitamin A is soluble in fats and in fat solvents. For human nutrition it is available preformed in animal tissues or as the provitamins (carotenes) in plant tissues. β-Carotene is the most effective vitamin A precursor because each molecule yields 2 molecules of the vitamin, whereas α-Carotene, γ-Carotene, and cryptoxanthine produce but one molecule of vitamin A for each molecule of carotene. Vitamin A may be detected through its characteristic ultraviolet absorption spectrum, and may be determined quantitatively by use of the intense blue color which it gives with antimony trichloride, in comparison with a standard.

Vitamin A is an unsaturated alcohol having the formula $C_{20}H_{30}O$. It contains a β-ionone structure.

$$H_3C \diagdown \quad CH_3$$

VITAMIN A

This formula represents the structure of Vitamin A_1. Vitamin A_2 differs from A_1 only by the presence of an additional double bond in the ring as far as has been determined. The two vitamins are identical in biological behaviour.

Fish liver oils are particularly good sources of vitamin A. Animal liver, milk, and egg yolk are also important sources, and the provitamin is found in butter, and in certain green and yellow vegetables. The carotenes are oxidized to form vitamin A by an enzyme in the liver. This oxidative process may fail in diabetic or myxedematous patients, and occasionally in people suffering from severe hepatic injury. Under such circumstances the carotenoid pigments accumulate in the blood and cause a yellow discoloration of the skin. This condition is called *carotenemia*. Its development probably requires a large intake of carotenoids and failure of the oxidative process in the liver over a fairly long period before it becomes detectable in the skin. The carotenoid nature of the yellow pigment in the blood can be determined by shaking the blood with petroleum ether in which the carotenes, in contradistinction to the bile pigments, are soluble.

Vitamin A deficiency is characterized by keratinizing metaplasia of epithelial structures. Besides the skin, the epithelial linings of the respiratory, gastro-intestinal, and urinary tracts are affected. Changes also occur in glandular structures, interfering with their normal secretory activity. Xerophthalmia and corneal ulceration are striking results of vitamin A deficiency.

Vitamin A, or a very closely related substance, is a component of the rhodopsin molecule, its synthesis or functioning is interfered with if vitamin A is lacking, resulting in nyctalopia. Deficiency of vitamin A leads to retarded growth. There may be a mechanical relation between retardation of bone development and certain of the effects involving the nervous system which have been observed in animals on vitamin A deficient diets.

Subjects maintained on a diet low in vitamin A usually show a relatively low level of the vitamin in the serum or plasma. This finding is not present invariably. The lower normal value in adults appears to be around 70 international units (approximately 20 micrograms) per 100 cc. of serum or plasma. Human beings do not show clinical evidence of deficiency until the concentration of vitamin A drops below 40 international units (approximately 12 micrograms). The level of carotene in the blood has been used as an index of absorption of adequate amounts of the provitamin. Carotene values fluctuate considerably because of variable factors such as, dietary intake, disorders of absorption, and hepatic disease. In normal adults carotene concentrations in serum or plasma are usually between 60 and 200 micrograms per 100 cc. The levels of vitamin A and carotene do not necessarily parallel each other. Children appear generally to have values for vitamin A and carotene similar to those of adults except that the carotene level is close to zero in infants until carotene-containing foods are added to their diet.

The *vitamin B complex* contains a number of vitamins which constitute a group because of their occurrence together in foods, and similarities in physiological functions. The role of some of the B complex members, thiamine, nicotinic acid, and riboflavin, in the enzymic oxidation-reduction systems has already been described in Chapter 5. Some of the nutritional aspects will be discussed in the following paragraphs.

Thiamine (Vitamin B_1) is the antineuritic or antiberiberi factor. It occurs widely in nature in plant and animal tissues, in the latter mostly in the phosphorylated form (cocarboxylase). The content of thiamine in many foods is inadequate for dietary needs. The vitamin is relatively stable upon exposure to boiling, but discarding of the aqueous medium in preparation of many foods results in losses of thiamine. Various forms of food processing may remove the largest part of the vitamin from white flour, polished rice, and other processed cereals, so that these grains may be deficient in thiamine. Macaroni products and refined sugar are also low, while whole grains, milk, liver, kidney, and heart tissues are usually rich in vitamin B_1. Smaller amounts occur in striated muscle meats. Thiamine is widely distributed in green leafy vegetables, legumes, and nuts. Yeast has a high thiamine content. It is common practice to enrich such foods as flour, bread, and cereals with thiamine.

Thiamine is destroyed readily by alkali and sulfite. A number of oxidizing agents convert thiamine to thiochrome, a yellow pigment with a characteristic fluorescence which is employed in the quantitative determination of thiamine by phosphofluorometric methods.

It has been shown previously that decarboxylation of pyruvic acid depends upon the enzyme cocarboxylase which contains thiamine. In thiamine deficient organisms the pyruvic acid content of blood is increased above normal. Even in mild cases this abnormal accumulation of pyruvic acid occurs under the influence of exercise or the intake of glucose. In actual pathological deficiencies there is decreased urinary excretion as well as decreased contents of cellular and extracellular thiamine. Diagnostic tests include determination of urinary content of thiamine. Such tests are more easily interpreted if they are done under standard conditions including the administration of a known amount of the vitamin. One commonly used test consists of the ingestion of 5 mg. of thiamine hydrochloride, an output of less than 20 micrograms in the urine in the following four hours being considered below normal. Standards for interpretation of such tests cannot be considered as absolutely reliable. However, a near-zero recovery is good evidence of a deficiency state.

Lack of thiamine in the diet inhibits growth of young animals. Continued deficiency of the vitamin results in polyneuritis in animals. For this reason, polyneuritis in human subjects with metabolic disorders is considered a manifestation of thiamine deficiency. Many such persons are undoubtedly benefited by administration of thiamine, but disappointing results of such therapy often lead the clinician to believe that factors other than thiamine deficiency are involved.

Beriberi is a symptom complex produced by thiamine deficiency. It is manifested by polyneuritis leading to progressive paralysis of motor and sensory functions, dilatation of the right heart, and often by edema and serous effusions (wet beriberi).

A functional inter-relationship of the various B complex vitamins is demonstrated by the observation that thiamine influences the mobilization of riboflavin in the liver, resulting in part of the riboflavin being excreted in the urine. Pantothenic acid acts similarly to thiamine in this respect.

Riboflavin (Vitamin B$_2$) deficiency of animals produces growth retardation, scaling of the skin, loss of hair, vascularization of the cornea, and cataracts. In man, deficiencies of the vitamin are commonly associated with ocular lesions, ranging from mild to severe vascularization of the cornea, photophobia, and gradual development of interstitial keratitis. The angles of the mouth develop fissures (cheilosis), the tongue may show inflammatory changes, and a greasy scaliness of the skin of the nose and ears is often observed.

The distribution of riboflavin in nature is practically the same as of thiamine. Leafy vegetables are comparatively richer in riboflavin than in thiamine. Riboflavin combines with proteins to form flavoproteins which function as enzymes in the respiratory processes of tissues. A deficiency state causes physiological abnormalities in the tissues resulting in the various clinical symptoms. The nature of these abnormalities is not known but it has been observed that there is a similarity of the pathological changes to those seen in nicotinic acid deficiency. It is possible that the tissue changes may not be specific for the particular enzyme, but may be a basic alteration capable of being produced by more than one deficient enzyme mechanism. Such speculation would help to understand the occurrence clinically of riboflavin deficiency in pellagra.

As in the case of thiamine deficiency the urinary excretion of riboflavin has been used as a diagnostic test. An oral test dose of 5 mg. should normally result in the renal elimination of not less than 200 micrograms of riboflavin in four hours. Such standards cannot be accepted as clearly established. As in other vitamin deficiencies a therapeutic test is often most deciding from a clinical standpoint.

Nicotinic acid (nicotinamide or niacin), is part of the phosphopyridine nucleotide enzymes which have been discussed in Chapter 5. Liver and kidney tissue, lean meat, eggs, milk, whole wheat, and green leafy vegetables are good sources of this vitamin. The minimum daily requirement of nicotinic acid in adults is approximately 10 mg.

Most of the symptoms of *pellagra* are referable to nicotinic acid deficiency. The gastro-intestinal, skin, and mental disorders clear up under administration of the vitamin. Other symptoms, such as polyneuritis and cheilosis, are manifestations of deficiencies of other members of the B-complex. It is to be expected that deficiency diseases involving the B-complex include symptoms ascribable to several of the members of this group because of their similar distribution in food.

It has been reported that corn contains a pellagragenic factor. Experiments on rats have shown differences in the requirement when pure nicotinic acid was fed, and when corn, containing an equivalent amount of nicotinic acid was substituted for it. Retardation of growth resulted and was counteracted by added nicotinic acid. Criticism has been applied to such experiments on rats because the low protein diets used produce a poor growth rate under any circumstances. However, comparable experiments with corn or other cereal grains with approximately the same nicotinic acid content show relatively more retardation of growth in the animals on the diet containing corn.

Corn is deficient in tryptophan; addition of tryptophan to a corn diet has a growth promoting action comparable to that of nicotinic acid. The relationship between tryptophan and nicotinic acid is not clear at present; it is possible that trytophan is a precursor of nicotinic acid as addition of certain tryptophan-containing ingredients to a diet may ameliorate symptoms of niacin deficiency. Changes in the intestinal flora brought about by such foods probably augment the enteric synthesis of nicotinic acid.

Pyridoxine (Vitamin B₆) is present in good supplies in meat, fish, corn, whole wheat, unpolished rice, and yeast. Animal experiments indicate that this vitamin has definite metabolic functions and it appears to be an essential factor in human nutrition. Compounds closely related to pyridoxine (pyridoxal, pyridoxamine) have the properties of the vitamin so that the various structures may be grouped together as the vitamin B_6 group.

Pyridoxine has a catalytic action on both transamination and decarboxylation of certain amino acids. Deficiency of this vitamin in rats results in reduced nitrogen utilization presumably because of failure of the above processes.

Kynurenic acid is an excretory substance which is considered to be the end product of tryptophan metabolism in certain animals such as the rat, guinea pig, and dog. If L-tryptophan is administered to rats on a pyridoxine-deficient diet, these animals excrete xanthurenic acid but not kynurenic acid. This metabolic phenomenon is not observed if D-tryptophan is used, nor does administration of kynurenic acid lead to excretion of xanthurenic acid in the pyridoxine deficient rat. In mice on synthetic diets the pyridoxine requirements increase with increases in proteins. On a low pyridoxine intake the animals survive longer if the protein intake is low.

Pyridoxine deficiency in rats, dogs, and chickens produces microcytic and mildly hypochromic anemia. Evidence is not available to link pyridoxine with erythropoiesis in man.

Pantothenic acid is widely distributed in foods which generally are rich in the B-complex. It is specific for the treatment of certain forms of dermatitis in chickens ('chick pellagra'), and a deficiency in the diet of the rat produces damage to the adrenal glands. Its essential nature for human nutrition has not been established.

Female rats fail to reproduce if they are placed on a pantothenic acid-deficient diet. Withholding of water from normal rats induces changes similar to those in the vitamin deficient state. The changes in water balance are assumed to be mediated through the effect of lack of pantothenic acid on the adrenal glands.

The lipotropic effect of *choline,* the base found in lecithin, has been dealt with in Chapter 6. Ethanolamine is the precursor in the biosynthesis of choline. Methylation of ethanolamine takes place step-wise to form monomethyl, dimethyl, and finally trimethyl, the compound which is choline. Interestingly enough, dimethylaminoethanol appears to serve as a methyl donor as well as acceptor.

Copeland and Salmon have observed malignant changes in the liver of a high percentage of rats maintained on a choline deficient diet for 8 months or longer. In a control series receiving the same diet supplemented with choline, the neoplastic changes did not develop. Diets containing insufficient amounts of choline or other methyl donors invariably produce cirrhosis of the liver in rats. It has been observed that choline deficiency in dogs produces severe anemia which may become irreversible, possibly because of permanent damage to the liver.

Biotin (Coenzyme R): This vitamin is found in kidney and liver. The latter organ serves as a source for isolation of the vitamin as the methyl ester. The synthesis of biotin has been accomplished.

The so-called 'egg white injury' appears in rats as a severe dermatitis. If the egg white is fed in large amounts to rats while they are deprived of biotin, addition of sufficient biotin to the diet will counteract the effect.

Biotin promotes the carcinogenic action of certain dyes such as butter yellow when fed to experimental animals. Tumor tissue generally contains more biotin than normal tissue and it has been suggested that a deficiency of biotin in the diet might retard neoplastic growth.

Biotin contains a sulfur atom in the molecule; this sulfur atom may be replaced by oxygen, the resulting substance being *oxybiotin*. Oxybiotin has physiological properties similar to those of biotin, and independent of the biological conversion of oxybiotin to biotin.

Inositol deficiency in mice results in retardation of growth and in alopecia. Biotin and/or inositol will prevent or cure these conditions, and this interchangeability of the two vitamins has been confirmed in various experiments. Biotin seems to have a slightly greater activity. Details of this relationship between inositol and biotin are not understood and the need for these vitamins in human nutrition has not been established.

Para-aminobenzoic acid is an essential growth factor for certain microorganisms, and for chicks. Some investigators have expressed the opinion that this vitamin is not a true growth factor because, at high concentrations, it often reduces growth. However, such action of essential nutritional components is not unusual and similar effects have been observed with other vitamins and amino acids. Para-aminobenzoic acid prevents chromotrichia in rats; a similar action has been observed in human subjects only if the graying of the hair is initiated by an acute deficiency state.

Para-aminobenzoic acid is particularly interesting because it 'antagonizes' the bacteriostatic effect of the sulfonamides. This antagonistic action appears to depend upon the competitive inhibition by the sulfonamides of an enzymic reaction involving the utilization of para-aminobenzoic acid. Some bacteria may grow in the absence of para-aminobenzoic acid provided adequate amounts of purine bases are present. Guanine and xanthine are mildly antagonistic to the sulfonamides. This antagonism depends upon the presence of methionine. Possibly the synthesis of methionine involves the utilization of para-aminobenzoic acid.

Para-aminobenzoic acid is a component of pteroylglutamic acid, or folic acid, which may be a primary intermediate in the synthesis of nucleic acid derivatives. Even though present knowledge of the functions of para-amino-benzoic acid is incomplete, the similarity in its acid-base properties to those of the sulfonamides may account for the anti-bacterial properties of the sulfa drugs. Para-aminobenzoic acid is used with good results in the treatment of rickettsial diseases, in which it seems to retard the spread of rickettsias.

Folic acid is of main interest in regard to its therapeutic effect in cases of macrocytic anemia. Remissions of the hematological changes have been brought about in pernicious anemia, sprue, and leucopenia. The response is characterized by a rise in the reticulocyte count, increase in the number of red and white cells and platelets, and an increase in the hemoglobin count of the red cells. The pathological changes in the central nervous system in pernicious anemia do not respond to treatment with folic acid. Folic acid is chemically characterized as a basic pteridine nucleus linked with p-amino-benzoic acid and glutamic acid. The chemical identification originally referred to the L. casei factor from liver, the name pteroylglutamic acid being applied. There are four major compounds in the folic acid group differing in their content of glutamic acid. Pteroic acid is the basic synthetic form obtained by substituting p-aminobenzoic acid for p-aminobenzoylglutamic acid. 'Teropterin' is pteroyltriglutamic acid. Pteroylheptaglutamic acid can be converted enzymically to pteroylglutamic acid. The name *folacin* is also applied to folic acid.

Evidence indicates that folic acid functions in the biosynthesis of purines and thymine or their equivalents. A number of investigations have been made on the nutritional relationship of thymine to folic acid. Originally it was observed that thymine was essential for the growth of S. lactis, and that S. lactis, L. casei, and other lactic acid bacteria require folic acid for growth. Subsequently it was shown that thymine (or the riboside derivative thymidine) could replace folic acid. The requirement of thymine was at least 5,000 times that of folic acid. Nutritional macrocytic anemia has shown response to treatment with large doses of thymine.

Xanthopterin, discovered as a pigment in yellow butterfly wings, is found widespread in nature. Chemically it resembles folic acid in that it has a pteridine base. Before the discovery of the chemical similarity xanthopterin had been demonstrated to have certain stimulating effects on blood cell formation. Administration of xanthopterin and folic acid to rats with sulfathiazole-induced anemia reveals an immediate effect on cell proliferation by the former and a delayed response by the latter, both of equal magnitude. Such observations have suggested that folic acid is converted to xanthopterin before it can exert its effect on the bone marrow to form new cells.

The *citrovorum factor* appears to be a metabolite of folic acid. It was discovered in a course of studies employing the micro-organism leuconostoc citrovorum. This factor is found in human and rat urine, the amount increasing after administration of folic acid. In vitro experiments with liver slices have shown that folic acid may be converted to citrovorum factor and that this conversion is accelerated by ascorbic acid.

Certain natural and synthetic substances have anti-vitamin properties. Pyridine-3-sulfonic acid has an SO_3 group substituted for a COOH group in nicotinic acid. It has antinicotinic acid properties being able to inhibit bacterial growth under certain experimental conditions. Such inhibition can be nullified by the addition of nicotinic acid. Similarly oxythiamine is an antivitamin B_1. The use of such antivitamins may become of therapeutic significance. For instance, it has been discovered in experimental animals that poliomyelitis develops slower in those deficient in thiamine.

Folic acid has several antagonists. *Aminopterin* is such a substance. It has been used to produce temporary remissions in acute leukemia. Toxic manifestations such as stomatitis and gastro-intestinal hemorrhages may follow its administration.

Vitamin B_{12} is a red crystalline compound containing cobalt. This vitamin is effective in relieving the neurological lesions and the glossitis as well as the anemia in pernicious anemia. Vitamin B_{12} may be identical with Castle's extrinsic factor or the anti-pernicious anemia factor of liver extracts. The vitamin is an important growth factor in animals, and its function in this respect has been demonstrated in children suffering from malnutrition. Thymine desoxyribose (thymidine) will replace vitamin B_{12} for the growth of L. lactis. This effect is not observed when thymine is employed. These facts have led to the hypothesis that B_{12} serves in the biosynthesis of thymidine in a manner parallel to that of folic acid in the synthesis of thymine. Thymidine has not shown erythropoietic activity in Addisonian pernicious anemia in the amounts tested.

Investigations using pure folic acid and vitamin B_{12} have shown an interesting interrelationship with the biological methylating agents, choline, methionine, and betaine. The transfer of methyl groups has been described previously. The original concept visualized an absolute need for extrinsic sources of 'labile' methyl groups, postulating total inability of the organism to produce such groups. It appears more correct at present to assume that such synthesis takes place but at a rate usually insufficient to meet demands. Furthermore, it appears that methyl donors may have their specific methyl acceptors, the process being catalyzed by specific enzyme systems. Vitamin B_{12} may function as part of such an enzyme system. The indicated relationship of folic acid and vitamin B_{12} to choline and methionine metabolism may mean that these substances may be found useful in the prevention and treatment of injury to the liver.

Vitamin C (Cevitamic acid) is the antiscorbutic vitamin. Its role as a hydrogen acceptor has been discussed in Chapter 5. This vitamin is water soluble and is distributed widely in nature in fresh fruits and vegetables. Such foods as citrus fruits, tomatoes, strawberries, bananas, cabbage, peas and beans, many green vegetables, green peppers, and asparagus are rich in vitamin C. Destruction of the vitamin occurs by oxidation which takes place readily in alkaline solution and is catalyzed by traces of copper. Acid media retard oxidation. The daily requirements of vitamin C in the normal adult have been stated by the Food and Nutrition Board of the National Research Council to be approximately 75 mg. It is doubtful if this is the minimum actually necessary because inhabitants of Britain during World War II received on an average 25 mg. per day without apparent manifestations of deficiency.

The adrenal cortex is rich in vitamin C. Injection of adrenocorticotropic hormone into the rat and guinea pig produces a prompt fall in ascorbic acid as well as in cholesterol content of the cortex. This phenomenon may be used as a means of assaying preparations of the hormone.

The destruction of vitamin C occurs by irreversible oxidation of dehydroascorbic acid while the physiological function of the vitamin seems to depend upon reversible oxidation and reduction of the two forms.

$$
\begin{array}{c}
CO \\
| \\
HOC \\
\| \quad O \\
HOC \\
| \\
HC \\
| \\
HOCH \\
| \\
CH_2OH \\
\text{ASCORBIC ACID}
\end{array}
\quad +O + H_2O \rightleftarrows \quad
\begin{array}{c}
CO \\
| \\
HOCOH \\
| \quad O \\
HOCOH \\
| \\
HC \\
| \\
HOCH \\
| \\
CH_2OH \\
\text{DEHYDROASCORBIC ACID}
\end{array}
$$

Vitamin D is an oil soluble vitamin which occurs in abundance in fish liver oils, egg yolk, butter, irradiated milk, and beef liver. Its importance in human nutrition in relation to the skeletal system has been discussed in Chapter 16. The minimum daily requirement for growing children, and pregnant and lactating women, is stated to be between 400 and 800 international units. The role of vitamin D in the adult metabolism has not been established with certainty, which fact makes it difficult for minimum daily requirements to be determined. The vitamin should probably be supplied to adults in quantities up to the minimum amount recommended for children.

Vitamin E consists of a mixture of α-, β-, γ-, and δ-tocopherols, of which the α-tocopherol has been synthesized. The tocopherols are insoluble in water, but are soluble in common fat solvents. Wheat germ and cotton seed oil, meat, egg yolk, and green leafy vegetables are good sources of tocopherols. The need for vitamin E for normal reproduction has been established in several animal species. Rats deprived of vitamin E show damage to the reproductive system of both the male and the female. In the male the spermatogenic epithelium degenerates, an early sign of vitamin E deficiency being loss of motility of the spermatozoa. In the female vitamin E deficiency does not prevent estrus or normal fertilization, but the embryos die early and are resorbed. The importance of an adequate supply of vitamin E in the human subject during gestation has not been established nearly as clearly as in animals although reports indicate that the use of vitamin E may be of distinct benefit in cases of habitual abortion. Several species of laboratory animals develop a form of muscular dystrophy when deprived of vitamin E. This nutritional muscular dystrophy of rabbits can be cured by the administration of α-tocopherol. Such observations have led to the use of vitamin E in human neuromuscular disturbances. It appears that treatment of amyotrophic lateral sclerosis has resulted in questionable improvement but that the destruction of the myelin sheaths and axis cylinders may be retarded by use of the vitamin.

The biological effect of the tocopherols seems to depend upon their ability to act as antioxidants; this has been demonstrated in feeding experiments involving vitamin A, showing that growth rates on small amounts of vitamin A are enhanced by the presence of tocopherols. There is strong evidence that vitamin E is important in human nutrition. Malnourished individuals have an average tocopherol blood level significantly below that of normals. Using animal data as criteria, it is estimated that the average human daily intake of tocopherol is approximately equal to the need, but that deficiencies may result if this intake is largely in the form of the physiologically less active tocopherols.

Vitamin K is the antihemorrhagic vitamin. It consists of a group of naphthoquinone compounds, a number of which have been prepared synthetically, and have the biological properties of vitamin K.

The antihemorrhagic properties of this vitamin were discovered by Dam and his associates; they found that alfalfa or a fatty non-sterol fraction of hog liver has the power to cure a hemorrhagic diathesis in newly hatched chicks.

It has not been possible to produce the hemorrhagic tendencies associated with hypoprothrombinemia in mammals by feeding them a vitamin K deficient diet. On such a diet the vitamin is formed through bacterial synthesis in the intestinal tract and hypoprothrombinemia occurs only when there is interference with absorption or utilization of the vitamin. Clinical aspects of vitamin K deficiency caused by disorders of the biliary system have been discussed in Chapter 10. Hypoprothrombinemia induced by drugs such as salicylic acid or dicoumarol, as well as the hemorrhagic diseases of the newborn related to hypoprothrombinemia may be counteracted by the administration of vitamin K.

Vitamin P is the name given to a substance or group of substances found in paprika and the peel of lemons and oranges. The name refers to the ability of this vitamin to restore abnormally increased capillary permeability back to normal. Szent-Györgyi and his co-workers isolated a crystalline substance "citrin" which contains 2 flavone dyes, hesperidin and eriodictyol glucoside. It has been postulated that these substances or similar crystalline compounds are precursors of the active vitamin which has not yet been identified chemically.

Pure hesperidin has no appreciable effect on capillary permeability but a yellow pigment from oranges has been identified as hesperidin chalcone. Possibly the vitamin effect is dependent on the greater solubility of the chalcone. Chalcones are unstable and hesperidin chalcone reverts easily to hesperidin with loss of biological activity. Methylation of hesperidin chalcone increases its stability and produces a substance with high vitamin P activity.

Recently another flavone glucoside, *rutin,* has been shown to be a rhamnoglucoside of quercetin. Rutin has vitamin P activity and it is being employed in treatment of conditions characterized by increased capillary permeability. Such conditions are encountered in a number of diseases including multiple vitamin deficiencies, diabetes mellitus, hypertension, and purpura. Lack of clinical response to the use of the substances with vitamin P activity may be occasioned by failure to recognize other factors as contributing to the changes in capillary permeability.

SUPPLEMENTARY READING

Curtis, G. M., and Fertman, M. B.: Iodine in nutrition. *J.A.M.A., 139*:28, 1949.

Elvehjem, C. A., and Krehl, W. H.: Imbalance and dietary interrelationship in nutrition. *J.A.M.A., 135*:279, 1947.

Frazier, L. E., Wissler, R. W., Steffee, C. H., Woolridge, R. L., and Cannon, P. R.: Studies in amino acid utilization: I. The dietary utilization of mixtures of purified amino acids in protein depleted adult albino rats. *J. Nutrition, 33*:65, 1947.

Hansen, A. E., and Burr, G. O.: Essential fatty acids and human nutrition. *J.A.M.A., 132*:855, 1946.

Luecke, R. W., McMillen, W. N., Thorp, F., Jr., and Tull, C.: The relationship of nicotinic acid, tryptophan and protein in the nutrition of the pig. *J. Nutrition, 33*:351, 1947.

Madden, S. C., Bassett, S. N., Remington, J. H., Martin, F. J. C., Woods, R. R., and Shull, F. W.: Amino acids in therapy of disease. *Surg. Gynec. & Obst., 82*:131, 1946.

McLester, J. S.: *Nutrition and Diet in Health and Disease.* W. B. Saunders Co., 1949.

NEWBURGH, L. H.: Obesity. *Arch. Int. Med.*, *70*:1033, 1942.

SALMON, W. D.: Some physiological relationships of protein, fat, choline, methionine, cystine, nicotinic acid and tryptophan. *J. Nutrition*, *33*:155, 1947.

SCHLENK, F., and SNELL, E. E.: Vitamin B_6 and transamination. *J. Biol. Chem.*, *157*:425, 1945.

WOOLLEY, D. W.: Some correlations of growth promoting powers of proteins with their strepogenin content. *J. Biol. Chem., 162*:383, 1946.

WOOLLEY, D. W.: The occurrence of a "pellagragenic" agent in corn. *J. Biol. Chem., 163*:773, 1946.

WOOLLEY, D. W.: Water-soluble vitamins. *Ann. Rev. Biochem., 16*:359, 1947.

YOUMANS, J. B.: Deficiencies of the fat-soluble vitamins. *J.A.M.A., 144*:34, 1950.

YOUMANS, J. B.: Deficiencies of the water-soluble vitamins. *J.A.M.A., 144*:307 and 386, 1950.

INDEX

This Book

Fundamentals of Biochemistry
in
Clinical Medicine

By Niels C. Klendshoj, M.D.

was set, printed and bound by The Collegiate Press of Menasha, Wisconsin. The page trim size is 7 x 10 inches. The type page is 30 x 48 picas. The type face is Linotype Baskerville, set 11 point on 13 point. The text paper is 60 pound White Winnebago Eggshell. The cover is Bancroft Arrestox B (3400) Red.

With THOMAS BOOKS *careful attention is given to all details of manufacturing and design. It is the Publisher's desire to present books that are satisfactory as to their physical qualities and artistic possibilities and appropriate for their particular use.* THOMAS BOOKS *will be true to those laws of quality that assure a good name and good will.*